ADVANCED NUTRITION AND METABOLISM:

WHAT IS THE QUEST?

2ⁿᵈ Edition

JONATHAN C. ALLEN,
Ph.D., C.N.S.

**North Carolina State University,
Department of Food, Bioprocessing,
&
Nutrition Sciences,
Raleigh, NC**

LINUS
Learning

Published by Linus Learning

Ronkonkoma, NY 11779

ISBN 10: 1-60797-727-3

ISBN 13: 978-1-60797-727-8

Printed in the United States of America.

This book is printed on acid-free paper.

Print Number   5   4   3   2   1

Table of Contents

Section 1:

Nutrient intake, digestion, absorption, and excretion related to nutrient balance.

By *Jonathan C. Allen, Maria Dolores Crespo Rodriguez, Saad Haque, Johari Jordan, Margaret Edem Mensah, and Kruti Ravaliya, Rini Basyamfar, Kristin Frankowski, Elise Hubbard, Ayeesha Khadeeruddin, Meghan Askew, Sharon Jackson, Eunice Kim, Melissa Loy, O Jesse Mendes, Catherine Mixon, Curtis Park, Yuting Qui, and Rebecca Stanley, Shalimbala Chizonda, Caroline Dickson, Samantha Duxbury, Christian Johansson, Kayla Lawson, Danielle Lucas, and Larry Witt*

Chapter 1.

The Common Goal of Nutritionists: Contributing to Appropriate Intake of Nutrients.

Chapter 2.

Regulation of food and nutrient intake. Does the body specifically regulate intake of these nutrients in any way?

Chapter 3.

Digestion and Absorption of Macronutrients. Mechanisms that Allow for Variable or Constant Absorption.

Chapter 4.

Digestion and Absorption of Micronutrients.

Chapter 5.

Section 2:

Storage and Functions of Nutrients in Organ Systems: If intake is not constant, how are nutrients stored?

By *Jonathan C. Allen, Sarah Brown, Raven Canady, Briana Massey, Rini Triani, Hind Sadis, Phillip Vaughn, Sopani R. Neba, Kimberly Palatini, Maryanne T. Perrin, Tierra Pressley, Jennifer Cole, Julie Chytka, Kristen Glossen, Eunice Kim, and Beverly Neffa, Kyle Craver, Mary Craver, Annie Lassiter, Neel Shah, George Stoforos, Stephanie Dill, Nazish Durrani Natalia Smith, Annita Wilborn, Christina Inserillo, Kyle Emery, Charles Giamberadino, Katie Shiraishi, Meaghan Bethea, and Weston Bussler*

Chapter 6.

Chapter 7.

Chapter 8.

Chapter 9.

Chapter 10.

Chapter 11.

Selected functions of vitamins and minerals:
Roles in differentiation, growth and development, antioxidants, and energy and protein metabolism.

Index

Section 1.

Nutrient intake, digestion, absorption, and excretion related to nutrient balance.

Chapter 1.

The Common Goal of Nutritionists: Contributing to Appropriate Intake of Nutrients

Chapter 2.

Regulation of food and nutrient intake. Does the body specifically regulate intake of these nutrients in any way?

Chapter Summary

Chapter 3.

Digestion and Absorption of Macronutrients. Mechanisms that Allow for Variable or Constant Absorption

Chapter 4.

Digestion and Absorption of Micronutrients

Chapter 5.

Excretion: How do animals get rid of excess or unneeded molecules?

Section 2.

Storage and Functions of Nutrients in Organ Systems: If intake is not constant, how are nutrients stored?

Chapter 6.

Bone as a Storage Site Associated with Minerals and Vitamins

Chapter 7.

Storage of Nutrients in Visceral Organs and Muscle.

Chapter 8.

Nutrients that Build and Comprise Blood

Chapter 9.

Storage, Body Structure and Metabolism: Carbohydrate

Chapter 10.

Lipid Storage, Metabolism, and Body Structure

Chapter 11.

Selected functions of vitamins and minerals
Roles in differentiation, growth and development, antioxidants, and energy and protein metabolism

Preface to Advanced Nutrition and Metabolism !

Edited from statements by students enrolled Summer 2013 in response to the question, "Writing in the format of a preface for our next text book, describe the overarching theme of this course. How will this course be useful to nutrition students whose main interest is not in metabolism as well as for those principally interested in nutrition at the biochemical, cell, and organismal level?"

This book, and the Advanced Nutrition and Metabolism course it is derived from, seeks to inform readers of the fundamental question that nutritionists in many different sub- disciplines approach from different perspectives: how do we arrive at the appropriate concentration of all the nutrients needed in the human body? On the grand scale, public health nutritionists look at policies that will help to provide appropriate quantities of foods to various populations. Community nutritionists and nutrition counselors work with individuals to assist them in choosing the appropriate foods that will provide the nutrients they need.

Nutritionists who work at the individual, organ system, and cellular levels try to understand how the body adapts to various levels of intake of each of these specific nutrients. The underlying mechanisms of digestion and absorption are explored in the context of feedback from the body's nutritional status to the rates of absorption and excretions. Knowing the optimum nutrient concentration for each cell, tissue, and organ system, allows us to work backwards to the appropriate quantity of intake of all of these nutrients each day, and to set the dietary reference intakes from that information.

Food is the link between human behavior and nutrition. What goes into our bodies can affect us negatively or beneficially. Understanding how and why foods affect us the way they do is important in maintaining our health. However, many people do not understand that it is not only the foods we eat that is important but the individual components of the food that are the essential part of our diets. This book is an overview of the necessary components needed for our body to function and maintain homeostasis.

Advanced nutrition and metabolism is a course that teaches students to understand the processes of and nutritional support for metabolic systems. The book will help you understand the important and fascinating metabolic cycles that drive physiological processes in your body. It will introduce you to the important nutrients utilized by the body to produce energy needed to walk, sit, read, run, cook, talk, swim and do all the things that we do in our daily lives. It will describe characteristics of nutrients from their structure, function, food source, symptoms of deficiency, and their interactions with other nutrients. Each nutrient has its own regulatory system, but all also work together in the totality of metabolism.

Initially, the book will delve into the realm of "essential" nutrients and what falls into that category. The class then moves on to the portion of the endocrine system that regulate satiety, hunger, and food intake. All together, Advanced Nutrition and Metabolism lends students a very well-rounded idea of the biological role of nutrients and real-world applications.

For those who are not particularly interested in metabolism this book will still be helpful because it will stimulate thinking about how one simple amino acid, trace element, or vitamin could upset the state of homeostasis in the body. It will challenge you to take a closer look into the biochemical pathways that are involved in order for the body to maintain energy. You will also gain a better understanding of why metabolism and biochemical processes are important and you will learn what types of foods, vitamins, or trace elements can disrupt the pathways. You will be able to explain with better knowledge how absorption and excretion work, how muscles are fueled with energy, how bones are remodeled. You will be able to explain biochemically and nutritionally how to avoid exceeding homeostatic limits through a proper diet. Some readers may find this a challenging, but fun course that allows you to expand your knowledge of biochemistry and apply it to better understand how organisms function. The description of nutritional function at the biochemical and cellular level will improve your understanding of metabolic processes as well.

The human body is a complex machine, and thus the nutritional needs and processes are also quite complex. Advanced Nutrition and Metabolism allows you to see, the big picture. From the moment of consumption through the processes of digestion, absorption, and excretion, the reader is able to zoom into a particular process as well as zoom out and see how all the nutrients work together to keep this complex machine running. You will also learn the background of nutrition as a science and how to analyze nutritional needs. In addition to the big picture, the details and biochemical "small pieces" will also be learned. How many classes are provide the details from a big picture view while shining light on the disease processes as well? Whether you are more interested in the process, the picture, or how the picture can go wrong, you are sure to learn it here and be left with a sense of gratitude for the wonder of the human body.

Learning Objectives
Students completing this course will be able to:

- Outline the metabolic pathways for macronutrients, and show where vitamins and minerals play important cofactor roles in metabolism.

- Contrast the homeostatic mechanisms used in humans to maintain nutrient content at a steady state with the role of nutrients in homeostasis of other physiological processes.

- Explain how optimum tissue nutrient content, other biomarkers, or adverse effects of too much or too little dietary intake are used to set the Dietary Reference Intakes for most nutrients.

- Design experiments to gather additional information to revise or establish new Dietary Reference Intakes.

- Explain how nutrients interact in the formation and maintenance of specific healthy tissues, such as bone, muscle, blood, and sensory systems.

- Describe a vision statement to cover the goals of nutrition scientists in a range of sub-disciplines.

Acknowledgements:

Coauthors for this text were all students in the course, Advanced Nutrition and Metabolism, at North Carolina State University, 2012 and 2013. Authors consented to publication of their contribution and appreciate the work of other scientists who have written papers and books to make the field of nutritional physiology and biochemistry understandable at the level of this course. The best efforts have been made by the authors and editor to properly cite the sources of information and illustrations. Illustrations have been selected from sources that are posted on the Internet with Creative Commons licensing to the greatest extent possible.

SECTION 1

Nutrient intake, digestion, absorption, and excretion related to nutrient balance.

Authors:

Jonathan C. Allen, Maria Dolores Crespo Rodriguez, Saad Haque, Johari Jordan, Margaret Edem Mensah, and Kruti Ravaliya, Rini Basyamfar, Kristin Frankowski, Elise Hubbard, Ayeesha Khadeeruddin, Meghan Askew, Sharon Jackson, Eunice Kim, Melissa Loy, O Jesse Mendes, Catherine Mixon, Curtis Park, Yuting Qui, and Rebecca Stanley, Shalimbala Chizonda, Caroline Dickson, Samantha Duxbury, Christian Johansson, Kayla Lawson, Danielle Lucas, and Larry Witt

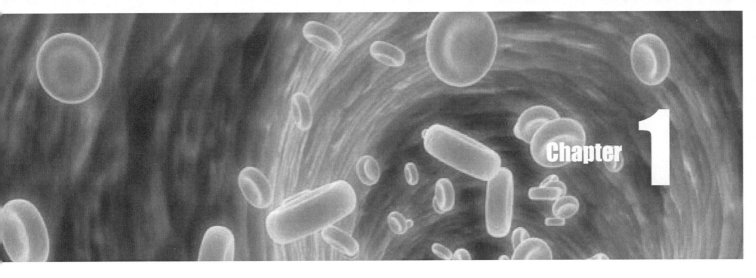

The Common Goal of Nutritionists: Contributing to Appropriate Intake of Nutrients

By Jonathan C. Allen

Learning Objectives

After completing this chapter, readers should be able to:

1. Describe a common objective for the practice of nutrition by scientists and policy makers in many nutritional fields.

2. Outline some events in nutrition history that led to the concept of essentiality and the establishment and revisions of the Dietary Reference Intakes.

3. Contrast molecules and substances that are essential, non-essential, or conditionally essential. Distinguish dispensable for indispensible (also called essential) components of foods based on a set of characteristics or experimental results.

4. Graphically depict the concept of variable nutrient requirements within a population and how that information helps claulate the RDA.

5. Appropriately apply the RDA to guidance for populations and individuals.

6. List some of the key discoveries leading to the establishment of nutrition as a scientific discipline.

7. Describe how nutrition science translates to public policy through the establishment of the Dietary Reference Intakes (DRIs).

8. Identify some of the strengths and weaknesses in the DRI recommendations.

1.1. Nutrient Requirements: History and Definitions

1.1.1. Introduction

The science of nutrition has expanded from its beginnings in the nineteenth century to a field with many branches and sub-fields. Can we look back through the development of each of the subfields to a common quest, or objective for all? The earliest nutritionists came to the realization that there were components of foods that were essential for health or for life. In the early twentieth century, nutrition branched from biochemistry by isolating and identifying the specific food components that made up the set of molecules referred to as nutrients, as opposed to metabolites that are commonly synthesized in other plants and animals. Clinical nutritionists and epidemiologists then performed the research needed to quantify the levels of intake of nutrients that results in adequate tissue concentrations for cells throughout the body to optimally perform the functions that depend on those nutrients. The sub-field of nutritional biochemistry still works to define the markers for adequate nutrient concentration in tissues for some of our nutrients. Many other nutritionists work to relate nutrient intake to the physiological markers of adequacy, to relate food selection to nutrient intake, to study the influences on human behavior that determine the quantity and quality of foods we choose to eat to supply the needed nutrients to our tissues, or to address similar issues in food animals to improve the food supply that humans have available to select from. With this view, we can define the **quest for most nutrition scientists** as contributing to the optimum concentration of all needed nutrients in cells and tissues throughout the bodies of humans.

Fortunately, we have help from evolution in maintaining those optimum tissue concentrations, and we do not have to rely on nutrition scientists to provide the perfect diet every day. There are a wealth of homeostatic processes that regulate the relative amount of absorption of nutrients from the foods we eat, excretion of excesses, and storage in specialized cells and tissues as reserves or inactive forms of our bodies' metabolites. This book will focus on those physiological processes for homeostatic control for nutrient concentrations in cells, as well as describe the marker systems for identifying the optimum tissue concentrations, which often involve preventing clinical or sub-clinical deficiency, or the converse, markers of health.

Ultimately, maintaining appropriate tissue concentrations of essential nutrients depends on having those nutrients in the foods we eat, and eating appropriate quantities. In the United States, the responsibility for defining the optimal nutrient intakes has been given to the Food and Nutrition Board, now part of the Institute of Medicine. Guidelines from this group are published in its latest form as the Dietary Reference Intakes. This book will also focus on the conversion of the science of nutrient homeostasis to these recommendations involving food selection. A desired outcome is that the readers will understand the biology behind nutrient regulation, and be able to put it into practice for evaluation of foods and diets.

1.1.2. History of Nutrients

Many authors have more expertise than this one in the history of nutrition. Readers are encouraged to refer to appropriate sources for details. Much of the following discussion comes from the review by Stipanuk [1].

Nutrients are chemical substances found in foods that are necessary for human life and growth, maintenance, and repair of body tissues. Nutrients encompass proteins, fats, carbohydrates (CHO), vitamins, minerals, and water. Protein intake must include 9 essential amino acids, sometimes several other amino acids that are conditionally essential, and enough total amino nitrogen to synthesize the remaining non-essential amino acids. Fat requirements include two families of essential fatty acids, which are usually minor constituents of our total dietary fat. Carbohydrates are not technically essential because we can synthesize all the monosaccharides used in the body from amino acid backbones. We generally recognize 12 or 13 vitamins and 15 minerals as essential.

Long before nutritional biochemistry was a science, ancient Greeks wrote that food was made up of "nutriment, medicines, and poisons". Today, if you try to learn about nutrition from the Internet, you may come to the same conclusion. Try to imagine the food industry 2000 years before Good Manufacturing Practices came along, when there was more reliance on hunting and gathering, in addition to agriculture. Plants could provide good sources of nutrients like ascorbic acid (vitamin C), or they could contain salicylic acid (a precursor of aspirin). Plants in the nightshade family provided starch in the roots or fruit and the neurotoxin, solanine, in the leaves. Now, we try to remove the poisons from processed foods, but we allow specific health claims, and even market medicinal foods; and we still have occasional problems of food poisoning, mostly associated with pathogenic microorganisms.

Many scientists, researchers, or clinical practitioners made discoveries and observations leading to the divergence of the science of nutrition from general medical practice. A few of the key events in the history of nutrition are those that follow [1].

In 1670, Thomas Sydenham, in Britain, observed that a tonic of iron in wine produced a clinical response in patients with chlorosis (which is now recognized as hypochromic or iron deficiency anemia). Thus, a bioavailable source of iron could cure an iron deficiency.

In 1747, James Lind, a Naval physician from Scotland, observed that consumption of citrus fruit (oranges and lemons) by sailors cured scurvy, whereas vinegar and some other folk remedies did not. Lind is credited with performing the first prospective, controlled, nutritional clinical trial.

Around 1770-1794, Antoine Lavoisier and Pierre-Simon Laplace concluded that the oxidation of carbon compounds was the source of energy for activity and other bodily functions in animals. Remember this concept; it will be a theme of some later chapters.

In 1827, William Prout, in London, proposed that the nutrition of higher animals could be explained by their need for proteins, carbohydrate, and fats, which he found in the body secretions. Prout also discovered, in 1823, that stomach juice contains hydrochloric acid; the proton was named, in part, for Prout and his biochemical research.

During the 1800's, Justus von Liebig, a chemist at the University of Giessen in Germany, postulated that energy-yielding substances (proteins, carbohydrates, and fat), together with a few minerals, represented the essentials of a nutritionally adequate diet and he predicted that their nutritional value could be calculated from their gross chemical composition. His work in plant nutrition led to the Law of Minimums, which can be thought of as an analogy to current concepts of complementary proteins. Liebig prepared tables of food values, which were facilitated with the help of Wilhelm Henneberg, who devised the Weende system (proximate analysis) for analyzing foods and feeds for protein, fat, fiber, nitrogen-free extract (CHO), and ash.

Christiaan Eijkman, working on causes for the disease beriberi in Java (now Indonesia) from 1888 to 1896, made the observation that a diet of polished rice fed to chickens caused beriberi-like symptoms, and changing the diet to unpolished or brown rice, which contains the germ and bran, cured the disease. In 1901, Gerrit Grijns, a Dutch physician who continued the work of Eijkman in the Dutch East Indies (Indonesia), interpreted the results of studies on the ingestion of a high starch diet and the formation of beriberi made by Christiaan Eijkman and Adolphe Vorderman to be correct. Grijns interpreted the research data to show that a nutritional component needed for health was lost in the rice polishing process, where as Eijkman originally thought the polished rice diet promoted a bacterial infection. Somewhat later Casimir Funk identified the component in the unpolished rice as a vitamin, thiamin, not a bacterial prebiotic or probiotic factor as Eijkman had postulated. These scientists provided the first clear concept of dietary deficiency disease; Eijkman was awarded a Nobel Prize in 1929 for his contribution.

In 1910, Elmer V. McCollum, in Wisconsin, and Thomas Osborne and Lafayette Mendel, in Connecticut, used rats to develop a new approach to the search for vitamins as well as in the discovery of essential amino acids, such as lysine, sulfur-containing amino acids, and histidine. By feeding purified diets, extracts of other foods could be added to reverse symptoms of apparent deficiency, or improve growth rates or reproductive efficiency.

The use of animal models was extremely important to the identification of essential nutrients. By 1915, six minerals, four amino acids, and three vitamins (A, B, and antiscorbutic factor) were identified as essential. In 1918, the concept of the presence of "accessory factors" or "minor constituents of foods" essential for health was established. Chemical purification and structural analysis of essential food components, along with the elaboration of metabolic and enzymatic pathways, proceeded at a rapid pace during the first half of the twentieth century. By 1950, most essential nutrients had been identified and explored, including 2 essential fatty acids, nine amino acids, 12 vitamins, and 11 minerals, plus three trace elements (molybdenum, selenium, and chromium).

Within these classes, the substances or molecules defined as **essential,** also called

indispensible, *are those that*

- Must be present in the diet for growth, health, reproduction, or survival;

- Can result in characteristic signs of a deficiency disease, possibly leading to death, when the substance is absent from the diet or intake is inadequate;

- Prevent growth failure and characteristic signs of deficiency when other substances do not;

- Can demonstrate a dose-response in the deficiency condition when intake is below the optimal or critical level of intake of the nutrient; i.e., the growth response or severity of signs of deficiency are proportional to the amount of nutrient consumed;

- Are not synthesized in the body in amounts that meet the needs for the critical function.

Today most scientists do not consider an element essential unless it has a defined biochemical function. Nielson [2] suggests that a nutritionally beneficial element be defined as "one with health restorative effects in response to an apparent deficient intake of that element, at intakes that are found with normal diets; these health restorative effects can be amplified or inhibited by nutritional, physiological, hormonal, or metabolic stressors". Defining essential mineral elements is a somewhat simplified case, since elements are neither created nor destroyed within the body, so all have to come from the diet. For minerals that have a requirement close to the level of detection (the traditional definition for "trace" elements), or the level of minimal body concentrations due to environmental contamination, defining an element as essential is somewhat more difficult. Neilson identified several

elements that probably have an essential function, due to interaction with other nutrients. Effects of boron deficiency can be amplified by a marginal vitamin D deficiency. Effects of vanadium deficiency can be amplified by deficient or excess dietary iodine. Beneficial effects of nickel are inhibited by vitamin B12, pyridoxine, or folic acid deficiency. (See Chapter 11 for a discussion on the possible metabolic need for arsenic.) Nielson also suggested four categories in which a trace element can be nutritionally essential:

- A dietary deprivation in some animal model consistently results in a changed biological function, body structure, or tissue composition that is preventable or reversible by an intake of an apparent physiological amount of the element in question.

- The element fills the need at physiological concentrations for a known in vivo biochemical action to proceed in vitro.

- The element is a component of known biologically important molecules in some life forms.

- The element has an essential function in lower forms of life.

Therefore defining an element as essential does not necessary mean it is essential for humans. Microorganisms require cobalt to synthesize cyanocobalamin, or vitamin B12, which they can pass on to animals. Humans require a dietary source of vitamin B12 and therefore need cobalt in the diet. However, humans cannot synthesize cyanocobalamin from cobalt alone.

Grazing sheep, on the other hand, are healthy when there is a source of elemental cobalt in their diet, and show clinical B12 deficiency symptoms when cobalt is absent. Symptoms of a clinical deficiency, or the required level of intake, can be influenced by the presence in the diet of substances for which the nutrient is a precursor, substances that interfere with the absorption or utilization of the nutrient, imbalances of other related nutrients, malabsorption of the nutrient, certain genetic defects, and the use of drugs that impair utilization of nutrients. Thus, defining an element as essential, as well as the more important problem of defining the required level of intake, is often a philosophical question open to various interpretations.

For organic nutrients there are other complications to the questions of essentiality. For example, vitamin D can be synthesized in the skin, but often this synthesis is inadequate to meet all biological functions. The vitamin niacin can be synthesized from the amino acid tryptophan, but the rate is dependent on tryptophan availability. Vitamin C (ascorbic acid) cannot be synthesized by humans and a few other herbivorous animals, but is readily synthesized by carnivores. The rate of synthesis of certain amino acids may not be adequate to meet the growth requirements of rapidly growing infants. For these and similar situations, Rudman and Feller [3] proposed the term "**conditionally essential**" for nutrients not ordinarily required in the diet but which must be supplied exogenously to specific populations that do not synthesize them in adequate amounts. The criteria for conditionally essential nutrients, first applied to amino acids in patients supported with total parenteral nutrition were: a decline in plasma concentrations of the nutrient into the subnormal range; appearance of chemical, structural, or functional abnormalities; and correction of both criteria by a dietary (or intravenous) supplement of the nutrient.

1.2. Establishing the Recommended Dietary Intakes

1.2.1. Guidelines for Food and Nutrient Intake: What are they and how did they develop?

Following the identification of the most of the essential nutrients that took place in the period from 1915 to 1950, evaluation of data to determine the amount of each nutrient needed in diets to meet the biochemical functions yet prevent excesses and imbalances was needed. With the realization that many conscripts to military service during World War II were not healthy enough for induction due to nutrient deficiencies, the Food and Nutrition Board of the National Research Council was organized in 1940 with the function of advising on problems of nutrition in connection with national defense. The first set of Recommended Dietary Allowances (RDA) for Americans was published in 1941. It has been updated ten times since, with the latest version being a set of comprehensive reviews of clusters of mostly indispensable nutrients that relate to each other by physiological function, rather than the earlier classification of nutrients by chemical properties. Given that the Food and Nutrition Board conducts these reviews to determine the best scientific consensus regarding the relationship of dietary intake of nutrients in foods to the markers of optimal nutrient status of individuals and populations, we can rely heavily on this source of information to aid in our quest of understanding how optimal cell and tissue nutrient concentrations are achieved.

The latest review of nutrient requirements by the Food and Nutrition Board differed from earlier versions in several key features [4]. The earlier Recommended Dietary Allowances terminology has been replaced by Dietary Reference Intakes. The new term allows RDA to be one of several recommendations regarding nutrient intake. Beginning around 1977, public concern about total food intake and health increased beyond just preventing deficiency diseases. Public awareness of malnutrition in the U.S. was highlighted by the report, Dietary Goals for the United States, also known as the "McGovern Report", after the chair of the United States Senate Select Committee on Nutrition and Human Needs, which authored it. The 8-year activities of this Senate Committee were largely transferred to a responsibility of the United Stated Department of Agriculture, (now within the USDA Center for Nutrition Policy and Promotion). The report from the "McGovern Committee" became the basis for the Dietary Guidelines for Americans, which are updated and published every five years by USDA-CNPP. Whereas, the Dietary reference intakes define appropriate nutrient intakes for health of the organism and its cells, the Dietary Guidelines for Americans translates the nutrient intake guidelines to recommendations for changes in food intake and selection to achieve health.

Other aspects of guidance on population and individual-based food intake promulgated by U.S. federal agencies include the Food Guide, formerly the Food Guide Pyramid, or MyPyramid and now MyPlate, (also supported by USDA), and nutrition labeling regulations (under the combined oversight of USDA and the Food and Drug Administration, FDA).

1.2.2. Dietary Reference Intakes

The *Dietary Reference Intakes* not only define nutrient intakes that prevent deficiencies, but they also define intake levels that can begin to cause adverse or toxic effects, a guideline termed the Tolerable Upper Intake Level (UL). In 1997, the Dietary Reference Intakes (DRI) became the new standard for measuring nutritional adequacy. replacing the older term Recommended Dietary Allowance. The DRI Committee of the Food and Nutrition Board determined that the DRI's can be used for both planning and assessing diets of individuals and groups, whereas the RDAs were designed to meet the nutrient needs of a large segment of a population, but individuals whose intake was less than the RDA were not necessarily likely to be deficient in that nutrient.

In contrast to the older RDA guidance system, using the complete set of DRIs as reference values now: a) includes upper levels of intake, where appropriate; b) incorporates chronic disease endpoints within the estimation of risk for some nutrients that may serve to establish adequate intake or upper intake levels; c) includes suggested intakes for some "non- classical" nutrients that may not constitute a single compound (e.g. dietary fiber), or be indispensible, such as beta carotene; and d) specifically highlight concepts of probability and risk for defining reference values. Detailed discussions of all of these concepts are beyond the scope of this chapter, so readers are referred to the associated publications intended to guide users of DRIs [4, 5, 6]. We will discuss how indicators of nutrient status relate to establishment of DRIs for many nutrients in later chapters.

Some chapters in this book generally follow the organization or logic of clustering nutrients into groups using categories that follow physiological functions. The organization of the six originals books written by separate committees, explaining the formation of the DRI for related nutrients, established this structure. Calcium, phosphorus, magnesium, vitamin D, and fluoride are nutrients involved in healthy bone formation, and were evaluated in the first publication in 1997 [7]; reevaluation of the vitamin D and calcium requirements was published in 2010 [8]. Thiamin, riboflavin, niacin, vitamin B6, folate,

vitamin B12, pantothenic acid, biotin, and choline have commonalities in intermediate metabolism [9]. Vitamin C, vitamin E, selenium, and carotenoids are considered together due to their role as antioxidants [10]. Vitamin A, vitamin K, arsenic, boron, chromium, copper, iodine, iron, manganese, molybdenum, nickel, silicon, vanadium, and zinc are generally cofactors for a wide range of enzymatic functions [11]. Energy, carbohydrate, fiber, fat, fatty acids, cholesterol, protein, and amino acids are considered as the main building material for body tissues, and as oxidizable substrates [12]. Water, potassium, sodium, chloride, and sulfate are all used in the quantity, charge, and osmolarity of different body fluids [13].

In addition to the RDA, which is still used for intake guidance for meal planning, the DRI guideline also includes the **Estimated Average Requirement** (EAR), which is the average daily nutrient intake level estimated to meet the requirement of half the healthy individuals in a particular life stage and gender group. These values allow for calculation of the RDA, when estimates of the varying requirements of individuals within that population is taken into account, as well as the variation of intake among individuals in a population when given the same nutrient guidance. The EAR can then be used as a benchmark for assessing the nutrient intake of individuals and allows for calculation of the probability that a given intake will result in deficiency.

Despite the careful review of available research, some nutrients have not been studied sufficiently in a way that allows for calculation of the EAR. In those cases, the DRI committees use available data, best judgment, and old techniques from former RDA committees to define **Adequate Intake** (AI), which is the recommended average daily nutrient intake level based on observed or experimentally determined approximations or estimates of nutrient intake by groups of healthy people that are assumed have low risk of deficiency for the population group.

As mentioned above, the **Tolerable Upper Intake Level** (UL) is the highest average daily nutrient intake level likely to pose no risk of adverse health effects to most individuals in the general population. As one increases intakes to levels above the UL the potential risk of adverse effects may increase.

Finally, the volume on energy and macronutrient metabolism [12], defined the **Acceptable**

Macronutrient Distribution Range (AMDR) as an intake range for an energy source (carbohydrate, fat, or protein) associated with reduced risk of chronic disease.

1.2.3. Some Limitations to the DRIs

When setting out to establish the DRIs, the Food and Nutrition Board set up a roadmap for guideline development that would be applied to each nutrient [5]. Because nutrients use a variety of physiological processes to maintain homeostasis, it is difficult to define adequate nutritional status and find endpoints for risk of inadequacy that apply to all nutrients. Ideally, dose-response studies should be available to determine the EAR distribution curves within a population, using the endpoints for risk of inadequacy for each nutrient as the response. In addition, the dose response data should consider bioavailability and bioequivalencies of food sources or nutrients added to diets. The EAR determined may not apply in exactly the same way to different foods. The DRI evaluation process has an emphasis on assessing variability in measurements. Normal distribution is assumed, yet often studies do not report or measure the variation in their data. Divergence from the normal distribution is hard to test if the raw data are not available. In some cases the EAR should be adjusted for outlying populations. For example the vitamin C requirement appears to be about 35 mg/day higher in people who smoke [4].

It may be equally hard to define endpoints for hazards (the inherent danger of the substance due to excess). Once a hazard has been identified from a review of the literature (excess exposure of nutrient x causes medical problem y in a certain percentage of the population), dose response-data are needed. These data provide a benchmark dose where the incidence of the medical problem approaches zero in that population. The benchmark dose is usually used as the UL, since the desired outcome of nutritional guidance is that no one is harmed by excess nutrient intake. If there are no dose-response data, an established no- observable-adverse-event-level (NOAEL) is used. In other words, if a dose that is know to cause medical problem y is known, and medical problem y has not been observed at another known dose, the lower dose is used as the UL even though the dose that begins to cause the problem in a small portion

of the population may be higher than the NOAEL. Frequently, measurement of variation is not available in dose-response studies for the UL. The UL is set based on the scientific estimate of the hazard, rather than policy implications of risk. For example, a majority of the U.S. population has a sodium intake that is greater than the UL for sodium. The sodium UL is based on the benchmark dose where a measureable portion of individuals experience sodium-sensitive hypertension. Food policies are pushing for sodium reduction to reduce the risk of hypertension in the population, but foods that exceed the UL are still permitted, and the UL is not raised to account for the fact that sodium reduction is difficult.

Often the data from dose-response studies are based on body weight of the subjects. Similarly, the true requirement for a nutrient by consumers can be actually dependent on their body mass. The DRI in those cases still needs to be provided in tables as a single value, rather than an equation. **Reference heights and weights** were established for each age-gender population group. The table of reference heights and weights (page 17 in reference [4]) can then be used by consumers or nutrition professionals to determine the EAR for an individual of a different size. The reference heights were determined from NHANES data of different age- gender groups. The reference weights were calculated from the mid-point of the ideal body mass index (BMI) using the reference height.

A few other caveats need to be kept in mind as we incorporate DRIs into our food selection and nutrient guidance. First, the DRIs were derived from data from healthy people and therefore the recommendations only apply to healthy people. Individuals with diseases, injuries, or genetic differences in metabolism may have different requirements and limitations. Furthermore, the guidelines apply to populations, and individuals within a population, but the Requirement for a specific individual is unknown. So, at least at the present time, and individual can only use the DRI in combination with their intake to estimate the probability or risk for deficiency or excess.

1.3. Summary

The science of nutrition became its own specialty in the first half of the 20th century. The first investigators came with convergent backgrounds from fields such as clinical medicine, biochemistry, chemistry, physiology and animal husbandry. The science of nutrition has also diverged of the last half to 3/4ths of a century to subspecialties such as global food security, community nutrition, nutritional epidemiology, nutrigenomics, clinical dietetics, and animal nutrition. For the big picture, nutritionists require understanding or work in areas related to economic, social, behavioral, as well as basic biochemical or biomedical science. Nutrition is not limited to scientific discovery and education of more nutritionists, but also involves public policy to promote the health and welfare and reduce costs to society. The overall quest of nutritionists in each of these fields is to provide food, modify behavior, make recommendations, or change policy so that people will consume diets that allow for optimum concentrations of nutrients in tissues and cells throughout the body. Fortunately, we have a lot of help from the evolution of physiological mechanisms that maintain nutrient homeostasis within our bodies. The following chapters of this book will describe many of those homeostatic principles, identify important metabolic processes that are dependent on the appropriate nutrient concentration, and illustrate how the quest of maintaining appropriate cellular nutrient concentrations and availability can be a touchstone for nutritionists who work in the biochemical, behavioral, and social science and public policy arenas.

1.4. References Cited

1. Stipanuk MH. 2006. Nutrients: History and Definitions. Ch 1 in: Stipanuk MH, Biochemical, Physiological, and Molecular Aspects of Human Nutrition. Saunders/Elsevier, St. Louis, MO.

2. Nielsen, FH. 2000. Importance of making dietary recommendations for elements designated as nutritionally beneficial, pharmacologically beneficial, or conditionally essential. Journal of Trace Elements in Experimental Medicine, 2000, 13, (1): 113 – 129

3. Rudman D, Feller A. 1986. Evidence of deficiencies of conditionally essential nutrients during total parenteral nutrition. J Amer Coll Nutr 5:101-6.

4. Otten JJ, Hellwig JP, Meyers LD, editors. 2006. Dietary Reference Intakes: The Essential Guide to Nutrient Requirements. The National Academies Press, Washington DC.

5. Food and Nutrition Board (FNB) 2008. The Development of DRIs 1994-2004: Lessons Learned and New Challenges: Workshop Summary. The National Academies Press, Washington DC.

6. Stark C. 2006. Guidelines for Food and Nutrient Intake. Ch 3 in: Stipanuk MH, Biochemical, Physiological, and Molecular Aspects of Human Nutrition. Saunders/Elsevier, St. Louis, MO.

7. Institute of Medicine. *Dietary Reference Intakes for Calcium, Phosphorus, Magnesium, Vitamin D, and Fluoride.* Washington, DC: The National Academies Press, 1997. (http://www.nap.edu/catalog.php?record_id=5776)

8. Institute of Medicine. *Dietary Reference Intakes for Calcium and Vitamin D.* Washington, DC: The National Academies Press, 2011. (http://www.nap.edu/catalog.php?record_id=13050)

9. Institute of Medicine. *Dietary Reference Intakes for Thiamin, Riboflavin, Niacin, Vitamin B6, Folate, Vitamin B12, Pantothenic Acid, Biotin, and Choline.* Washington, DC: The National Academies Press, 1998. (http://www.nap.edu/catalog.php?record_id=6015)

10. Institute of Medicine. *Dietary Reference Intakes for Vitamin C, Vitamin E, Selenium, and Carotenoids.* Washington, DC: The National Academies Press, 2000. (http://www.nap.edu/catalog.php?record_id=9810)

11. National Research Council. *Dietary Reference Intakes for Vitamin A, Vitamin K, Arsenic, Boron, Chromium, Copper, Iodine, Iron, Manganese, Molybdenum, Nickel, Silicon, Vanadium, and Zinc.* Washington, DC: The National Academies Press, 2001. (http://www.nap.edu/catalog.php?record_id=10026)

12. National Research Council. *Dietary Reference Intakes for Energy, Carbohydrate, Fiber, Fat, Fatty Acids, Cholesterol, Protein, and Amino Acids (Macronutrients).* Washington, DC: The National Academies Press, 2005. (http://www.nap.edu/catalog.php?record_id=10490)

13. National Research Council. *Dietary Reference Intakes for Water, Potassium, Sodium, Chloride, and Sulfate.* Washington, DC: The National Academies Press, 2005. (http://www.nap.edu/catalog.php?record_id=10925)

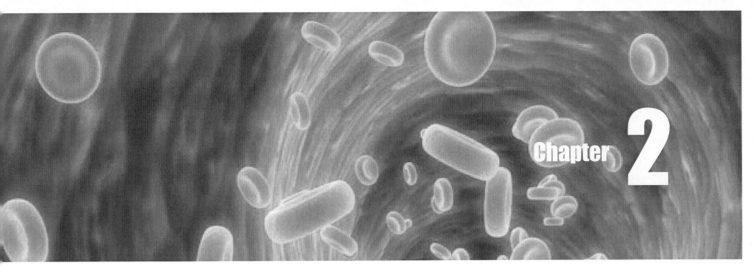

Chapter 2

Regulation of food and nutrient intake.

Does the body specifically regulate intake of these nutrients in any way?

By Maria Dolores Crespo Rodriguez, Saad Haque, Johari Jordan, Margaret Edem Mensah, and Kruti Ravaliya

---

Learning Objectives

At the conclusion of this chapter, you should be able to explain or describe;

1. Regulation of carbohydrates (glucose) and lipid intake by homeostatic and non-homeostatic mechanisms;

2. How protein quality and quantity affects protein balance;

3. Regulatory systems that exist in the body to ensure a supply of protein that is adequate for growth and turnover.

4. Regulation, uptake, and DRIs for potassium, magnesium, phosphorus, and calcium;

5. Integration of signals controlling food intake

6. Hormones and peptides implicated in food intake regulation

Chapter Summary

A better knowledge of all the factors affecting appetite and food intake, can lead to effective treatments against obesity, and associated pathologies such as diabetes, cardiovascular diseases, and micronutrient deficiencies.

A first step in control of the nutrients contained in our bodies is regulation of the quantities and types of foods that we eat. Regulation of intake quantity is a function of huger and appetite, which initiate food consumption, and satiation, which causes food intake to cease (or portion control, where the food available for intake is limited). The balance of the foods we select constitute our diet, which is a function of taste, appetite, culture, and nutrition knowledge. Because individual foods almost always contain different nutrient profiles, the identities and quantities of foods that make up the diet control nutrient intake.

Carbohydrates that convert to glucose in the body are an important source of energy from the diet. In turn, appetite control is crucial for maintaining body energy homeostasis. Contributing to this achievement, homeostatic and non-homeostatic mechanisms play together for controlling carbohydrate intake where endocrine, vascular and nervous systems have an interactive role.

Lipids are found in locations as diverse as the yolk of eggs and the human nervous system and are important members of bacterial, plant and animal membranes. Lipids are a diverse set of compounds that can be grouped according to their function, properties, or structure. Lipids are not water soluble, but instead soluble in organic solvents such as chloroform and ether. There is often a misperception of lipids as harmful, but lipids are needed to protect the body and its organs and function in essential metabolic pathways. This chapter will discuss some basics of lipid digestion and absorption and lipid effects on the regulation of food intake.

Adequate daily quality protein consumption is important in order to maintain normal body functions. Unlike carbohydrates and fats, the body does not store excess proteins for later use. Considering the importance of proteins in the body, it is hypothesized that homeostatic regulatory systems ensure adequate supply of proteins needed for growth and maintenance. Few of the many papers in food intake regulation have looked at whether the body regulates the intake of protein in a specific way. It is likely that both the quantity and quality of dietary protein influence protein intake. Rats tend to avoid diets containing inadequate or excessive amounts of proteins and diets that are imbalanced in amino acids but the nature of signals that drive rats to do this remains obscure. Activation of GCN2 in the APC contributes to the avoidance of amino acid imbalanced diet. Leucine may also plays a role in regulating protein intake by mTORC1 pathway but the mechanism is still unclear.

Macrominerals are an important component of many biochemical reactions, and must be consumed to replenish levels within the body that are necessarily excreted. Macrominerals (potassium, magnesium, phosphorus, sodium, chloride, calcium), those that are found in the body in greater quantities than trace minerals (iron, zinc, copper, manganese), participate in a variety of bodily functions, such as blood pH buffering, cellular build-up and breakdown, DNA transcription, oxidative phosphorylation. As such, they are critical, and must be consumed on a daily basis to ensure adequate levels within the body. This discussion focuses on the minerals potassium, magnesium, phosphorus and calcium, however, many more minerals (micro and macro) are involved in the seemingly simple maintenance of the human body, especially during times of stress or growth. Recommended dietary intakes and adequate intake estimates have been established for these minerals, however, for some of them, such as calcium, the American population falls sharply short of optimum dietary intake. A deeper understanding of the pathways may aid in the development of means to ensure a more well-rounded approach to human nutrition, and better implementation strategies to improve nutrition in at-risk groups.

Interestingly, sodium appears to differ from most minerals in that intake maybe be physiologically controlled within a narrow range. There is also tight regulation of water balance, with homeostatic mechanisms acting on both intake and excretion.

2.1. Regulation of carbohydrates intake: an integrative system

2.1.1. Carbohydrates as a source of energy

Carbohydrates constitute the main energy source for the body. Carbohydrates present in the diet must be hydrolyzed during digestion to their smaller constituents, monosaccharides, prior absorption into the body. From all the monosaccharides (glucose, fructose and galactose), glucose is the main representative of the carbohydrate family since it is the primary source of energy for cells. It is particularly relevant in the brain, which has limited storage of glucose and needs a continuous supply of this monosaccharide from the blood [1, 2]. Foods containing different types of carbohydrates will provide glucose after digestion more or less rapidly. The velocity at which the glucose is obtained from a particular food is known as glycemic index. Technically, the glycemic index of a food has been defined as the "Incremental area under the blood glucose response curve of a specific portion of a test food expressed as a percent of the response to the same amount of carbohydrate from a standard food taken by the same subject" ("Glycemic Index Defined". Glycemic Research Institute. http://www.glycemic. com/Index.htm).

2.1.2. Homeostatic and non-homeostatic mechanisms controlling carbohydrate intake

In general, food intake and more specifically carbohydrates intake, is regulated by multiple factors that can be divided in two main groups of mechanisms: homeostatic and non-homeostatic [3]. Both mechanisms play together in the complex process of appetite control, a key factor in the regulation of energy intake. Endocrine, vascular and nervous systems interact to maintain energy homeostasis controlling the functions of cells, tissues and organs. Hormones secreted by the endocrine glands, are transported through the blood stream to the target organs or tissues and nervous system where a response is generated providing feedback information [3, 4]. The brain plays a crucial function on appetite control regulating food intake. In fact, a key point on appetite regulation is assigned to the gut-brain axis [5]. A better understanding about the central regulation of appetite as well as the mechanisms influencing eating behavior, may contribute to deal with obesity, diabetes, or cardiovascular disease and to develop efficient treatments to fight them [3, 4, 6].

Multiple factors configure the eating behavior, especially regarding to size and meal selection [6]. Eating behavior is influenced by homeostatic or physiological factors (such as gastrointestinal tract secretions and motility, secretion of peptides and hormones) and non-homeostatic factors like psychological, social and also genetic variables. These non-homeostatic factors are thought to influence meal quantity, frequency and timing. Also, the genetic variability of digestive

regulatory hormones like CCK, ghrelin or leptin may have an effect on appetite control [6]. Food selection is also influenced by food palatability (configured by a group of senses like sight, taste, smell) [2]. Basically, there are five oral perceptions for defining taste: sweet, sour, bitter, salty and umami (L-glutamate) [2, 6]. Taste receptors for all of them have been found in stomach, small intestine and colon [7, 8]. The contents in the lumen may activate these taste receptors, inducing an increase in intracellular Ca^{2+}, which stimulates the release of peptides like CCK, GLP-1 and PYY (described below) that are responsible for satiety signals [8]. Specifically associated with glucose, a relationship between dietary sugars (sweet stimulation) and chemosensing control of glucose absorption may influence the secretion of GLP-1 by enteroendocrine L cells in the intestine [7, 8]. The sweet-sensing receptor T1R2/T1R3 has already been identified and described. T1R2/T1R3 is expressed in the oral cavity (taste buds) and also within the gastrointestinal tract, showing sensitivity for natural sweet molecules such as glucose, fructose or sucrose as well as for synthetic sweeteners [8]. Interestingly, it has been shown that in people affected by obesity and diabetes, and thus with an increased blood glucose level, the expression of these taste receptors is reduced [8]. Taste is also intimately related to the 'reward value' of food and satiation [8]. Scientific findings proposed that eating meals composed primarily by carbohydrates may have an effect on increasing blood tryptophan levels, and that leads to serotonin production by the brain which causes a positive effect on mood [9]. However, proteins in the diet can block this mechanism [9]. Indeed, activation of different brain regions of special interest are the dopaminergic limbic and the prefrontal reward areas) will determine the evaluation of a food stimulus [3, 7]. For instance, eating delightful tasting foods such as chocolate, cause the release of endorphins that create a pleasant feeling [9].

2.1.3. Glucose homeostasis

Back in the early 20th century, several associations between appetite and blood glucose levels emerged. Carlston, in 1916, already suggested that low glucose concentration in plasma may function as a stimulator of appetite (meal initiation), and on the contrary, high levels of glucose in plasma could stimulate satiety (meal termination) [10]. In the 1950's, Jean Mayer proposed a "glucostatic hypothesis" by which "glucoreceptor" neurons located in the hypothalamus would detect fluctuations of glucose in plasma, with the consequent generation of signals for meal termination when the concentration of glucose is high. Based on this theory, glucose may function as a satiety factor [11, 12, 13]. In the 80's, Louis-Sylvestre and Le Magnen showed the relationship between the fall in blood glucose and meal initiation in rats, thus, its implication on the short-term appetite control [11]. The concepts of short- and long-term regulation of food intake are associated with the quantity of food ingested. Mainly, the short-term regulation prevents an overeating during each particular meal, maintaining a control on the calories ingested via satiation signals, whereas, a long-term regulation is associated with a control on the body energy storage as fat primarily regulated by adiposity signals (Fig. 1) [4, 14]. Other research also supported the association between the postprandial increase in blood glucose after carbohydrate consumption and the secretion of satiety signals, and also a positive correlation between the period of time of elevation of glucose in plasma, and the interval of time between meals [12]. However, some other studies still found controversial the association between postprandial glycemic status and insulin responses with appetite control, and thus, did not support the "glucostatic theory" [12].

Current scientific research is still dealing with relationships among glycemic levels, weight control, diabetes, obesity and other related pathologies [11, 15], as well as whether glucose homeostasis and metabolism has regulatory factors controlling carbohydrate intake [16]. Recent studies have characterized gluco-sensing neurons, located in the ventromedial hypothalamus and elsewhere in the hindbrain and forebrain, [13]. Gluco-sensing neurons play a critical role on body energy homeostasis due to their function as metabolic sensors that are able to receive and integrate not only glucose concentration but a diversity of hormonal, metabolic and neural peripheral signals [13].

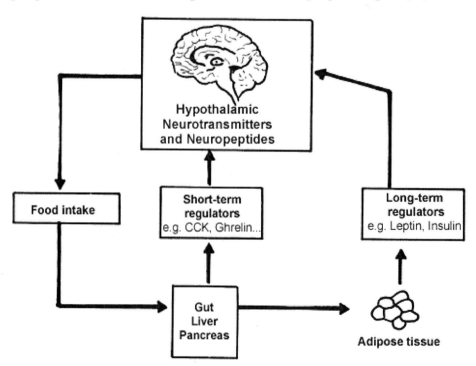

Figure 2.1-1: "Schematic view of the short- and long-term regulation of food intake mediated by ghrelin, insulin and leptin. NPY, neuropeptide Y; AgRP, agouti-related protein; α-MSH, melanocyte-stimulating hormone; CCK, cholecystokinin; PYY, peptide YY; GLP, glucagon-like peptide". (redrawn from: Gil-Campos M, Aguilera CM, Canete R, Gil A. Ghrelin: a hormone regulating food intake and energy homeostasis. Br J Nutr 2006;96:201-26.)

2.2. Lipid Digestion and Absorption and the Regulation of Food: A Review

2.2.1. Introduction

Lipids are a group of naturally occurring compounds that fall into this single category of substance because of their common physical property dissolving in organic solvents such as acetone, ether or chloroform with little or no solubility in water. There are two major categories of lipids, those that contain open-chain compounds that have polar heads and nonpolar tails and those that consist of fused-ring compounds. However, lipids can be categorized into three categories with importance to their dietary sources or their function. Those categories are as follows: simple lipids, compound lipids and derived lipids.

2.2.2. Lipid Digestion

A brief description of the digestion of lipids is needed to understand the involvement of lipids on the regulation of food intake. The most abundant class lipids consumed and digested by humans and other mammals are triacylglycerols (TAG), with lesser amounts of phospholipids and sterols. In the average western diet, approximately 150 g of triglyceride and 4-8 g of phospholipids, mainly lecithin, is consumed daily with two thirds of that amount coming from animal fats. There is also about 7-22 g of endogenous phospholipid, or phospholipids secreted by the body in bile into the gut lumen. Three main steps involved with the digestion of lipids must occur in sequential order: dispersion of bulk fat globules into emulsion particles, hydrolysis of fatty acid esters, and the desorption and dispersion of insoluble lipids [17]. The process of the digestion of lipids begins in the mouth with the lingual lipase breaking the lipids found in the food products. Lipids must be broken down or emulsified into small enough sizes to eventually become absorbed by the body because they are not water-soluble. This emulsification is achieved in the stomach through the action of peristalsis and continues in the small intestine with the assistance of bile salts. Persistalsis is a wavelike motion that moves food through the entire digestive tract [2]. Although chewing food

aids in reducing the size of fat droplets, it is in the stomach that the lipids found in the food eaten are mainly emulsified into smaller particles with the aid of stomach acids [17]. The surface area of dietary lipid droplets that is accessible for digestion is increased tremendously through emulsification. The availability of fat for enzymatic digestion is increased further by the emulsifying actions of the bile salts and binding of lipases to co-lipases. Bile salts are effective emulsifiers because of they have hydrophilic and hydrophobic ends, or amphipathic properties. Esterases, the digestive enzymes responsible for breaking down dietary lipids in the gastrointestinal tract cleave esters bonds that are within the triacyglycerols, phospholipids and cholesterol esters [2,17].

The digestion of triacylglycerols in the mouth due to lingual lipase, in the stomach dues to gastic lipase secreted by serous glands or von Ebner glands, and in the small intestine lumen through the action of pancreatic lipase. Lingual lipases are considered true lipases that act only on aggregated substrates that are insoluble. Lingual lipases are specific for primary ester bonds found in triglycerides. Both lipases and other esterases are more active on triglycerides with short-chain than on those with long-chain fatty acids [17]. Emulsification of lipids by chewing allows a sufficient surface area of the substrate to become exposed to lingual lipases. Emulsified product leaves the stomach and moves to the duodenum as fine lipid droplets. In the duodenum, emulsification continues complemented by bile, which is released by the gallbladder because of the stimulation of cholecystokinin (CCK). Bicarbonate and pancreatic lipase are released from the pancreatic duct at the same time. When bile salts and phospholipids are not present, lipase binds to the triglyceride-water interface via hydrophobic interactions. This interaction causes the activation of pancreatic lipase, assisted by protein colipase, calcium ions and bile salts. The colipase binds to the bile salt providing an anchor site for the lipase. Colipase, is a peptide composed of about 100 amino acids residues that is formed in the lumen from procolipase by the action of trypsin. The digestion of lipids to form absorbable cholesterol and phospholipids use a different pathway and other specific enzymes.

Cholesterol, also categorized as a steroid, can be found membranes and helps in the modification of membrane bound proteins. Cholesterol has many functions, one of which is to serve as a precursor for other steroids and Vitamin D3. However, when in excess, cholesterol can have harmful effects on the health of individuals. Phospholipids are formed when the alcohol group of glycerol is esterified to a phosphoric acid derivative instead of a third fatty acid. Digestion of cholesterol esters uses cholesterol esterase enzymes to yield free cholesterol and a fatty acid. During digestion of phosholipids, a C-2 fatty acid of lecithin is removed by an esterase specific for that carbon position, phospholipase A2, yielding lysolecithin and a free fatty acid.

The products of this enzymatic reaction combine with the bile salts involved in the digestion process to form micelles that are negatively charged. The small size of these micelles allows them to enter spaces that other micelles and lipid droplets are unable to travel. The negative charges on the micelles make them more absorbable by effectively making them water-soluble [18].

Once lipids have reached the size needed through the emulsification process, it can now be absorbed into the body for uses in other chemical processes.

2.2.3. Lipid Absorption

During the absorption process the micelles are absorbed by the enterocytes or mucosal epithelial cells. Lipids taken up by the enterocytes are incorporated into chylomicrons for export to the lymphatic system [25]. While fatty acids are absorbed by enterocytes using both protein- dependent and protein independent processes, cholesterol is dependent upon three specific enzymes that compete with one another in the membrane.

How lipid micelles are carried across the brush border membrane is not fully understood [19]. While considered an energy-independent passive diffusion process, cholesterol is taken up by enterocytes with a high efficiency. The absorption of cholesterol is a 2-fold process incorporating an uptake process then a transport process to complete the absorption. Because of distinctions in the efficiency of intestinal cholesterol absorption, a transporter-facilitated mechanism is implicated [20, 21]. The cholesterol uptake transporter, referred to as Niemann- Pick C1 like 1 (NPC1L1), and ATP-binding cassette (ABC) proteins, ABCG5 and ABCG8, transporters for cholesterol efflux have been

identified [22-25]. Further investigation into NPC1L1 shows that there is a sterol element in the promoter that is in charge of regulating cholesterol absorption in response to the intake of cholesterol. When the expression of NPC1L1 is reduced at the level of transcription the absorption of cholesterol is reduced. When *NpcIII* in mice is deleted there is also a reduction of cholesterol absorption. There is a cholesterol absorption inhibitor, ezetimibe, that acts in the same manner, by targeting NPC1L1 [26]. The reduction of the *NpcIII* gene expression has also been shown in patients who have colon abnormalities. Nuclear liver X receptors (LXRs), scavenger receptor class B type I (SR-B1) and ER membrane-localized enzymes have all been implicated in the absorption of cholesterol. Of these, LXRs have been shown to have an affect on lipogenesis, and may be involved in the regulation of lipid metabolism.

2.2.4. Lipid Intake Regulation

Lipid digestion and absorption allows lipids to be involved in the regulation of the intake of food. When lipids are consumed and the digestion process begins, CCK is stimulated to promote introduction of bile salts that assist in the digestion of lipids. In addition, CCK provides satiety or reduces appetite [27]. Regulation of lipid metabolism can be linked to carbohydrates. Fatty acids that are formed in the liver are either transported using the enzyme carnitine acyl transferase I or, they are converted into TAG and phospholipids. Malonyl CoA is formed when the concentration of mitochondrial citrate is increased making the mitochondria permeable and allowing the citrate to escape into the cytoplasm. This typically occurs when there are not sufficient amounts of glycerophosphate for fatty acids to form triacylglycerol because there has been an increase in free fatty acids. Excess malonyl CoA inhibits carnitine acyl transferase I, increases the synthesis of fatty acids, and suppresses the oxidation of the fatty acids, thereby causing excess glucose to be stored as TAG because lipogenesis has become stimulated. LXRs affect lipogenesis and increase plasma triglycerides through fatty acid synthase up-regulation. Lipogenesis and triglyceride synthesis are linked because LXRs signal conversion of carbohydrate to lipid [28]. Acyl

CoA:cholesterol acyltransferase (ACAT) and other regulatory enzymes connected to LXRs link cholesterol levels and cardiovascular disease.

2.3. In search for a mechanism for protein intake regulation

2.3.1. Introduction:

Proteins are a vital component of our diets. They play important roles in maintaining healthy body functions. They serve as enzymatic catalysts, are used as transport molecules (hemoglobin transports oxygen) and storage molecules (iron is stored in the liver as a complex with the protein ferritin); they are used in movement (proteins are the major component of muscles); they are needed for mechanical support (skin and bone contain collagen-a fibrous protein); they mediate cell responses (rhodopsin is a protein in the eye which is used for vision); antibody proteins are needed for immune protection; control of growth and cell differentiation uses proteins (hormones) [29]. Basically, they are involved in virtually all cell functions.

In situations where protein intake is inadequate, the body may show certain deficiency symptoms. When protein intake is inadequate, but total caloric intake is sufficient, a condition known as **kwashiorkor** may occur [30]. Symptoms of kwashiorkor include an enlarged stomach, loss of hair and hair color, and an enlarged liver. Conversely, if protein and caloric intake are both inadequate, a condition known as marasmus occurs [31]. **Marasmus** symptoms include stunted growth, extreme muscle loss, and weakness.

Protein can take the place of some fat and carbohydrate, for example in supplying the body with energy, but fat and carbohydrate cannot serve in place of the body's need for protein. Also unlike carbohydrates and fats the body does not store extra proteins [32]. Only plants and prokaryotic microorganisms fix non-protein nitrogen into amino acids. That is why the minimum amount of protein, from a good source, must be consumed daily. Considering the importance of protein intake, it is hypothesized that there is an existence of homeostatic regulatory systems that ensure adequate supply of proteins needed for growth and physiology [32]. This regulatory system is affected by

the quality and/or quantity of protein intake [32, 33] but the question is whether they actually reflect a specific, homeostatic regulation of protein intake or regulation of food intake in general.

2.3.2. Quality of Proteins

Protein quality is a term used to describe how well a protein from food matches the body's requirements, i.e. the biological value of the protein. This biological value is dependent on the building blocks that make up the protein; called **amino acids**. There are 20 primary amino acids and proteins are formed by the linking of different combinations of these twenty amino acids. Out of the twenty, nine of them cannot be synthesized by the body on its own [34]. These are considered "essential" and must come from the diet. The nine essential amino acids include: leucine, histidine, isoleucine, lysine, methionine, phenylalanine, threonine, tryptophan and valine.

According to their quality, proteins can be classified as complete or incomplete. A complete protein contains adequate amount of all of the essential amino acids that should be incorporated into a diet [35]. Such proteins are mostly found in animal sources such as meat, poultry, fish and milk. An incomplete protein (also referred to as partial protein) is any protein that lacks one or more essential amino acids in correct proportions [35]. These are normally found in plant sources such as corn, rice, and beans. By combining foods from two or more incomplete proteins, a complete protein can be created. The amino acids that may be missing from one type of food can be compensated by adding a protein that contains that missing amino acid. An example is combining legumes with cereals. Legumes contain relatively low quantities of the essential amino acid methionine, but adequate amounts of lysine whereas cereals have just the opposite ratio [36]. These are considered complementary proteins when they are combined to compensate for each other's lack of amino acids.

2.3.3. Quantity of Protein Intake/ Protein Requirements

The amount of protein required in a person's diet is dependent on the age, body size, physical state of the person, overall energy intake, physical activity level and the quality of proteins. Sedentary or non-growing individuals need to eat enough protein to match whatever they lose daily from protein breakdown to maintain a state of protein equilibrium or protein balance. Currently, the recommended dietary allowance (RDA) for protein is 0.8 grams of protein per kilogram of healthy body weight [37]. This is an estimate for the amount of protein required for nearly all adults to maintain protein equilibrium [37]. Healthy weight is used as a reference in the determination of protein needs because excess fat storage doesn't contribute much to protein needs and the body cannot store excess protein once it is consumed, so it is converted into glucose or fat and then stored as fat or metabolized for energy needs.

Protein requirements are higher during childhood for growth and development, during pregnancy or when breast-feeding in order to nourish a baby, when the body needs to recover from an illness, malnutrition or trauma and when physical activity level is high [37, 38]. In such cases it is said that the body needs to be in a state of positive protein balance i.e. protein intake exceeds related protein losses. Alternatively, if protein intake is less than related protein losses, such as is often seen during acute illness, then the body is said to be in a state of negative protein balance.

2.3.4. How Dietary Protein Quality and Quantity Affects Protein Intake

A large number of behavioral studies have demonstrated that protein intake is influenced by the protein or amino acid content of the diet [32, 33]. For example when rats are offered a choice between two diets they will select: a diet containing an adequate amount of protein in preference to one that is deficient in protein; a diet containing a moderate amount of protein in preference to one containing an excessive amount; a diet containing an adequate amount of an indispensable amino acid in preference to one that is deficient in that amino acid; and a diet with a balanced pattern of amino acids in preference to one containing disproportionately high amounts of one or more indispensable amino acids [32, 33].

Such observations suggest that protein intake and selection are controlled through mechanisms that enable the rat to recognize when the amount of protein consumed is inadequate or excessive and if the diet contains appropriate proportions of indispensable amino acids.

2.3.5. Physiological Regulation of Protein Intake

Research studies on how the body regulates food intake have mainly been in the context of energy intake despite the fact that food intake is influenced by more than just the energy content of the diet. It is less well understood whether the body regulates the intake of proteins specifically, and whether mechanisms in the body exists that allow individuals deficient in protein to gravitate towards protein diets or individuals exceeding their protein requirements to reduce high protein intake.

The hypothalamus plays a major role in appetite regulation associated with the homeostatic regulation of energy balance, and it would be logical to hypothesize that the hypothalamus contributes to the homeostatic regulation of protein balance. The hypothalamus receives neural and hormonal signals from the gastrointestinal tract (GIT) such as cholecystokinin (CCK), ghrelin, pancreatic polypeptide, peptide YY and glucagon-like peptide-1 (GLP-1) that have been shown to influence (stimulate or inhibit) food Intake [39, 40]. Peptide YY (PYY), pancreatic polypeptide and glucagon-like peptide-1 suppress appetite, whilst ghrelin increases appetite. The mechanisms by which these gut hormones modify food intake are the subject of ongoing investigation. Whiles these hormones regulate food intake in general, the question still remains if any of these hormones specifically regulate protein intake and selection.

An early hypothesis made in the early 1970's by Fernstrom and Wurtman [41] was that serotonin or its precursor, tryptophan, might provide a unique signal related to dietary protein intake [32, 41]. They reported that a high correlation was observed between brain tryptophan concentration and the ratio of the plasma concentration of tryptophan to the sum of the concentrations of the large neutral amino acids (LNAA) that compete with tryptophan for entry into brain (Trp/LNAA) [42]. A high correlation was also observed between plasma Trp/LNAA ratio and brain serotonin concentration. Anderson and Ashley [43] proposed, in view of the observations of Fernstrom and Wurtman [41], that changes in brain serotonin concentration in response to changes in protein intake might serve as a signal for a system in the brain that controlled long-term protein intake independently of energy intake. Although these observations show a likely involvement of serotonin in regulation of protein intake, much of the supporting evidence is based on pharmacological experiments and the use of extreme diets, and as such, there seems to be limited support for this mechanism for regulation of protein intake.

More recent experiments have suggested leucine (one of the branched chain amino acids (BCAAs) as likely to present a physiological signal of hypothalamic amino acid availability.

Leucine is known to stimulate muscle protein synthesis and decrease the rate of protein degradation, when injected into the brain by acting locally within the mediobasal hypothalamus [32], via activation of mTOR (mammalian target of rapamycin) and/or inhibition of AMPK signaling. mTOR is an important receptor affecting various anabolic pathways, including protein synthesis. Leucine also stimulates a temporary increase in insulin concentration, which also somehow affects mTOR indirectly. Leucine therefore suppresses food intake. While these data collectively provide a cellular and neural mechanism for leucine dependent decreases in food intake, the role of these signaling systems in the specific regulation of protein intake is still unclear. There are no data connecting this mechanism to larger issues of protein homeostasis [32].

Currently, the strongest evidence supporting physiological regulation of protein intake is amino acid imbalance and its effect on the brain, specifically the anterior piriform cortex (APC) [44]. An explanation for rats' ability to detect and avoid diets that are imbalanced in amino acids relates this "learned aversion" behavior to critical molecular events within the APC that results in an accumulation of uncharged tRNAs for the missing amino acid [45]. This accumulation of uncharged tRNA activates the kinase GCN2 locally within the APC, and replacement of the missing amino acid locally within the APC or deletion of GCN2 is sufficient to attenuate this learned aversion [45, 46].

2.4. Regulation of Food Intake: Integration of appetite signals by central nervous system

The hypothalamus, together with other brain areas, constitute a key site in the central neural system associated with feedback control of food intake and appetite and has a crucial role maintaining peripheral energy homeostasis (Fig. 2) [4, 5]. Main areas of the brain implicated in the integration of satiation signals, adipose signals and other signals also related with appetite and food intake are represented and described in figures 2 and 3.

The brain is constantly receiving information about energy levels from peripheral organs, as well as information about nutrient absorption rate and fluctuations on energy homeostasis (Fig. 2) [1, 4, 47, 48]. After integrating this information the brain is able to regulate the level of glucose and other nutrients in storage organs (i.e. glycogen in the liver or fat in adipose tissue). Blood glucose concentration is strictly regulated by the neuroendocrine system [1, 2]. Glucose metabolism may be partly regulated through the circadian clock located in the nuclei of hypothalamus, as well as by integrating signals from the periphery [49]. In response to peripheral stimuli the brain sends signals through the autonomic nervous system stimulating the secretion of metabolically active hormones that differentially activate the metabolic pathways of glycogenesis, glycogenolysis or gluconeogenesis, in concert with regilation by the pancreatic hormones insulin and glucagon and glucocorticoid hormones secreted by the adrenal cortex [2, 4].

2.4.1. Pancreatic Hormones with Effects on Glucose Homeostasis and Food Intake

Insulin is a hormone secreted in the fed state by β-cells located in the pancreas in response to an elevation in glucose blood levels (i.e. after ingestion of carbohydrates). It is involved in glucose, lipid and amino acid synthesis and storage [2]. On the other hand, the hormone glucagon is secreted in a fasted state by pancreatic α-cells, in response to a reduction in plasma glucose concentration and is stimulated along with glucocorticoid hormones such as cortisol [50].

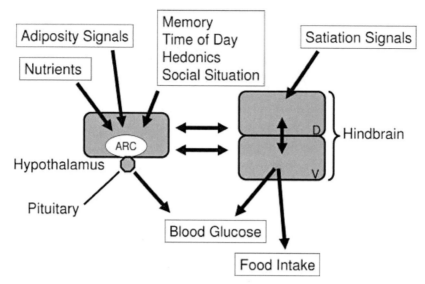

Figure. 2.4-1: Satiation signals with origin in the gastrointestinal system reach the dorsal hindbrain (D). Dorsal hindbrain sends satiation signals and is directly connected with the ventral hindbrain (V), which controls blood glucose levels through the autonomic nervous system. The center controlling eating behavior (food intake) is located in this ventral part as well. The dorsal hindbrain also transmits information from other factors from anterior areas to the hypothalamus and other brain areas, which integrate satiation and adiposity signals. Also at this area information about available nutrients, memory or experience, timing, hedonics or social situation is integrated. This information is then transmitted to the ventral hindbrain and pituitary, where several variables of energy homeostasis are controlled. (Taken from: Woods SC, D'Alessio DA. Central control of body weight and appetite. J Clin Endocrinol Metab 2008;93:S37-50. [4])

Fluctuations in the secretion of these two hormones modulate glucose metabolism and maintain glucose homeostasis. For instance, the consumption of carbohydrates leads to an increase in plasma glucose concentration, which stimulates the secretion of insulin and reduces glucagon. In contrast, when glucose levels in plasma are decline, glucagon secretion is stimulated and insulin inhibited [2]. Neural centers located in the hypothalamus and nucleus of the solitary tract (NTS) *in the* caudal brainstem play a crucial role controlling plasma glucose through appetite regulation, and thus impact energy balance (Fig. 3) [1, 4, 47, 48]. Examples are the hypothalamic receptors for leptin and insulin that integrate adiposity signals from the periphery (Fig. 3) [54]. Insulin as an adiposity signal, together with the hormone leptin secreted in adipocytes, is implicated in the long-term food intake regulation (Fig. 1), and its secretion is directly proportional to body fat content [4]. In addition, insulin in circulation can influence the production of glucose in the liver via NPY secretion in the arcuate nucleus (ARC) in the hypothalamus [49].

2.4.2. Other neuropeptides affecting food intake

Other peptides secreted in the gastrointestinal tract, adipose tissue and brain affect appetite and eating behavior involved in the regulation of the food intake. The identification of a wide diversity of neuropeptides with hormonal activity has supported the evidence of the interdependent activity of endocrine and central nervous systems [2]. Many of these peptides involved in appetite control are directly related with caloric intake (i.e. CCK or PYY). Hormones that may have a direct relationship with glucose intake, metabolism and homeostasis, are insulin, glucagon, leptin, GLP-1 and ghrelin.

At the upper gastrointestinal tract level, between the absorptive and exocrine cells, can be found highly specialized endocrine cells. These endocrine cells are responsible for secreting hormones such us CCK, secretin, GIP or gastrin [5]. The roles of the gastrointestinal tract in affecting appetite and satiety leads to its consideration as a physiological target for

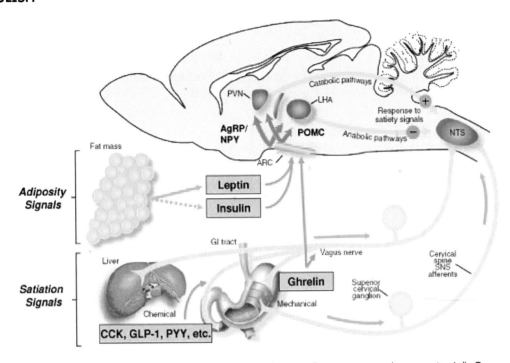

Figure. 2.4.2-1: "Model summarizing different levels of control over energy homeostasis". Several signals emerge during and after meals, for example distension of the stomach and the secretion of peptides in the intestine, like CCK, GLP-1 and others, constituting the satiation signals. These signals activate the sensory nerves sending nerve impulses to the hindbrain, activating neurons in the nucleus of the solitary tract (NTS) with the consequent influence on meal size. At the same time, the hormone ghrelin secreted in the stomach, also stimulates neurons directly in the ARC through vagal stimulus. On the other hand, adiposity signals related to body fat content, fundamentally leptin and insulin, reach the ARC through the blood-brain barrier. In response, proopiomelanocortin (POMC), NPY and AgRP are synthesized. ARC neurons also interact with other hypothalamic areas, such us the PVN and the LHA. The PVN response is catabolic, promoting the intensity of satiation signals in the hindbrain. On the contrary, LHA output is anabolic, thus suppressing the activity of the satiation signals. (Taken from: Woods SC, D'Alessio DA. Central control of body weight and appetite. J Clin Endocrinol Metab 2008;93:S37-50. [4])

weight control strategies and treatments [3]. Adipose cells, also function as an endocrine tissue, secreting the hormone leptin that is implicated in body fat mass regulation, constitute another key point in appetite control [2, 51]. The production of hormones by specialized peripheral cells is stimulated by different chemical signals such as blood concentrations of glucose, fatty acids, or amino acids, and pH fluctuations [2]. The hormones secreted by the peripheral endocrine glands in response to the energy yielding substrates in blood include ghrelin, leptin, CCK, GLP- 1, and PYY [8].

Table 1 summarizes the information about the peptides described below and their influence on appetite.

Cholecystokinin (CCK) is secreted by I cells in duodenum and jejunum and also by the brain and enteric nerves [2, 4, 5]. It stimulates secretion of enzymes and pancreatic juice by the pancreas and also stimulates gallbladder contraction, releasing bile, both into the duodenum, as well as stimulating gastric motility [4]. CCK secretion is particularly sensitive to lipids orproteins in the chyme entering the duodenum [6]. CCK secretion stimulates local nervous receptors in the duodenum that transmit the signal through the vagus nerve to the brain to elicit a short-term satiation signal [4, 5].

Glucagon-like peptides (especially GLP-1) are secreted from the ileum and colon by L cells, where they coexist with PYY and oxyntomodulin, and also by the nervous system [2, 4, 5]. GLP-1 secretion is triggered by fats and carbohydrates in the diet [5]. GLP-1 can influence glucose metabolism because it increases glucose-dependant insulin secretion and decreases glucagon production, and also promotes the growth of pancreatic β-cells [5].

Peptide tyrosine-tyrosine (PYY), **neuropeptide Y** (NPY), and **pancreatic polypeptide** (PP) constitute the pancreatic polypeptide–fold (PP-fold) family. PYY is secreted by distal intestinal L cells in the ileum, which also co-express GLP1 [2, 5]. PYY production is proportional to caloric intake. It inhibits gastric acid and pancreatic juice secretions and also has an inhibitory effect on gastric and intestinal motility [4, 5]. PYY and GLP-1 are secreted in the postprandial state and both are components of an inhibitory feedback mechanism regulating the transition of nutrients in the gastrointestinal tract known as "ileal brake" [4, 5]. Both peptides have an inhibitory effect on appetite and food intake when administered to humans. Although both interact with receptors in the brain, the detailed mechanism of action remains unknown. The anorectic effect of these intestinal hormones, have been investigated as possible therapeutic targets for obesity treatment [4, 5].

NPY is secreted primarily in the hypothalamus and it is known for its strong effect increasing appetite [4, 5, 51]. The hypothalamus is connected to receptors in the brainstem for other hormones that regulate appetite.

Pancreatic peptide (PP) is secreted in the pancreas in the postprandial state and is regulated by vagal stimulus. PP affects gastric acid, exocrine pancreas and biliary secretion and gastrointestinal motility [4, 5]. There are some controversies regarding to the role of this peptide in energy homeostasis since some studies showed that peripheral administration decreases appetite and food intake but central administration showed the opposite effect [4].

Oxyntomodulin is secreted by L cells in the distal intestine. This proglucagon-derived peptide acts to decrease hunger and therefore constitutes a satiety factor. The mechanism of its action still remains unknown but it is thought that GLP-1 receptors expressed at the arcuate nucleus of hypothalamus is involved [4, 5]. GLP1 activates neurons in the hindbrain whereas oxyntomodulin activates neurons in the hypothalamus [5].

Glucose-dependent insulinotropic peptide (GIP), formerly known as **gastric inhibitory peptide** is secreted by enteroendocrine K cells in duodenum and jejunum. GIP and GLP-1 are classified as incretins because they stimulate insulin secretion through a glucose-dependent mechanism. GIP also inhibits gastric secretions and motility [52].

Amylin is a hormone secreted by pancreatic cells (like insulin) and also by gastric and intestinal endocrine cells. It delays gastric emptying and inhibits gastric acid and glucagon secretion [2, 4, 5]. Amylin seems to directly stimulate the area postrema of the hindbrain [4].

Apolipoprotein A-IV (APO A-IV) is a glycoprotein secreted in the intestine and also synthesized by the arcuate nucleus in the hypothalamus. APO A-IV is related to lipid absorption. APO A-IV may be a link between the short and long-term regulation of body fat [4, 5].

Enterostatin is a peptide also related to lipid digestion that originates from colipase secreted by the exocrine pancreas. Administration of enterostatin, systemically or directly into the brain in animals, reduced food intake, specifically fats, but not carbohydrate or protein. However, these findings, as for apo A-IV as for enterostatin, are not yet proved in humans [4, 5].

Bombesin-family peptides include the amphibian peptide bombesin and the mammalian analogs, **gastrin-releasing peptide** (GRP) and **neuromedin B** (NMB). Gastrin-releasing peptide (GRP) is released from enteric nerves. GRP enhance the release of gastrin and other peptides such as glucagon-like peptides, CCK and somatostatin. The administration of these peptides, both systemically and centrally, can cause a decrease in food intake. Mice presenting a reduced number of GRP receptors eat bigger meals and develop obesity [4].

Ghrelin is a peptide primarily secreted in the fasting state by endocrine cells located in the stomach and small intestine that stimulates food intake. Ghrelin is known for increasing appetite when injected either centrally or peripherally, as well as being the only hormone in humans and animals increasing short-term food intake [5, 14]. It increases gastrointestinal motility and decreases insulin secretion. Plasma levels of ghrelin rise shortly before meals, inversely to satiation peptides, and the ingestion of nutrients, especially carbohydrates, suppress its production. Thus, it is associated with short-term control of feed intake [4, 14] (Fig. 2.4.1). This suppression is mediated by non-vagal intestinal signals stimulated by insulin. Indeed, ghrelin also stimulates the secretion of neuropeptide Y. One peculiarity of ghrelin is having a direct effect on receptors located in the hypothalamus (like other gastrointestinal signals such as GLP-1 or CCK). However, it seems to be also interacting with receptors located on vagal sensory nerves with a function unrelated to satiation [4]. Novel findings also suggest an important role of ghrelin in regulating the secretion of leptin and insulin and vice versa [14].

Leptin is secreted mainly by white adipocytes and has a suppressing effect on food intake, acting on the satiety center located in the hypothalamus. Leptin travels through the circulatory system until reaching the central nervous system where it interacts with specific receptors, ob-R [56]. Leptin secretion is proportional to body fat stores and its activity intensifies energy expenditure with a potential outcome of reducing body weight [51]. Its action on satiety or hunger inhibition is due to its effect on other peptides and via the sympathetic nervous system [4]. For instance, it inhibits hypothalamic neurons from secreting NPY and agouti-related protein (AgRP), suppressing the effect of these appetite-stimulating peptides. Indeed, it stimulates the melanocyte-stimulating hormone (α-MSH), an inhibitor of hunger formed by cleavage of proopiomelanocortin (POMC) secreted by neurons in the arcuate nucleus of hypothalamus, and also stimulates the appetite suppressant neuropeptide cocaine amphetamine-regulated transcript (CART) secreted in the hypothalamus (Fig. 3) [4, 51]. Moreover, the corticotropin-releasing factor (CRF) is also associated with the suppression of food intake generated by leptin. It is thought that GLP-1 is also implicated in the metabolic activity of leptin [4, 51]. Besides its central actions, leptin is considered one key factor on peripheral glucose homeostasis regulation, through peripheral pathways such as its effect on insulin secretion by pancreatic β-cells. Experimental findings have revealed that insulin levels may have a direct effect on leptin secretion. Insulin also participates in other metabolic process such as fat metabolism, reproductive functions, and hematopoiesis [51]. Other scientific findings have elucidated a link between a deficiency in leptin or leptin receptors and obesity as well as an increase in insulin resistance and glucose intolerance, both associated with diabetes [51]. Leptin is thought to be involved in long-term control of feeding, basically associated with the maintenance of normal levels of energy stored in the body as fat (Fig. 1) [14, 51].

Further research in the field of food intake and control of appetite is still needed due to the complexity of all the mechanisms and molecular pathways implicated. Of special interest can be applications of research for developing new therapies targeting specific neuroendocrine cells or receptors, or interventions on different regulatory mechanisms for addressing the epidemics of obesity, diabetes and cardiovascular disease.

*Modified from: Cummings DE, Overduin J. Gastrointestinal regulation of food intake. J Clin Invest 2007;117:13-23, [5] and Woods SC, D'Alessio DA. Central control of body weight and appetite. J Clin Endocrinol Metab 2008;93:S37-50. [4]

2.5. Macrominerals and Regulation of Intake

2.5.1. Introduction

Minerals are an important component to human nutrition that required in varying concentrations daily to meet adequate nutrition. Macrominerals include the common minerals calcium, phosphorus, magnesium, sodium, potassium, chloride, and sulfur. Other minerals are also required for bodily functions in lower concentrations, and are referred to as microminerals or trace elements, and these include minerals such as iron, zinc, copper, manganese, and others.

There are varying definitions on the required concentrations of minerals to be considered macrominerals. If the requirement constitutes at least 0.01% of the total body weight or greater than 100 mg/day, or the mineral occurs in a minimum quantity of 5 g per 60 kg human body, these definitions would fit macrominerals.

As macrominerals are required for daily metabolic function, a minimum quantity must be consumed. However, a maximum level of consumption must also

TABLE 2.5-1: Peptides with effect on food intake and its main site of production *

Peptide	Main site of synthesis	Effect on food intake
CCK	Proximal intestinal I cells	Decrease
Apo A-IV	Intestinal epithelial cells	Decrease
GLP-1	Distal-intestinal L cells	Decrease
PYY	Distal-intestinal L cells	Decrease
Oxyntomodulin	Distal-intestinal L cells	Decrease
PP	Pancreatic F cells	Decrease
Glucagon	Pancreatic α cells	Increase
Insulin	Pancreatic ® cells	Decrease
Amylin	Pancreatic ® cells	Decrease
Enterostatin	Exocrine pancreas	Decrease
GRP/NMB	Gastric myenteric neurons	Decrease
Leptin	White adipose/gastric chief and P cells	Decrease
Ghrelin	Gastric X/A–like cells	Increase
Agouti-related protein (AgRP)	Arcuate nucleus- hypothalamus	Increase
Neuropeptide Y (NPY)	Hypothalamus	Increase
Melanocyte stimulating hormone (α MSH)	Arcuate nucleus- hypothalamus	Decrease
Neuropeptide cocaine amphetamine-regulated transcript (CART)	Ventral tegmental area (VTA)- brain	Decrease

be established since all minerals have the potential for toxicity. It is important to be mindful of these potential issues issues of toxicity and deficiency, which can vary among population types based on race, age, gender, and physiological state (pregnant, lactating, etc.) In order to maintain appropriate levels of minerals within the body, they are transported to and from where they are needed via the blood, and can be found in cells, as well as in the extracellular matrix.

2.5.2. Potassium

Potassium is a major intracellular cation that makes up about 0.35% of total human body weight. Potassium intake is largely regulated by food choices. Potassium can be found in a variety of foods, such as prunes, bananas, cantaloupe and honeydew. The absorption and transportation of potassium is not entirely known, though the majority is through the small intestine via passive diffusion or sodium-potassium ATPase pumps [2]. The amount absorbed varies among individuals

and may be affected by the quantity consumed. Numerous studies link increased consumption levels of potassium to lowered blood pressure [53, 54]. Potassium consumption was linked to lower excreted urinary calcium [56, 57], but this observation does not necessarily mean that bone calcium levels are maintained. Potassium is balanced in the body through the kidney, where kidney potassium levels mirror that of the blood. Aldosterone maintains blood potassium levels, through reciprocal maintenance of sodium and potassium [2]. However, abnormally high blood potassium (hyperkalemia) can lead to toxic side effects as well, such as cardiac disorders. Generally, potassium does not build up in the body, as normal circulation and renal function maintain adequate concentrations. However, during times of excessive fluid loss through vomiting or diarrhea, hyperkalemia can occur. It is possible to develop a potassium deficiency, which is associated with high blood pressure and increased urinary calcium excretion. An adequate intake of potassium has been developed at 4700 mg of potassium per day; however, most Americans do not meet this requirement, and as such are potentially potassium deficient. The average potassium intake in the US measured in the 1990's was approximately 2.6 g/day [74].When adequate potassium is supplied, the body is able to maintain a healthy blood level, and as such, an upper limit for intake has not been developed [2].

2.5.3. Magnesium

Magnesium is the fourth most common cation present in the body, with a normal adult body content of about 25 g distributed between the skeleton and soft tissues [58]. Much of the magnesium found within the body is associated with bone. Of the magnesium that is not bound to bones, up to 90% can be associated with ATP or ADP, and can aid in the hydrolysis of the phosphodiester bond of ATP [2]. Food sources of magnesium include coffee, nuts, legumes, and whole-grain cereals. Magnesium is present in many food, but few at high concentrations. It plays a role in a wide variety of physiological functions, such as enzyme substrates, direct enzyme activation, and influencing membrane properties and specifically in cellular functions such as oxidative phosphorylation, glycolysis, DNA transcription and protein synthesis. Magnesium homeostasis is maintained by a very efficient system, centered in the kidney, and is very closely monitored for slight changes. The magnesium concentration in the kidney mirrors that of the blood, and can regulate blood concentration of magnesium. It can be absorbed passively (in situations where high levels of magnesium are consumed), or actively (when low levels of magnesium are consumed). The most efficient magnesium absorption occurs in the distal small bowel, though absorption occurs throughout the entire intestinal tract. The estimated average requirement for magnesium is 265 mg per day for females, and 320 mg per day for males, and the recommended daily allowance for females is 350 mg per day and 420 mg per day for males, however, average consumption of this mineral falls below these limits with averages for females around 228 mg per day and males 328 mg per day. Long-term disease has not been directly and clearly linked to low levels of consumption of magnesium, however, some studies have suggested relationships. During times of

magnesium depletion, blood levels of potassium also decrease, while levels of calcium and sodium increase [58]. Dietary interactions between magnesium and other minerals can cause an increase or decrease in the amount of absorbed or excreted magnesium. Diets high in caffeine, calcium, sodium and protein can cause unwarranted excretion of magnesium. No hormone has been identified as primarily involved in magnesium metabolism [58]. Conversely, higher levels of vitamin D can improve magnesium absorption in the small intestine, and monosaccharides and disaccharides, such as fructose and lactose, can promote the absorption of magnesium in the gastrointestinal tract [58].

2.5.4. Phosphorus

Another macromineral that is widely found in the human body is phosphorus. It makes up about 0.8-1.2% of total body weight, with the majority present in the skeleton. Phosphorus is found in a wide variety of foods, including meat, poultry, eggs, and dairy products, with animal- based products being better sources than plant-foods. Phosphorus may be high in some processed foods because it is added to improve function and stability. The phosphorus in many plants is in the form of phytic acid, which has limited bioavailability and can interact negatively with other macrominerals (such as calcium and magnesium), to prevent their absorption [64]. Bioavailability of phosphorus from phytates is low because mammals do not have the ability to break down and digest phytate, through a lack of phytase. However, some microflora in the gastrointestinal tract are able to digest phytate, but only when they are not linked to cations such as calcium or iron. Therefore, although total phosphorus intake is largely governed by the quantity in foods that are selected, the amount available for tissue homeostasis may not be directly proportional to intake. The majority of phosphorus absorption occurs in the small intestine, via similar pathways as magnesium, through active (when lower levels of phosphorus are consumed), and passive diffusion (when higher levels of phosphorus are consumed). Phosphorus is usually in an environmental scarcity, in comparison to other macrominerals such as calcium [60], although it may be high in processed foods due to its diverse functions as a food additive. Roughly 200 mmol of phosphorus is filtered and reabsorbed through the kidney on a daily basis. Parathyroid hormone and fibroblast growth factor 23 (FGF-23) are key in maintaining levels of serum phosphorus. FGF-23 acts on reuptake of inorganic phosphate; as serum levels of inorganic phosphate increase, FGF-23 is produced, inhibiting reuptake of the inorganic phosphate from renal tubule fluid, thereby reducing the serum concentration of inorganic phosphate. Alternatively, PTH responds to low inorganic phosphate to promote osteoclastic release of bone mineral, and increase serum calcium and phosphate levels. Cells do not store very much inorganic phosphate, and as such rely on ECF to deliver phosphate stored in bone when necessary. Phosphorus deficiency is termed hypophosphatemia, and is very rare, usually occurring concurrently with metabolic disorders. There are many manifestations of hypophosphatemia, and include anorexia, osteomalacia, rickets, confusion and even death. Alternatively, excessive phosphorus in the body is termed hyperphosphatemia, and is generally concurrent with renal failure. Manifestations of this condition include calcification of arteries and higher risk of cardiovascular disease [60]. An estimated average requirement has been established for phosphorus, at 580 mg per day, and RDAs are 700 mg per day for males and females who are 19 years and older [2].

2.5.5. Calcium

Calcium, the most abundant divalent cation in the body, represents about 2% of total body weight, with the vast majority (99%) contained in the bones and teeth. Calcium is available in a variety of foods, such as dairy products, seafoods, cruciferous vegetables and dark leafy greens. In some fruits and vegetables, calcium inhibitors, such as oxalic acid or phytic acid can significantly reduce calcium. Oxalate has a low solubility, and is difficult to ionize in the gastrointestinal tract, making calcium absorption difficult [61]. Alternatively, there are some salts that promote absorption of calcium, such as calcium citrate malate. It has a very high solubility, and can dissociate easily in the gastrointestinal tract, increasing the likelihood of calcium absorption [61].

Calcium absorption from foods in the intestine is inefficient and dependent on a variety of factors, such as serum calcium levels, and physiological state

(such as age, pregnancy, etc), and calcium concentration in the meal itself. As higher levels of calcium are consumed, it is less likely to be efficiently absorbed, and is therefore recommended that calcium be consumed in lower doses more frequently throughout the day. Absorption can occur in two different methods, as in other macrominerals, via a passive diffusion or an active transport [61]. In the passive diffusion method, the lumen concentration of calcium dictates the amount of calcium absorbed. In the active transport method, calcium-binding proteins, such as calbindin, are stimulated by the increased production of calcitriol, and calcium transporters transport calcium through calcium channels within the cell membrane [62].

Recommended dietary intakes of calcium have been established for a variety of age groups and genders, however, for most adults, ages 19-51, 800 mg per day is recommended by the Institute of Medicine. At ages greater than 51, for females, the recommendation increases to 1000 mg, in order to attempt to counteract the decrease in ability to absorb calcium as humans age. However, the same recommendation is not made for men greater than 51 years. The recommendation is maintained at 800 mg per day [61]. Calcium deficiency is common among many Americans, especially young, adolescent females. Low levels of calcium are associated with a variety of disorders, including kidney stones and osteoporosis, as well as hypertension, and polycystic ovarian syndrome in women. Low calcium intakes increase bone turnover rate, and cause an increase in production of PTH. Conversely, there are also issues associated with excessive consumption of calcium. Conditions associated with high calcium levels or hypercalcemia, include vascular calcification, myocardial infarction, prostate health issues, and kidney stones [61]

2.5.6. Sodium appetite

It is possible that a significant portion of many populations consume excess sodium and/or chloride. The UL for sodium is 2300 mg/day, based on the fact that many people with hypertension will respond to sodium intake above that level with a dose responsive rise in blood pressure [63]. The RDA was established at 1500 mg per day based on short term studies of EAR in groups of individuals. In contrast, a metaanalysis of research on sodium intake found an average of nearly

3700 mg/day [64] in populations from around the world and over a time frame of 50 years. The USDA has promoted reduced sodium intake in its Dietary Guidelines for Americans [65] and in appeals to the food industry to lower the sodium content of processed foods. Many salt substitutes are now available and reduced sodium versions of many processed foods are in the market place. Some ethnic cuisines use more salt in foods than others, yet the sodium intake was reported to be consistent across time and populations [64]. A specific appetite for sodium or salt is known to occur in animals [66]. Sodium appetite increases when intake is low and renin-angiotensin-aldosterone hormonal signal that conserves sodium by reducing excretion is stimulated. Agriculturalists take advantage of this mechanism to provide dietary supplements to animals by placing trace-element impregnated salt blocks in pastures and rangelands. A recent report from the Institute of Medicine [67] "explains that there is no consistent evidence to support an association between sodium intake and either a beneficial or adverse effect on most direct health outcomes other than some [cardiovascular disease] outcomes (including stroke and CVD mortality) and all-cause mortality." Although the appropriate sodium intake may still be subject to debate, it is clear that most humans will seek out salty foods to take in a quantity of sodium that is above the UL. This specific appetite is not recognized for other mineral nutrients.

2.5.7. Conclusions

It is clear that there are a variety of interactions between the various macrominerals that are required for daily function, and it is also clear that it is a very delicate balance that is struck for optimal digestion and nutrient absorption. The body can compensate for a small swing on either side of the balance; however, it is possible to fall into the deficient or toxic levels. There is little evidence that humans actively seek foods to balance intake of most minerals. Most elements are widely distributed in the foods we eat and selection of a variety of foods of different colors and flavors is likely to provide intake of all essential mineral elements. Homeostatic mechanisms that vary rates of absorption, excretion and storage are usually adequate to provide a healthy range of physiological concentrations in cells

and tissues over a wide range of intakes that provide adequate energy. Exceptions noted above, include potentially suboptimum intake of potassium and calcium in many individuals that may be contributing to higher than necessary incidence of hypertension and osteoporosis. The other exception is the demonstrated appetite for sodium that seeks foods that will provide a usual intake of about 2600 to 4800 mg per day.

2.6. Regulation of water intake

2.6.1. Introduction

Water is a critical molecule that is responsible for supporting the lives of all organisms on Earth. It helps maintain cellular homeostasis and many of functions of life and can act as a solvent for various biochemical reactions. The balance of water in an organism's body is carefully maintained to reduce incidence of chronic disease and maintain its health. Various physiological triggers such as "thirst" are in place to make certain adequate amounts of water are ingested. In humans, the kidney is the main organ through which water and ion levels are conserved. As water makes up around 60-65% of the total body weight of humans, the kidneys and its associated hormones are crucial to a healthy individual [68, 69]. Despite extensive study and review of data, the only DRI for water that has been set is the AI to help prevent the effects of dehydration on bodily function [68].

2.6.2. Properties of Water and Body Composition

Water has many scientifically useful properties. In the human body, its high specific heat is used to absorb heat generated by metabolic activity and keep an equal osmotic pressure in both intracellular and extracellular spaces. The total water weight in the body is divided between around 30% intracellular fluids (ICF, inside all the cells in the body) and around 25% extracellular fluids (ECF, everything outside the cells) water weight [70]. Fat-free body mass is around 70-75% water with adipose tissue being around 10-40% water. Thus more athletic individuals have a higher total body water percentage due to a higher fat-free mass.

Water also keeps blood flowing through blood vessels by holding the volume of the blood relatively constant and allowing for pressure gradients. Blood flow provides nutrient transport and waste removal. Waste products, mostly urea and chlorides, can only be concentrated to a certain extent in humans and necessitate excretion of water. The removal of liquid waste is important for maintaining salt concentrations within the body during normal body functioning. In times of exercise and heat exposure, salt excretion through sweat gland pulls extra water as a cooling mechanism.

2.6.3. *The Adequate Intake of Water*

The AI is the value based on experimentally derived intake levels or approximations of observed mean nutrient intakes by a group (or groups) of healthy people. The AIs for children and adults are expected to meet or exceed the amount needed to maintain a defined nutritional state or criterion of adequacy in essentially all members of a specific apparently healthy population [68]. For water, AI has been set because there is insufficient data to determine an EAR for individuals in the different life stages and reference heights and weights. The water comes from foods and beverages that contain water in addition to ingested water. The UL for water was not set even though toxic effects have been observed if very large amounts of fluids that can exceed the kidney's excretion rate are rapidly ingested. Healthy individuals with functioning kidneys and a healthy urinary system should not have complications with excess water excretion [1] [5]. In a normal, U.S. diet, individuals should not have to worry about water deficiency or even excess. The liquid beverages and various foods supply more than enough water to maintain a healthy amount of water and sodium levels in healthy individuals. Concerns about adequate water intake would occur during illnesses that reduce water content such as fever or diarrhea [68, 71].

2.6.4. *Water Regulation*

The primary indicator of water levels in the body is the plasma or serum osmolality. The pituitary secretes a hormone called the Antidiuretic Hormone (ADH) that regulates the water content in the blood in relation to salt concentration. This causes the kidneys to reabsorb more water, and at the same time, Aldosterone (ALD), from the adrenals, helps to increase sodium absorption [70]. Hypotonic salt solutions act in the body as mixtures of isotonic solutions and water. The water, in excess of what is required to form an isotonic solution, is excreted immediately, while the salts are retained. The amount of chloride ions (salts) excreted increases with the increased excretion of urine [71]. Drinking excess water does not have an effect on the water content of blood and tissue as the water exchange between the ICF and ECF is nearly instantaneous and the salt balance is tightly regulated..

Osmotic gradients are responsible for water movement across the cell and epithelial membranes in the body. Water moves from areas of lower to higher concentrations of solutes (salts) by osmosis. This equalizes the concentrations on both sides of a cell membrane or keeps it at a level a specific part of the body needs for proper functioning. Sodium cations are abundant in the ECF while chloride and bicarbonate ions are the anions. The ICF contains potassium and magnesium cations with proteins as anions. The ICF/ECF boundary is controlled by sodium-potassium active transport pumps to maintain correct ratios of the ions. These systems are even present in the developing fetus to provide a stable growth environment and removal of harmful concentrations of ions in circulation [72]. The growing kidney tubules start to separate the primary solutes of sodium and chloride while still partially using the mother's excretion system. Over time, regulation of this homeostatic process is so precise that plasma osmolality rarely varies by more than 2%, when access to water is unrestricted [73].

Thirst is the stimulus for water-seeking behavior and water intake, analogous to hunger for food intake. Thirst and water intake are an essential component of the homeostasis of body water content that controls blood volume and osmolality. Thirst is also impacted by plasma sodium concentration and arterial blood pressure. Signals that are excitatory for thirst are:

- increased plasma osmolality detected by cerebral osmoreceptors;

- decreased blood volume presumably detected by cardiac stretch receptors in the heart;

- increased circulating levels of angiotensin II detected by angiotensin II receptors in the subfornical organ, a highly vascularized region of the brain not subject to the blood-brain barrier; and

- increased gastric sodium load apparently detected by putative sodium receptors in the abdominal viscera.

In contrast, signals that inhibit thirst include:

- decreased plasma osmolality detected by cerebral osmoreceptors;

- increased arterial blood pressure detected by arterial baroreceptors; and increased gastric water load that dilutes the gut sodium, apparently detected by putative sodium receptors in the abdominal viscera [75].

Water loss can result from many sources such as respiration, gastrointestinal loss, exercise, fevers, diarrhea, burns, or other trauma. For a non-sedentary healthy individual, water loss through just urine is about 1-2 L/day. Loss through daily perspiration averages about 0.5 L/day, with far more or less depending on the climate and strenuous exercise, potentially leading to a loss of several liters [68]. Problems occur when the water and salt balance in the body is not maintained.

Hyponatremia occurs where fluid replacement is insufficient to keep up with water loss. It can lead to seizures, hypotension, tachycardia and a wide variety of debilitating conditions [68, 73]. Hyponatremia shares symptoms with dehydration because in both conditions water excretion is far lower than normal, but the salt concentrations are different.

Another odd case with water balance occurs in astronauts or others who experience microgravity situations. Water that is normally pooled into the lower extremities is pumped headward. This causes the kidneys to signal for increased excretion of urine, which leads to demineralization effects on weight-bearing bones [69, 70]. Normally, any blood vessel that is below the heart has an increased pressure compared to those vessels above due to the effect of gravity. In reduced gravity environments, the blood is redistributed upwards, increasing arterial pressure and decreasing ADH levels in the kidney, leading to a lessened need to urinate. Studies have shown that astronauts lose large amounts of calcium due to the bone demineralization and the calcium is released into the bloodstream which is increasingly absorbed by the kidneys and excreted via the urine [70].

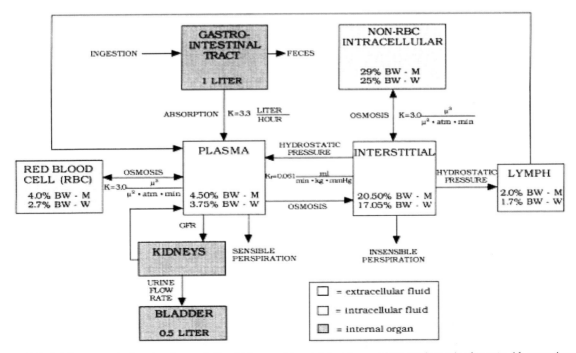

Figure 2.6-1: Movement of water through the kidneys, blood, bladder, and gastrointestinal tracts. K=membrane permeability. The size of the compartment can differ in males (M) and females (F) where BW=body weight. From reference [70].

2.7. References cited

1. Ritter S, Dinh TT, Li A. Hindbrain catecholamine neurons control multiple glucoregulatory responses. Physiol Behav 2006;89:490-500.

2. Gropper SAS, Smith JL, Groff JL. Advanced nutrition and human metabolism. Australia; United States: Wadsworth/Cengage Learning, ©2009; 2009.

3. De Silva A, Salem V, Matthews PM, Dhillo WS. The use of functional MRI to study appetite control in the CNS. Exp. Diabetes Res. 2012;2012:Article ID 764017, 13 pages.

4. Woods SC, D'Alessio DA. Central control of body weight and appetite. J Clin Endocrinol Metab 2008;93:S37-50.

5. Cummings DE, Overduin J. Gastrointestinal regulation of food intake. J Clin Invest 2007;117:13-23.

6. Grimm ER, Steinle NI. Genetics of eating behavior: Established and emerging concepts. Nutr Rev 2011;69(1):52–60.

7. Sclafani A, Ackroff K. Role of gut nutrient sensing in stimulating appetite and conditioning food preferences. Am J Physiol – Regulatory, Integrative and Comparative Physiology 2012;302:R1119-33.

8. Geraedts MCP, Troost FJ, Saris WHM. Gastrointestinal targets to modulate satiety and food intake. Obesity Reviews 2011;12:470-7.

9. Benton D. Carbohydrate consumption, mood and anti-social alcific. In: Benton D, editor. Lifetime nutritional influences on cognition, alcific and psychiatric illness. Publisher: Woodhead Publishing Series in Food Science, Technology and Nutrition, 2011;223: 160-179.

10. Mobbs C, Isoda F, Makimura H, Mastaitis J, Mizuno T, Shu I, Yen K, Yang X. Impaired glucose signaling as a cause of obesity and the metabolic syndrome: the glucoadipostatic hypothesis. Physiol Behav 2005;19;85(1):3-23.

11. Chaput J, Tremblay A. The glucostatic theory of appetite control and the risk of obesity and diabetes. Int J Obes (Lond) 2009;33(1):46-53.

12. Levin BE, Routh VH, Kang L, Sanders NM, Dunn-Meynell AA. Neuronal Glucosensing: What Do We Know After 50 Years? Diabetes 2004;53:2521-8.

13. Gil-Campos M, Aguilera CM, Canete R, Gil A. Ghrelin: a hormone regulating food intake and energy homeostasis. Br J Nutr 2006;96:201-26.

14. Maljaars PWJ, Peters HPF, Mela DJ, Masclee AAM. Ileal brake: A sensible food target for appetite control. A review. Physiol Behav 2008;95:271-81.

15. Flatt JP. Misconceptions in body weight regulation: implications for the obesity pandemic. Crit. Rev. Clin Lab Sci 2012;49:150-65.

16. Carey, M.C., D.M. Small, and C.M. Bliss. 1983. Lipid digestion and absorption. Annual Review Physiology 45:651-77.

17. Yao, L., J.E. Heubi, D.D. Buckley, H. Fierra, K.D. Setchell, N.A. Granholm, P. Tso, D.Y. Hui and L.A.

18. Woollett. 2002. Separation of micelles and vesicles within luminal aspirates from healthy humans: Solubilization of cholesterol after a meal. Journal of Lipid Research 43:654-660.

19. Iqbal, J. And M.M. Hussain. 2009. Intestinal lipid absorption. American Journal of Physiology-Endocrinology and Metabolism 296:1183-1194.

20. Yang, L.Y., A. Kuksis and J.J. Myher. 1995. Biosynthesis of chylomicron triacylglycerols by rats fed glyceryl or alkyl esters of menhaden oil fatty acids. Journal of Lipid Research 36:1046-1057.

21. Moreau, R.A., B.D. Whitaker and K.B. Hicks. 2002. Phytosterols, phystostanols, and their conjugates in foods: Structural diversity, quantitative analysis, and health-promoting uses. Progress in Lipid Research 41:457-500.

22. Altmann, S.W., H.R. Davis, Jr., L.J. Zhu, X. Yao, L.M. Hoos, G. Tetzloff, and M.P. Graziano. Niemann- Pick C1 like 1 protein is critical for intestinal cholesterol absorption. Science 303:1202-1204.

23. Berge, K.E., H. Tian, G.A. Graf, L. Yu, N.V. Grishin, J. Schultz, P. Kwiterovich, B. Shan, R. Barnes and

24. H.H. Hobbs. 2000. Accumulation of dietary cholesterol in sitosterolemia caused by mutations in adjacent ABC transporters. Science 290:1771-1775.

25. Lee, M.H., K Lu, S. Hazard, H. Yu, S. Shulenin, H. Hidaka, H. Kojima, r. Allikmets, N. Sakuma, R. Pegoraro, A.K. Srivastava, G. Salen, M. Dean and S.B. Patel. 2001. Identification of a gene, ABCG5, important in the regulation of dietary cholesterol absorption. Nature Genetics 27:79-83.

26. Lu, K., M.H. Lee, S. Hazard, A. Brooks-Wilson, H. Hidaka, H. Kojima, L. Ose, A.F. Stalenhoef, T. Mietinnen, I. Bjorkhem, E. Bruckert, A. Pandya, H.B. Brewer, Jr., G. Salen, M. Dean, A. Srivastava and S.B. Patel. 2001. Two genes that map to the STSL locus cause sitosterolemia: genomic structure and spectrum of mutation involving sterolin-1 and sterolin-2, encoded by ABCG5 and ABCG8, respectively. The American Journal of Human Genetics 69:278-290.

27. Garcia-Calvo, M., J. Lisnock, H.G. Bull, B.E. Hawes, D.A. Burnett, M.P. Braun, J.H. Crona, H.R. Davis Jr., D.C. Dean, P.A. Detmers, M.P. Graziano, M. Hughes, D.E. Macintyre, A. Ogawa, K.A. O'neill, S.P. Iyer,

28. D.E. Shevell, M.M. Smith, Y.S. Tang, A.M. Makarewicz, F. Ujjainwalla, S.W. Altmann, K.T. Chapman and

29. N.A. Thornberry. 2005. The target of ezetimibe is Niemann-Pick C1-Like 1 (NPC1L1). Proceedings of the National Academy of Sciences USA 102:8132-8137.

30. Woods, S.C., R.J. Seeley, D. Porte, Jr., and M.W. Schartz. 2012. Signals that regulate food intake and energy homeostasis. Science 280(5368):1378-1383.

31. Schultz, J.R., H. Tu, A. Luk, J.J. Repa, J.C. Medina, L. Li, S. Schwendner, S. Wang, M. Thoolen, D.J. Mangelsdorf, K.D. Lustig and B. Shan. 2000. Role of LXRs in control of lipogenesis. Genes and Development 14(22):2831-2838.

32. Dunford, M. and Doyle, J. A. Nutrition for Sport and Exercise. 2nd Ed. Cengage Learning publishers. Pp 154-157. 2011

33. Krebs NF, Primak LE, Hambridge KM. Normal childhood nutrition & its disorders. In: Current Pediatric Diagnosis & Treatment. McGraw-Hill.

34. 31.. Suskind, Robert M. "Malnutrition and the immune response." Kroc Foundation Series 7 (1977).

35. Morrison, C.D., Reed, S. D., Henagan, T. M. Homeostatic Regulation of Protein Intake: In search of a mechanism. Am J Regul Integr Comp Physiol 302:R917-R928, 2012

36. Harper AE, Peters JC. Protein intake, brain amino acid and serotonin concentrations and protein self-selection. J Nutr 119: 677–689, 1989.

37. McKean, C. M., D. E. Boggs, and N. A. Peterson. "The influence of high phenylalanine and tyrosine on the concentrations of essential amino acids in brain." Journal of neurochemistry 15.3 (2006): 235-241.

38. Pellett, PL, and Young VR. "Nutritional evaluation of protein foods." Food and Nutrition Bulletin Suppl. 4 (1980).

39. Steinke, FH, and Hopkins DT. "Complementary and supplementary effects of vegtable (sic vegetable) proteins." Cereal Foods World 28 (1983).

40. Campbell WW, and Leidy HJ. "Dietary protein and resistance training effects on muscle and body composition in older persons." Journal of the American College of Nutrition 26.6 (2007): 696S-703S.

41. Lemon, P. W. R. "Do athletes need more dietary protein and amino acids?." International Journal of Sport Nutrition 5 (1995): 39-39.

42. Berthoud HR, Morrison C. The brain appetite, obesity. Annu Rev Psychol 59: 55–92, 2008.

43. Suzuki K, Simpson KA, Minnion JS, Shillito JC, Bloom SR. The role of gut hormones and the hypothalamus in appetite regulation. Endocr J 57: 359 –372, 2010.

44. Fernstrom J. D. & Wurtman,R. J. Brain serotonin content: Increase following ingestion of a carbohydrate diet. Science 174: 1023-1025. 1971

45. Fernstrom J. D. & Wurtman,R. J. Brain serotonin content: Physiological regulation by plasma neutral amino acids. Science 178: 414-416. 1972

46. Ashley V.M.& Anderson G,.H. Correlation between the plasma tryptophan to neutral amino acid ratio and protein intake in the self-selecting weanling rat. /. Nutr. 105: 1412-1421. 1985

47. Gietzen DW, Hao S, Anthony TG. Mechanisms of food intake alcifi- sion in indispensable amino acid deficiency. Annu Rev Nutr 27: 63–78, 2007

48. Hao S, Sharp JW, Ross-Inta CM, McDaniel BJ, Anthony TG, Wek RC, Cavener DR, McGrath BC, Rudell JB, Koehnle TJ, Gietzen DW. Uncharged tRNA and sensing of amino acid deficiency in anterior piriform cortex. Science 307: 1776–1778, 2005.

49. Maurin AC, Jousse C, Averous J, Parry L, Bruhat A, Cherasse Y, Zeng H, Zhang Y, Harding HP, Ron D, Fafournoux P. The GCN2 kinase biases feeding behavior to maintain amino acid homeostasis in omnivores. Cell Metab 1: 273–277, 2005.

50. Mayer J. Regulation of energy intake and body weight: The glucostatic theory and the lipostatic hypothesis. Ann N Y Acad Sci 1955;63:15-43.

51. Schwartz GJ. Integrative capacity of the caudal brainstem in the control of food intake. Phil Trans R Soc B 2006;361:1275–1280.

52. Kalsbeek A, Bruinstroop E, Yi CX, Klieverik LP, La Fleur SE, Fliers E. Hypothalamic control of energy metabolism via the autonomic nervous system. Ann N Y Acad Sci 2010;1212:114-29.

53. Somogyi V, Gyorffy A, Scalise TJ, Kiss DS, Goszleth G, Bartha T, Frenyo VL, Zsarnovszky A. Endocrine factors in the hypothalamic regulation of food intake in females: a review of the physiological roles and interactions of ghrelin, leptin, thyroid hormones, oestrogen and insulin. Nutrition Research Reviews 2011;24:132.

54. Tucholski K, Otto-Buczkowska E. The role of leptin in the regulation of carbohydrate metabolism. Endokrynol Pol 2011; 62(3):258-62.

55. McIntosh CHS, Widenmaier S, Kim S. Chapter 15 Glucose☐ Dependent insulinotropic polypeptide (gastric inhibitory polypeptide; GIP). In: Vitamins & Hormones. Academic Press p. 409-71.

56. Houston, Mark C. "The Role of Cellular Micronutrient Analysis, Nutraceuticals, Vitamins, Antioxidants and Minerals in the Prevention and Treatment of Hypertension and Cardiovascular Disease." Ther Adv Cardiovasc Dis 4, no. 3 (June 1, 2010): 165–183.

57. Houston, Mark C., and Karen J. Harper. "Potassium, Magnesium, and Calcium: Their Role in Both the Cause and Treatment of Hypertension." The Journal of Clinical Hypertension 10, no. 7 (2008): 3–11.

58. Whelton PK , and He J. "Potassium in Preventing and Treating High Blood Pressure." Seminars in Nephrology 19, no. 5 (September 1999): 494.

59. Lemann, J., Adams, N.D., Gray R.D.. "Urinary Calcium Excretion in Human Beings." N Engl J Med 301, no. 10 (1979): 535–541.

60. Rafferty, K., Davies K.M., and Heaney, R.P.. "Potassium Intake and the Calcium Economy." J Am Coll Nutr 24, no. 2 (April 1, 2005): 99–106.

61. Rude, R. K. "Magnesium Deficiency: A Cause of Heterogenous Disease in Humans." J Bone Miner Res 13, no. 4 (1998): 749–758.

62. Heaney, R. P., and B. E. C. Nordin. "Calcium Effects on Phosphorus Absorption: Implications for the Prevention and Co-Therapy of Osteoporosis." J Am Coll Nutr 21, no. 3 (June 1, 2002): 239–244.

63. Heaney, R.. "Phosphorus." In: Present Knowledge in Nutrition. Eds. John W. Erdman, Jr.; Ian A. Macdonald; Steven H. Zeisel. Ames: Wiley Blackwell, 2012. 447-458.

64. Weaver, C. "Calcium." In: Present Knowledge in Nutrition. Eds. John W. Erdman, Jr.; Ian A. Macdonald; Steven H. Zeisel. Ames: Wiley Blackwell, 2012. 434- 446.

65. Song, Y., X. Peng, A. Porta, H. Takanaga, J.-B. Peng, M. A. Hediger, J. C. Fleet, and S. Christakos. "Calcium Transporter 1 and Epithelial Calcium Channel Messenger Ribonucleic Acid Are Differentially Regulated by 1,25 Dihydroxyvitamin D3 in the Intestine and Kidney of Mice." Endocrinology 144, no. 9 (September 1, 2003): 3885–3894.

66. Institute of Medicine, Food and Nutrition Board. Dietary Reference Intakes for Water, Potassium, Sodium, Chloride, and Sulfate, 2005.

67. McCarron, DA, . Kazaks AG, Geerling JC, Stern JS, Graudal NA. Normal Range of Human Dietary Sodium Intake: A Perspective Based on 24-Hour Urinary Sodium Excretion Worldwide. Am J Hypertens (2013) doi: 10.1093/ajh/hpt139

68. US Department of Agriculture, US Department of Health and Human Services. Dietary Guidelines for Americans, 2010.

69. Geerling JC, Loewy AD. Central regulation of sodium appetite. Exp Physiol 2008; 93:177–209.

70. Institute of Medicine. Sodium Intake in Populations: Assessment of Evidence. May 14, 2013. National Academies Press <http://www.iom.edu/Reports/2013/Sodium-Intake-in-Populations-Assessment-of- Evidence.aspx>

71. Panel on Dietary Reference Intakes for Electrolytes and Water, Standing Committee on the Scientific Evaluation of Dietary Reference Intakes. "1 Introduction to Dietary Reference Intakes." Dietary Reference Intakes for Water, Potassium, Sodium, Chloride, and Sulfate. Washington, DC: The National Academies Press, 2005.

72. Blanc et al. "Energy and Water Metabolism, Body Composition, and Hormonal Changes Induced by 42 Days of Enforced Inactivity and Simulated Weightlessness." The Journal of Clinical Endocrinology & Metabolism. December 1, 1998 vol. 83 no. 12 4289-4297.

73. Doty, S.E., and R.C. Seagrave. "Human water, sodium, and calcium regulation during space flight and exercise." Acta Astronautica. 46.9 (2000): 591-604.

74. Adolph, Edward F. "The Regulation of the Water Content of the Human Organism". The Journal of Physiology. 55.1-2 (1921): 114–132.

75. McCance, RA., Widdowson, EM. "Water Metabolism." Cold Spring Harbor Symposia on Quantitative Biology. 1954. 19: 155-160.

76. Hannon et al. "Disorders of Water Homoeostasis in Neurosurgical Patients." The Journal of Clinical Endocrinology & Metabolism. May 1, 2012 vol. 97 no. 5 1423-1433

77. USDA Food Surveys Research Group. Food and Nutrient Intakes by Individuals in the Unites States, by Income, 1994-96. <webharvest.gov/peth04/20041025164331/http://www.barc.gov/bhnc/foodsurvey/pdf/income/pdf>

78. Stricker EM, Syed AF. 2000. Thirst. Nutrition, 16(10): 821 – 826.

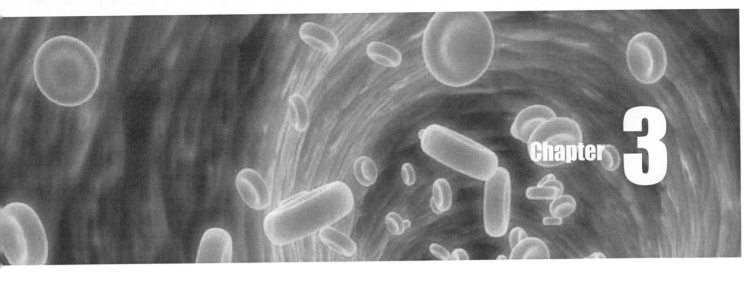

Digestion and Absorption of Macronutrients. Mechanisms that Allow for Variable or Constant Absorption

By Rini Basyamfar, Kristin Frankowski, Elise Hubbard, and Ayeesha Khadeeruddin

Learning Objectives

1. Define the difference between digestion and absorption
2. Understand the roles the gastrointestinal (GI) tract organs and the major accessory organs (salivary glands, liver, gallbladder and pancreas) play in digestion and absorption
3. Identify the layers and sublayers of the GI tract and their functions
4. Identify the modes of absorption
5. Match enzymes to breaking which carbohydrate bonds
6. Explain how carbohydrates are absorbed in the small intestine
7. Identify which absorption transporters are used for which sugars
8. Identify a common disorder that can affect carbohydrate digestion and absorption
9. Identify the products of lipid hydrolysis
10. Explain the role of bile acids in lipid absorption
11. Name common disorders that interfere with lipid digestion and absorption
12. Diagram or explain the process of protein denaturation
13. Explain how a protein is digested and absorbed in the body
14. Name common disorders associated with digestion and absorption

3.1. Overview of digestion and absorption

Digestion is the process by which foods are broken down in the gastrointestinal (GI) tract into a form (nutrients) the body can use. Absorption is the uptake of nutrients from the GI tract into the blood or the lymph. The GI tract is sometimes defined as the esophagus, stomach and the small and large intestines. For our purposes we will define the GI tract as the entire path food takes as it travels through the human body including the oral cavity and the anus.

3.1.1. *The gastrointestinal tract*

The GI tract, which is approximately 16 feet in length [2], from mouth to anus, along with the salivary glands, liver, gallbladder and pancreas (accessory organs) comprise the digestive system. The foods we eat and the fluids we drink provide the body with most of the nutrients our bodies require. These nutrients are arranged in six classes: carbohydrates, lipids, proteins, vitamins, minerals, and water. The digestive tract is the set of tissues, structures and organs that break down the things we consume into nutrients that are useful

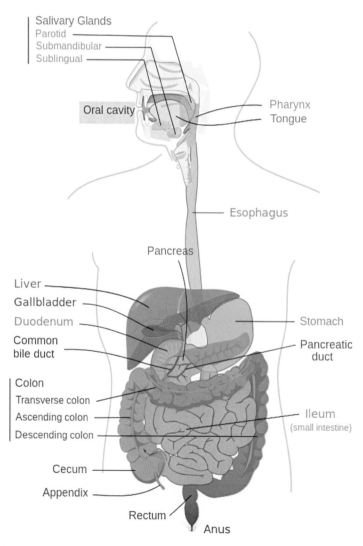

Figure 3.1-1: The GI tract.
From https://en.wikipedia.org/wiki/File:Digestive_system_diagram_edit.svg#/media/File:Digestive_system_diagram_edit.svg

to the body and absorb those nutrients into the blood and lymph.

The GI tract starts with the oral cavity, the entry point for the things we eat, continues through the esophagus which connects the oral cavity to the stomach. Food from the stomach travels through the small and large intestines and finally exits the body through the anus. The inside cavity (the inside of the tube) of the GI tract is known as the lumen. It is from the contents of the lumen that the digestive system breaks down the food into nutrients and absorbs those nutrients into the body.

3.1.2. GI tract layers

The GI tract has 4 main layers and the lumen in the interior. These layers are the mucosa, submucosa, muscularis and the serosa.

3.1.2.1. Mucosa

The mucosa is the inner most layer of the GI tract and is in contact with the contents of the lumen. The mucosa has three sublayers: epithelium, lamina propria and the muscularis mucosa. The epithelium, which is in contact with the lumen, contains exocrine and endocrine cells. The exocrine cells secrete a variety of enzymes and juices into the lumen and the endocrine cells secrete hormones into the blood. The lamina propria, the next sublayer moving outwards, contains connective tissues and small blood vessels and lymphatic vessels. The lamina propria also contains lymphatic tissue containing white blood cells which protects against microorganisms in the lumen. The outermost sublayer is the muscularis mucosa, a thin layer of smooth muscle tissue.

3.1.2.2. Submucosa

The submucosa is the second layer and is made up of connective tissue, lymphoid tissue, mucosal glands, and a network of nerves known as the plexus. The lymph tissue protects the body from foreign bodies, just as the lymph does in the mucosa. The plexus (plexus of Meissner) contributes to the control of secretions from the mucosal glands and regulates mucosal movements

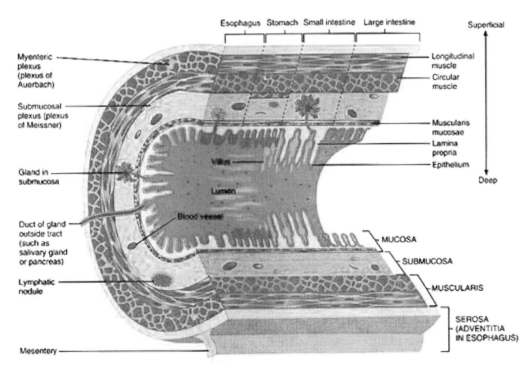

Figure 3.1-2: Sectional view of the layers of the GI tract.
From http://www.apsubiology.org/anatomy/2020/2020_Exam_Reviews/Exam_3/tunics%20diagram.jpg

and blood flow. The submucosa binds or connects the mucosa to the muscularis externa.

The physical shape of the mucosa and submucosa varies along the GI tract from relatively smooth in the esophagus to an elongated, bumpy, surface in the small intestine and back to a relatively smooth surface in the large intestine. The physical contour of the layers presents a relatively larger or smaller surface area to the lumen as required to support the varying functions in the different parts of the GI tract.

3.1.2.3. Muscularis externa

The muscularis externa is made up of circular and longitudinal muscle that provide rhythmic muscle contractions. The muscularis externa also contains the myenteric plexus which controls the contractions of the muscularis. These muscles and the regulating nervous tissue are important for peristalsis, the movement of the lumen contents along the GI tract.

3.1.2.4. Serosa

The serosa is made up of connective tissue and the visceral peritoneum. The peritoneum surrounds the organs in the abdomen and the pelvic cavities. In the abdomen the visceral peritoneum surrounds the stomach and intestines and the parietal peritoneum lines the abdominal cavity. The space between them is known as the peritoneal cavity. Each of these membranes are highly vascularized and semi-permeable.

3.1.3. Oral cavity

The oral cavity is the mouth and pharynx (throat) and is the entry way for food into the GI tract. Digestion begins in the mouth as the food is chewed and mixed with saliva. Saliva is produced by the three salivary glands (the first of the accessory organs to aid in digestion and absorption); the sublingual, submandibular and the parotid; located in pairs in the lining of the oral cavity. Approximately 1 liter of saliva is produced daily due to the activity of the parasympathetic and sympathetic nervous systems. The parotid salivary glands produce water, electrolytes and enzymes. The sublingual and submandibular glands produce water, electrolytes, enzymes and mucus. Saliva is 99.5% water which helps dissolve the food.

The electrolytes include sodium, potassium and chloride which participate in buffering the pH values in the mouth to prevent the teeth from dissolving. The mucus lubricates the food to facilitate swallowing and coats and protects the oral mucosa. The primary enzyme produced is α-amylase which begins the digestion of starches by hydrolyzing the α1-4 bonds.

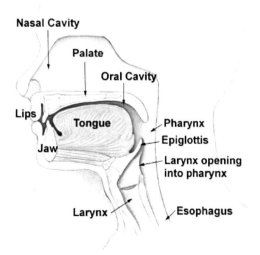

Figure 3.1-3: The oral cavity and salivary glands. From https://commons.wikimedia.org/wiki/File:Illu01_head_neck.jpg

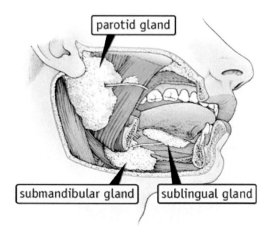

Figure 3.1-4: Salivary glands. From http://avenuedentalgroup.com/what-your-bad-breath-says-about-overall-health-puyallup-dentistry/

As the food is chewed it moves into the back of the oral cavity or pharynx which triggers an involuntary swallowing reaction. The epiglottis moves downward covering the entrance to the trachea as the larynx moves upwards preventing food from entering the trachea.

3.1.4. Esophagus

The esophagus connects the oral cavity to the stomach penetrating the diaphragm which separates the chest cavity from the abdominal cavity. The upper part of the esophagus has striated muscles (voluntary control) and the lower part of the esophagus has smooth muscles (involuntary control) that together produce a wave like contraction and relaxation of the esophagus known as peristalsis that moves the food bolus along the esophagus. The time from mouth to stomach is approximately 10 seconds.

At the lower end of the esophagus (distal end) is the gastroesophageal sphincter. This sphincter acts as a valve allowing food to exit the esophagus into the stomach and preventing gastroesophageal reflux, which is the return of stomach contents into the esophagus. During swallowing, the pressure within the sphincter lowers allowing food the pass into the stomach. At other times the pressure remains high, closing the valve. Neuronal and hormonal signals participate in the control of the pressure within the sphincter.

3.1.5. Stomach

The stomach is primarily a digestive organ and other than minimal water and lipid soluble nutrients it does not participate in absorption.

The stomach is consists of 5 regions: The cardiac region (cardia) which is adjacent to the gastroesophageal sphincter, the fundus which is above and beside the cardia. The body which makes up the bulk of the stomach, the antrum (pyloric antrum) which makes up the lower one third of the stomach and the pylorus which is the area that connects the stomach to the duodenum via the pyloric sphincter.

The stomach, when empty, has a volume of approximately 50 ml and has visible folds (rugae) in all regions other than the antrum. When full, the stomach can hold 1 to 1.5L and the rugae disappear as the stomach expands.

The cardia receives the food from the esophagus which then passes on to the body of the stomach which acts as a reservoir and the primary producer of gastric juices. The antrum is the area where the food is ground and mixed with the gastric juices resulting in chyme, a thick semi- liquid mixture of partially digested food. The antrum produces strong peristalsis which facilitates the exit, in small amounts at regular intervals, of the chyme through the pylorus and the pyloric sphincter into the duodenum.

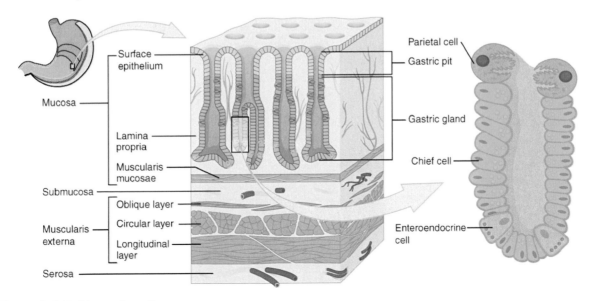

Figure 3.1-5: Stomach wall.
From https://cnx.org/contents/FPtK1zmh@6.5:O9dvCxUQ@3/The-Stomach

Gastric juice is produced by the gastric glands which consist of three functionally different types and are located in the gastric pits of the mucosa. The cardiac glands are found in a narrow area in the cardia where the esophagus empties into the stomach. Oxyntic glands which are found in the body of the stomach and pyloric glands found in the antrum.

The cell types in the gastric glands consist of:

1. Neck (Mucus) cells, close to the surface of the mucosa, which secrete bicarbonate and mucus.

2. Parietal (Oxyntic) cells which secrete hydrochloric acid and intrinsic factor.

3. Chief (Peptic) cells which secrete pepsinogens.

4. Enteroendocrine cells which secrete a variety of hormones.

The cardiac glands consist of Mucus, Chief, and Enteroendocrine cells. The oxyntic glands contain all of the cell types as does the pyloric glands which also have special Enteroendocrine cells known as G-cells.

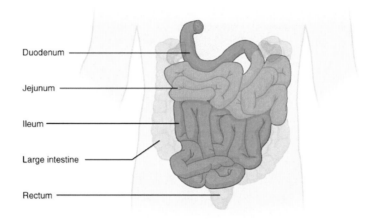

Figure 3.1-6: Small intestine.
From http://sains-phd.blogspot.com/2016/03/anatomi-letak-dan-fungsi-usus-halus.html

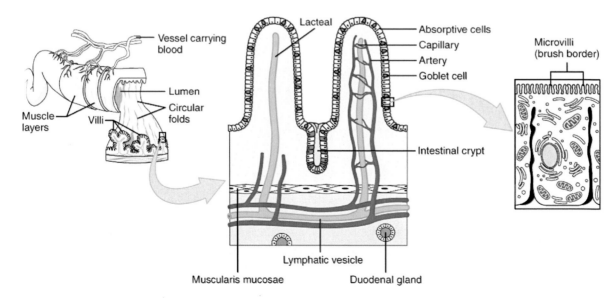

Figure 3.1-7: Lining of the small intestine.
From https://www.boundless.com/biology/textbooks/boundless-biology-textbook/animal-nutrition-and-the-digestive-system-34/digestive-systems-195/digestive-system-small-and-large-intestines-750-11983/

The gastric juice has a very low pH of around 2 because of the large amounts of hydrochloric acid (HCl) present. The HCl, in addition to its digestive role, converts the pepsinogens into active pepsin. The mucus, which contains bicarbonate, coats and protects the mucosa from damage from the HCl.

Very little chemical digestion takes place in the stomach other than the denaturation of proteins in the acidic environment and the initiation of protein hydrolysis by pepsin.

Additionally some residual hydrolysis of starches continues by α-amylase in the saliva that survives the low pH environment.

3.1.6. Small intestine

The small intestine is the primary digestive and absorptive organ. It is consists of three main functional areas. The duodenum, jejunum and the ileum. The duodenum is the first approximately 30 cm of the

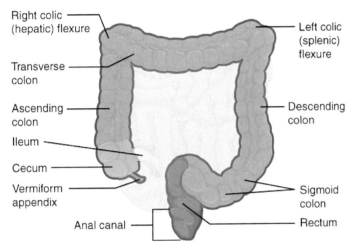

Figure 3.1-8: Large intestine.
From https://courses.lumenlearning.com/ap2/chapter/the-small-and-large-intestines/

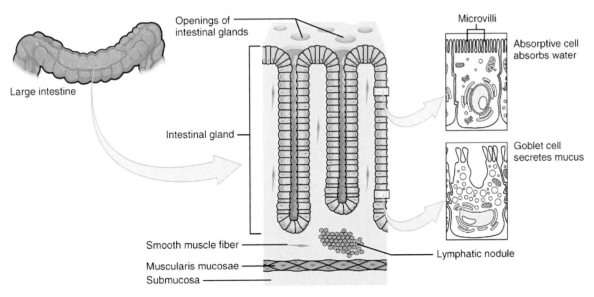

Figure 3.1-9: Lining of the large intestine.
From https://courses.lumenlearning.com/ap2/chapter/the-small-and-large-intestines/

small intestine, the jejunum is the central area and the ileum is the final area. The jejunum and the ileum are approximately 270 cm in length. Overall the small intestine has a surface area of approximately 250 m² due to the highly folded structure of the mucosa. This large surface area is necessary to support the nutrient absorption that takes place in the small intestine.

The folds of the mucosa are further folded into villi which themselves contain microvilli. The villi and microvilli, also known as the brush border, and are parts of the enterocytes which are the absorptive cells in the small intestine.

Chyme enters the duodenum at approximately 1.5 ml every 30 seconds. Brunner's glands in the first few cm of the duodenum secrete a viscous mucus with a pH of approximately 9 that neutralizes the acid chyme. Digestion occurs along the entire length of the small intestine utilizing the digestive enzymes embedded in the brush border. Absorption also occurs along the length of the small intestine.

3.1.7 Large intestine

Unabsorbed materials enter the large intestine (colon) from the ileum through the ileocecal sphincter into the cecum. From there they move through the ascending, transverse and descending colon, which is approximately 150 cm long. As the material moves through the colon the majority of the water is absorbed from the fluid like chyme. Unabsorbed carbohydrates are fermented in the colon by the bacterial flora present.

3.1.8. Accessory organs

The salivary glands, liver, gallbladder and pancreas are collectively known as the accessory organs of the digestive system. The salivary glands produce α-amylase that breaks down starches and mucus that lubricates the ingested food.

The liver produces bile which is stored in the gall bladder via the bile duct. Bile, which is made up of bile acids, is primarily responsible for emulsifying lipids.

The pancreas produces pancreatic digestive enzymes, which are responsible for digesting 50% of all ingested carbohydrates and proteins, and 80% of all ingested fats. These enzymes are secreted into the duodenum as pancreatic juice.

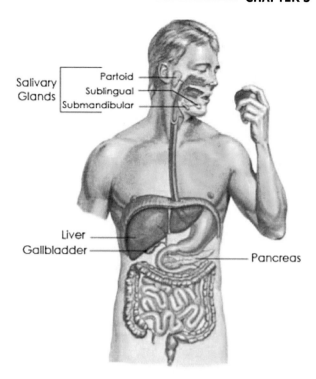

Figure 3.1-10: Accessory organs. From https://insidehumanbodies.wikispaces.com/Digestive+System+%26+Excretory+System

3.1.9. Types of absorption

Absorption primarily takes place in the small intestine. This absorption takes place in four ways:

1. Passive diffusion. This takes place when the concentration of a nutrient is higher in the lumen than in the absorptive cells. This difference in concentration, or gradient, forces nutrients into the absorptive cell. Fats and water are some of the nutrients absorbed by passive diffusion.

2. Facilitated diffusion. Facilitated diffusion takes place when the concentration in the lumen is slightly higher than in the absorptive cells. Carrier proteins carry the nutrients into the absorptive cells. The sugar fructose is absorbed by facilitated diffusion.

3. Active absorption. This takes place when both a carrier protein and energy (ATP) is required to move a nutrient into the absorptive cell. Active transport can take place with the higher concentration of the nutrient on either side of

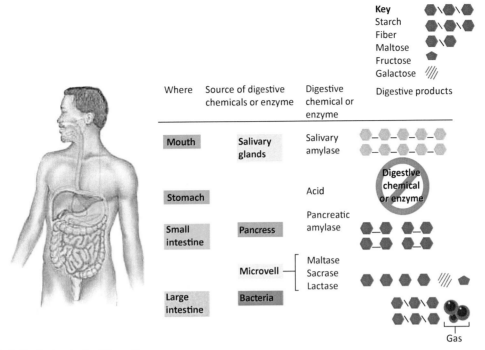

Figure 3.2-1 Carbohydrate Digestion.
Copyright @ 2014 by Jones & Bartlett Learning, LLC, an Ascend Learning Company. www.jblearning.com
From http://slideplayer.com/slide/10205646/

the cell membrane. Amino acids and glucose are actively absorbed.

4. Endocytosis. In this type of active absorption the absorptive cell encloses the nutrient in a invagination of its cell membrane that forms a vesicle. The vesicle then *pinches off* inside the absorptive cell. Large protein particles in breast milk are absorbed in this way.

3.2. Digestion and Absorption of Carbohydrates

3.2.1. Carbohydrates

Carbohydrates are a major component of the human diet, accounting for about half of the calories that are ingested [9]. There are many different types of carbohydrates. The simplest being the monosaccharide; which is only one sugar unit, such as glucose or fructose. A more complicated carbohydrate would be disaccharides which are two joined sugars such as lactose and sucrose. The major sugars in the diet are glucose,

fructose, and sucrose [10]: of which sucrose accounts for 30% of the western diet [9]. More complicated yet are the polysaccharides which consist mostly of starches. Starch accounts for 60% of the carbohydrates in the average diet [9]. Starch is composed of amylose and amylopectin where amylose is composed of straight chain glucose polymers and amylopectin is composed of branched glucose molecules. Sugar alcohols can also be included in carbohydrates; these are often made up of monosaccharaides and disaccharides [10].

3.2.2. Hydrolysis of complex sugars

The process of digestion of carbohydrates begins in the mouth for complex carbohydrates. α-Amylase begins the breakdown of carbohydrates. This is an endosaccharidase that is specific for α-1,4 glycosidic bonds. The α-amylase can only cleave that one specific kind of linkage disaccharide sugars remain. These sugars are maltose, isomaltose, and α-limit dextrins.

The α-amylase that is present in the saliva is secreted in its active form but is deactivated by the low pH environment in the stomach. If the enzyme is protected in a large food bolus it may continue function in a limited fashion but this hydrolysis does not contribute to carbohydrate digestion significantly.

From the stomach the partially digested starches move into the small intestine. This partially digested food enters the small intestine along with pancreatic juices containing enzymes and bicarbonates that neutralize the low pH of the chyme. Digestion continues by the breakdown of polysaccharides by pancreatic α-amylase in the lumen. Like the salivary amylase pancreatic α- amylase is restricted to hydrolyzing only the α1,4 glycosidic linkage. The process to this point results in amylose and amylopectin hydrolyzed to dextrin by salivary and pancreatic α-amylase. Dextrin from amylose is hydrolyzed to maltose by pancreatic α-amylase, and dextrin from amylose pectin is hydrolyzed to maltose, maltotriose, and limit dextrins by pancreatic α- amylase.

These sugars are not yet available for absorption and further hydrolysis is required. Enzymes from the brush-border in the intestinal epithelial cells now continue to breakdown sugars in the lumen. These enzymes are able to cleave sugars in different areas than the α- amylases. There are many different brush border enzymes and they are found in different areas of the intestine. Maltase (β-glucoamylase) hydrolyzes the α1,4 links between glucose molecules and at the tail of polymers. Isomaltase is the enzyme that is responsible for breaking down α1,6 links at branching points of the sugar molecules.

Within the brush-border other enzymes continue the digestion. Sucrase cleaves the link between glucose and fructose breaking down sucrose. The other major brush border enzyme is lactase. This is the enzyme that breaks down lactose into glucose and galactose. The hydrolysis of lactose by lactase occurs only half as fast as hydrolysis of other sugars; lactose hydrolysis is the rate limiting factor for carbohydrate digestion and absorption. Trehalase breaks down the disaccharide trehalose by hydrolyzing the α1,1 linkage between glucose molecules.

After the hydrolysis of these sugars by various enzymes 80% is broken down to the monosaccharide glucose. Many things can affect the digestion of sugars in the small intestine. Some of these include the food form, the type of preparation, type of starch, transit time, and the amount for fat, fiber, and proteins [12].

3.2.3. Carbohydrate absorption in the small intestine

Absorption of monosaccharides by the small intestine is done in two ways: active transport and facilitated diffusion. Glucose and galactose are taken up by the

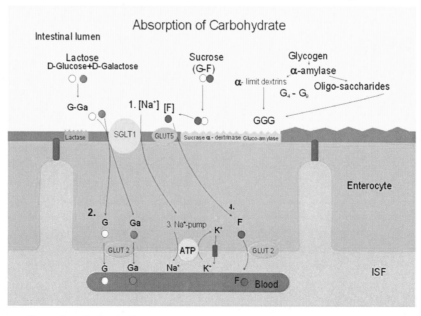

Figure 3.2-2: Absorption of carbohydrates.
From http://www.zuniv.net/physiology/book/images/22-11.jpg

enterocytes by Na- glucose transporter 1 (SGLT1). The number of this transporter site is highest in the jejunum and duodenum. The transporter is sodium dependent and the concentration of sodium determines the rate of sugar transport. One glucose molecule is brought into the cell for every 2 molecules of sodium. When sodium is low the glucose binds to SGLT1 with a lower affinity than when there is a higher concentration of sodium. When there is a high concentration of sodium present there is a conformational change in SGTL1, which allows for this higher binding affinity of glucose to the molecule. The first conformational change that occurs is when sodium binds to the transporter it causes a change that allows glucose to bind to it. Then once glucose binds the transporter brings them into the cell. Then sodium disassociates into the cytoplasm of the cell and allows glucose to also disassociate. Sodium is pumped across the membrane to create a sodium gradient between the interior of the cell and the lumen of the intestine by the hydrolysis of ATP. Glucose leaves the cell by facilitated diffusion transporter type 2 (GLUT2). When the concentration of glucose is very high in the lumen, glucose can be absorbed directly by the GLUT2 facilitated transporter.

Fructose uses a different method of transport from glucose or galactose; it uses facilitated diffusion to both enter the cell and leave the cell. It is diffused in direct proportion to its concentration. Fructose is brought into the cell independent of glucose concentration, but uptake into the cell is slower than glucose or galactose entry. Fructose requires a specific co transporter known as glucose transporter 5 (GLUT 5). GLUT5 functions independently of sodium unlike GLUTs used for transportation of glucose and galactose. Fructose in the presence of glucose or sucrose is more efficient in being transported than when fructose is present alone.

Sugar alcohols use passive diffusion to enter the cell. Sugar alcohols have the slowest rate of absorption. Passive diffusion does not require energy or a transporter. The molecules are small enough to pass through the membrane without additional energy or another molecule based on the concentration gradient. They are partially digested by the same brush border enzymes and then diffuse across the membranes.

3.2.4. Carbohydrates in the large intestine

Carbohydrates that contain β1-4 covalent bonds such as cellulose are not broken down by amylase, but can promote fermentation in the large intestine. Microflora in the large intestine can break down some components of dietary fiber. The results are monosaccharaides and gases such as methane.

Resistant starches also pass through the small intestine undigested and are partially digested by the micro flora in the large intestine. These resistant starches fall into one of four classes:

1. RS1: Inaccessible, digestible, starches such as those found in seeds, legumes, and some unprocessed grains

2. RS2: Naturally occurring semi-crystalline granules found in uncooked potatoes and green bananas

3. RS3: Resistant starches formed during cooking such as from legumes and high amylose corn.

4. RS4: Specially processed starches intended to be resistant.

Remaining undigested starches pass out of the body in the stool.

3.2.5. Disorders of carbohydrate digestion and absorption

Problems can arise when sugars are not fully digested in the small intestine. When the sugar is not digested it cannot be absorbed by the small intestine and will travel to the large intestine. Once it reaches the large intestine it will be fermented by bacteria that are present and cause gastrointestinal discomfort.

Disorders either in digestion or absorption can result in undigested carbohydrates passing through into the large intestine. These disorders can be either something that a person is born with or can be acquired later in life. Lactose intolerance is a well-known disorder. In lactose intolerance the person does not have lactase so lactose is not hydrolyzed into smaller monosaccharrides. Because disaccharrides cannot be absorbed into the small intestine the sugar continues onto the large intestine and causes gastrointestinal discomfort. Disaccharride mal- absorption is a genetic disease that is caused by a mutation in SGTL1. The major symptom of this would be profuse diarrhea after sugar is consumed. This is usually present in small children and can be fatal because of fluid loss. Removal of sugars from the diet has been shown to stop the diarrhea. Such infants are often not fed starch in the first few months of life.

3.3. Lipid Digestion and Absorption

3.3.1. Lipids

Dietary fats are important human nutrients because they are a major source of energy and also assist in the absorption of essential fat-soluble vitamins. Common sources of dietary fat and fat soluble vitamins are dairy fats (butter), milk, and fat from meat, eggs, baked goods, vegetables oils, and nuts. They consist of polar and non-polar lipids among which the most common is **triglyceride** (TAG). Dietary fats also consist of phospholipids (PLs), sterols, and other lipids including fat-soluble vitamins.

In the human diet many different fats and oils are relevant as sources of TAGs. These include oils that originate from fruits such as palm oil and olive oil, or from seeds such as corn, rapeseed, and soybean oil. Fats from adipose tissues and intramuscular fat droplets from pigs, cattle, poultry, and lamb as well as fish oils are used in the human diet. These fats contain complicated fatty acid profiles involving a range of fatty acids, which could extend to 30 or more different fatty acids, with various chain lengths, saturation or unsaturation and fatty acid isomers.

3.3.2. Lipid hydrolysis

As with many nutrients, the digestion of dietary fats begins in the oral cavity with the exposure to lingual lipases found in saliva. The process of digestion continues as some lipids are absorbed along with water by the stomach. In addition, the stomach is a major site for the emulsification of dietary fat and fat-soluble

vitamins. Grinding and mixing of gastric content as well as gastric motility contribute to dispersion of lipid droplets. The mixture then proceeds to the small intestine where bile and pancreatic juice provide bile salts and digestive enzymes such as pancreatic lipase or co-lipase.

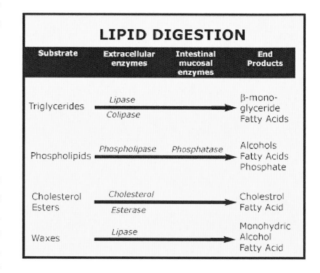

Figure 3.2-3: Lipid Digestion.

Water-soluble lipase enzymes are vital in the process of lipid hydrolysis leading toward digestion and absorption of dietary lipids. Like other enzymes, lipases have varying degrees of selectivity towards various substrates they react with. This selectivity influences not only the range of substrates but also the efficiency with which the lipase catalyzes a substrate. Binding to an insoluble emulsified or aggregated substrate activates lipases. This process is highly dependent on the concentration and type of compound present as well as the properties of the aqueous phase (pH and ionic strength) [15]. Lipases hydrolyze medium chain fatty acids faster than long chain fatty acids and cleave them at the sn-3 position. In adults it is estimated that 10– 30% of ingested lipids are digested in the stomach yielding diglycerides and free fatty acids.

These products contribute to an efficient intestinal lipolysis after propulsion of the gastric content into the duodenum. In the duodenum the pH is considerably increased due to secretion of $NaHCO_3$. The presence of bile salts increases the surface pressure for lipase and prevents denaturation. The pancreas secretes at least three lipase enzymes: pancreatic lipase, carboxyl ester hydrolase and phospholipase A2. Pancreatic lipase has a high turnover number of long-chain triglyceride molecules/min. Carboxyl ester hydrolase is considered to be minor; it catalyzes the hydrolysis of water-soluble esters such as triacetin and lysolecithin and insoluble esters such as esters of cholesterol and vitamins A, D and E. Pancreatic phospholipase A2 is involved in the hydrolysis of long chain triglycerides. This lipase also performs a limited amount of hydrolysis of phospholipids resulting in the enhanced binding of pancreatic lipase. These enzymes primarily yield Sn-2 monoglycerides and FFAs.

Phospholipids

Phosphatidylcholine is the most common phospholipid present in the lumen of the small intestine. It is primarily found in mixed micelles also containing cholesterol and bile salts.

Digestion of this lipid is primarily carried out as a response to food intake by enzymes such as pancreatic phospholipase and other enzymes secreted by the pancreas. These enzymes interact with the lipid at the sn-2 position to yield FFAs and lysophosphatytidylcholine. These products are easily removed from the water-oil interface when they interact with bile salts and form micelles. As hydrophobic and hydrophilic components of micelles, bile salts are essential in facilitating mixed micelle formation. [2]

Triglycerides (TAG)

The structure and source along with other factors affect the digestion and absorption of TAGs. The digestion of TAG takes place both in the stomach and intestine. Pre-duodenal lipases significantly increase the success of digestion; however, TAGs are primarily digested by pancreatic lipase in the upper segment of the jejunum, a portion of the stomach. Pre-duodenal lipase is important because it begins the process of fat dispersion and aids in the formation of the food bolus. The majority of the digestion of TAGs results from hydrolysis by pancreatic lipase. The presence of TAG causes the C-cells in the duodenal mucosa to secrete cholecystokinin. In response, the gall bladder or liver release bile acids that increase the surface area of the TAG droplets. The interaction of the pancreatic lipase and TAG yields 2-monoacylglyerol (2-MAG), and free fatty acids (FFAs). 2-MAG can undergo

further hydrolysis to form glycerol and FFAs or can be absorbed through the small intestine.

Cholesterol

Cholesterol is a unique lipid because it can originate from within the body (endogenous) or from dietary sources (exogenous). The digestion and absorption of cholesterol depends on its form. Non-esterified cholesterol can be incorporated into acid micelles and absorbed by enterocytes; however, most dietary cholesterol in the form of free sterol must be hydrolyzed by cholesterol esterase. Following this process the primarily hydrophobic molecule is processed with bile salt and incorporated into a mixed micelle along with other lipid products, and is ready for absorption.

Vitamin E

Vitamin E is one of the most abundant lipid-soluble anti-oxidants found in humans.

While the hydrophobic nature of Vitamin E is necessary for its nutritional functions, this property creates challenges for the body regarding digestion, uptake, transport and delivery to various tissues. Similar to other dietary fats, micelle formation is required for the absorption of Vitamin E through the intestine. The vitamin E entry to the circulation occurs primarily through the secretion of chylomicrons (fat transporters) into the lymphatic system and has been shown to be rapid, susceptible to saturation, oleic acid dependent, and temperature-dependent.

Vitamin A

Vitamin A activity in the diet derives from two sources: pre-formed vitamin A in foods from derived from animals, and provitamin A carotenoids, such as β-carotene, α-carotene, and β-cryptoxanthin that are found in plant-derived foods. The conversion of preformed vitamin A gives rise to retinol. Dietary vitamin A is digested and absorbed in the form of dietary retinyl esters that are hydrolyzed in the intestine by the pancreatic enzyme and other enzymes, such as pancreatic triglyceride lipase, intestinal brush border enzyme, and phospholipase B. Some retinol is taken up by the enterocyte and is complexed by the cellular retinol-binding protein type 2. The retinyl esters are then incorporated into chylomicrons, intestinal lipoproteins containing other dietary lipids.

3.3.3. *Lipid absorption*

Dietary fats and fat soluble vitamins are broken down by hydrolysis, stabilized by polar bile salts, and become part of micellar particles that are water soluble. Digested lipids include FFAs, 2-monoacylglycerols, cholesterol, and lysophosphatidylcholine. These particles can penetrate the unstirred water later that surrounds the absorptive cells in the small intestine. Once the micelle enters this water layer, the lipid contents of the micelle can interact with the brush border of the cell and diffuse into the enterocyte. Following absorption, enzyme acyl CoA synthase re-forms FFAs that are 10-12 carbon atoms into triacylglycerols, phosphatidylcholine and cholesteryl esters.

3.3.4. *Disorders of lipid digestion and absorption*

Lipid Malabsorption results in increased lipids including fat soluble vitamins in the stool.

It can be caused by pancreatic insufficiency from cystic fibrosis, pancreas disease, or surgical removal of the pancreas. Bile duct obstruction, celiac disease and crohn's disease are also causes of lipid malabsorption.

Consuming products that contain short chain fatty acids such as milk or coconut milk are therapeutic.

3.4. Protein Digestion and Absorption

3.4.1. *Protein*

Protein is the major functional and structural component of every cell in the body. Proteins act as precursors for nucleic acids, hormones, membranes and vitamins, so ample supply is necessary to maintain cell integrity and function, and for health and reproduction. Approximately 16 percent of protein is made from amino nitrogen making it the most important component from a nutritional aspect. Therefore, nitrogen metabolism is synonymous with protein metabolism.

Complete proteins contain all nine essential amino acids and are found in animal sources such as meat, poultry, fish, eggs, milk, cheese and yogurt. Incomplete proteins that are found in plant sources such as legumes, grains, nuts, seeds and vegetables are deficient in one or more of 9 amino acids. A third category called

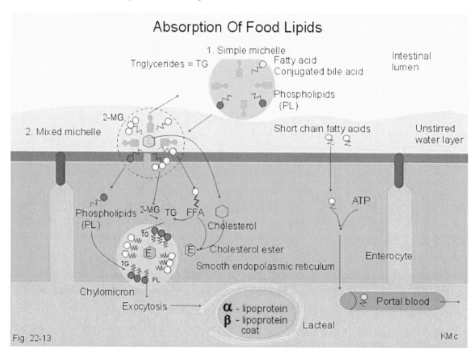

Figure 3.3-1: Absorption of lipids.
From http://slideplayer.com/slide/4560563/

conditionally essential amino acids is a mix of proteins from both sources.

3.4.2. Protein digestion

There are many mechanisms for digestion and absorption of proteins: dietary intake in the form of proteins or de novo synthesis by the body. After a protein in eaten and enters the stomach, it is denatured by the stomach acid. Then, it is cleaved into peptides by pepsin that activates after protein reaches the stomach. Proteins then enter small intestine where many enzymes hydrolyze the peptide bonds and all the amino acids are free flowing. Then, they enter the mucosal cells where they either enter the blood stream or get further metabolized within the cells. Absorbed amino acids enter the liver where some are used by liver and others by peripheral tissues. The liver and intestine together contribute about 50 percent of total body protein turnover. Of the total protein content in the body, about 43 percent goes to skeletal muscle, 15 percent to skin and blood, 10 percent to active visceral tissues and the rest to brain, heart, lung and bone. Half of the total proteins in body are myosin, actin, collagen and hemoglobin.

Intraluminal phase

The first phase, intraluminal phase, is divided into first, the gastric phase and second, the pancreatic phase. It starts from the stomach where proteolysis starts by two pepsins. These are the major gastric proteases whose actions make large polypeptides, small oligopeptides and some free amino acids. The gastric phase is not too crucially important to the digestion because patients with total gastrectomy can also digest proteins the same way.

The pancreatic phase of protein digestion is important in converting the protein to a mixture of small oligopeptides and free amino acids. To do this, many proteolytic enzymes are made by pancreatic acinar cells as inactive zymogens. These zymogens get activated in the duodenum by enteropeptidase, an enzyme associated with brush border membrane and localized to the duodenal enterocytes, (after the pH becomes more basic which inactivates the gastric pepsins). This activation starts by trypsin and follows to chymotrypsin elastase, and carboxypeptidases A

and B. Trypsin, chymotrypsin and elastase cleave the interior peptide bonds of proteins and polypeptides. These enzymes are classified as serine proteases because they have a serine amino acid residue at their active site. Trypsin cleaves peptide bonds that have on the carboxyl side a basic amino acid, chymotrypsin cleaves bonds where the amino acid on the carboxyl side is aromatic, and elastase cleaves bonds where the carboxyl group is part of an aliphatic amino acid.

Carboxypeptidases A and B are major exopeptidases in pancreatic fluid. Both are zinc-containing metallopeptidases that remove single amino acids from the carboxy terminal ends of proteins and oligopeptides. Due to their specificities, a majority of dietary proteins are converted to free amino acids and oligopeptides. Thus, the pancreatic phase of digestion is more important than the gastric phase.

Small intestinal phase

The small intestinal phase, where the final steps in digestion of peptides take place, occurs in the intestinal lumen and is associated with small intestinal mucosal cells. These cells are highly polarized and present a brush border membrane that contains peptidases. These peptidases are dimeric, integral membrane proteins attached to glycosyl- phosphatidylinositol. The active site is identified with a large hydrophilic portion of the peptide chain that projects into the lumen of the intestine. These enzymes then are translated and synthesized in the rough endoplasmic reticulum, glycosylated in the Golgi apparatus and then inserted into brush border membrane.

Each enzyme has a specific function: aminopeptidase N removes the N- terminal amino acids rom short oligopeptides usually containing a proline residue. Dipeptidyl aminopeptidase IV and aminopeptidase P cleave prolyl peptides from the amino terminus. Angiotensin-converting enzyme and carboxypeptidase P work in a concerted fashion to hydrolyze prolyl peptides from the carboxy terminal end. These enzymes have complementary functions to the pancreatic enzymes because the pancreatic enzymes cannot hydrolyze proline peptide bonds. Even the endopeptidases in brush border membranes are different than the pancreatic ones. These enzymes initiate the hydrolysis of large proteins such as alpha-casein, fibrinogen, and histone, which reduces them to small peptides and amino acids even without the action of pancreatic insufficiency. The purpose of phases 1 and 2 is to reduce the dietary protein to free amino acids, and tiny polypeptides that enable the carrier-transporters to carry out their function in the next phase.

3.4.3. Protein absorption

Protein absorption has four carrier-mediated active transport systems that move amino acids against a concentration gradient in concert with a transfer of positive charge. There are two facilitated diffusion pathways and one simple diffusion that take up amino acids in the intestinal lumen as they get high in concentration. Two sodium-coupled transporters in the basolateral membrane transfer amino acids from the blood into the enterocyte. Peptide transport also occurs by an independent process from the amino acids. This has important nutritional significance in that the intraluminal digestion products include a lot of small peptides and many amino acids are more efficiently

absorbed in peptide form. Therefore, even patients with defects who cannot take up regular amino acids can absorb them if they are in peptide form. A majority of the peptides that are absorbed are hydrolyzed by peptidases in the cytoplasmic fraction of intestinal enterocytes. The few remaining peptides go into the bloodstream.

3.4.5. Disorders of protein digestion and absorption

Celiac disease is the inability to digest the plant protein, gluten. It leads ultimately to atrophy of intestinal villi and impaired absorption of all nutrients. The treatment for celiac disease is the remove gluten from the diet.

3.5. Summary

1.1   The digestive system is the gastrointestinal tract and the associated accessory organs.

1.2   Carbohydrate digestion starts in the mouth. The majority of digestion and absorption takes place in the small intestine.

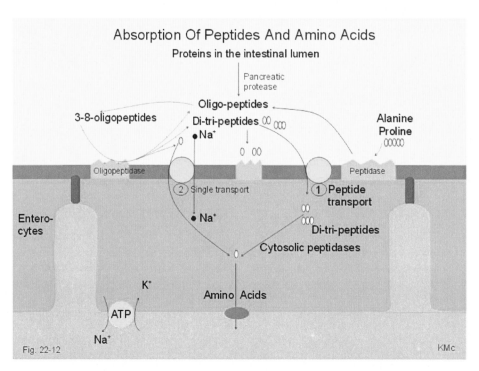

Figure 3.4-1: Protein absorption.
From http://the-nutrition-academy.com/how-much-protein-do-you-need-for-weight-loss/

1.3 Lipid digestion and absorption is dependent on the emulsification of fats with bile salts

1.4 Protein digestion starts with the denaturation of proteins in the mouth and stomach and is completed in the small intestine.

3.6. References

1. Ruiz M. Diagram of a human digestive system [Internet]. 2006.

2. Gropper SS, Smith JL. Advanced Nutrition and Human Metabolism. Belmont, CA: Wadsworth, Cengage Learning; 2013. p. 33--35.

3. Anonymous. Sectional views of the GI tract. [Internet]. [cited 2013 Aug 2]. Available from: http://www.easynotecards.com/upl oads/358/22/593ab409_13673075871 8 000_00000007.jpg.

4. Anonymous. Organs of the digestive system. [Internet]. 2007 [cited 2013 Aug 2]. Available from: https://www.boundless.com/physiology/ the--digestive-- system/organs--of--the--digestive-- system/pharynx----2/.

5. Anonymous. Consumer Updates, The Role of Saliva. [Internet]. 2011 [cited 2013 Aug 2]. Available from: http://www.fda.gov/ucm/ groups/fdagov-- public/documents/image/ ucm254587.jpg.

6. OpenStax College. The stomach. [Internet]. 2013 [cited 2013 Aug 2]. Available from: http://cnx.org/content/m46517/ latest/?collection=col11496/latest.

7. OpenStax College. The small and large intesines. [Internet]. 2013 [cited 2013 Aug 2]. Available from: http://cnx.org/content/ m46512/latest/?collection=col11496/latest.

8. Anonymous. Digestive System Basics. [Internet]. 2013 [cited 2013 Aug 2]. Available from: http://www.ghthealth.com/products/ digestivesystemoverview.aspx.

9. Gray G. Carbohydrate digestion and absorption. Physiology in medicine. 2012;292(23):225- -1230.

10. Southgate DAT. Digestion and metabolism of sugars. American Journal of Clinical Nutrition 62(suppl)203s--11s. 62(Supplimental):203s- -211s.

11. Paul M. Insel RETDR. Nutrition. Sudberry, MA: Jones & Bartlett Learning; 2003. p.74.

12. Goodmen BE. Goodman BE. 2010. Insights into digestion and absorption of major nutrients in humans. Advances in Physiology Education. 2010;34:44--52.

13. Anonymous. Absorption of Carbohydrates. [Internet]. [cited 2013 Aug 2].

14. Available from: http://bigoakridge.org/ wp-content/uploads/2012/12/carbohydrate- absorption.jpg.

15. Stevens C. E. aHID. Comparative Physiology of the Vertebrate Digestive System.

16. 2nd ed. New York: Cambridge University Free Press; 1995.

17. Kuksis A SNHA. Lipid Absorption and Metabolism. Environmental Health Perspectives. 1979;33:45--55.

18. Gustavo Zubieta--Calleja PEP. New Human Physiology. 2nd ed. Copenhagen: Department of Medical Physiology, University of Copenhagen; 2004.

3.7. Study questions

A. True or False

Questions:

1. Saliva contains the fat-digesting enzyme pepsin.

2. The gallbladder makes bile which helps in digestion and absorption of fat.

3. Food is chewed and mixed with saliva in the esophagus.

4. Glands in the digestive tract released a viscous fluid called mucus.

5. Microvilli increase the surface area available for absorption.

6. Enteroendocrine cells produce hormones.

7. The majority of chemical digestion in the stomach occur in body and pylorus.

B. Short answer

Questions:

8. Which part in digestive tract plays the biggest role in digestion and absorption?

9. What happen when people have a lack of digestive enzymes?

10. What is gastric juice?

11. The inside cavity of the gastrointestinal tract is called

C. Multiple choice

Questions:

12. Which part is not a segment of stomach?

    a. Body

    b. Fundus

    c. Trachea

    d. Antrum

13. The gastric phase and the pancreatic phase is part of the_____in protein digestion and absorption.

    a. Transport and absorption phase

    b. Intraluminal phase

    c. Small intestinal phase

    d. Extraluminal phase

14. What is not a main layer in GI tract?

    a. Muscularis

    b. Mucosa

    c. Serosa

    d. Epiglottis

15. The enzyme responsible for breaking down the $\alpha 1$-6 link in a polysaccharide?

    a. Isomaltose

    b. Maltase

    c. Lactase

    d. Alphatase

16. The most common phospholipid present in the lumen of the small intestine?

    e. Palmitoleic acid

    f. Phosphatidilcholine

    g. Docosapentanoic acid

    h. Pholoieic acid

17. The gastric juice in the stomach has a pH of__ because of large amounts of hydrochloric acid (HCl) are present.

    a. 14

    b. 7

    c. 4

    d. 2

18. Absorption of monosaccharaides by the small intestine is done in two ways.

    a. Active transport and facilitated diffusion.

    b. Osmosis and facilitated transport

    c. Facilitated diffusion and osmosis transport

    d. Osmosis diffusion and active transport

19. Fructose requires a specific co-transporter known as?

    a. GLUT 1

    b. GLUT 3

    c. GLUT 5

    d. GLUT 7

Answers:

1. (F) contain the protein-digesting enzyme pepsin

2. (F) Liver

3. (F) Esophagus has function to move food to the stomach 4. (T)

4. 5. (T)

5. 6. (T)

6. 7. (F) Body and fundus

Answers:

7. Small intestine

8. Malnutrition, weight loss, poor digestion, and poor absorption.

9. A mixture of water, mucus, hydrochloric acid, and an inactive form of the protein- digesting enzyme pepsin.

10. Lumen

Answers:

11. c (Trachea)

12. b (Intraluminal phase)

13. d (Epiglotis)

14. a (Isomaltase)

15. b (Phosphatidilcholine)

16. d (pH 2)

17. a (Active transport and facilitated diffusion)

18. c (GLUT 5)

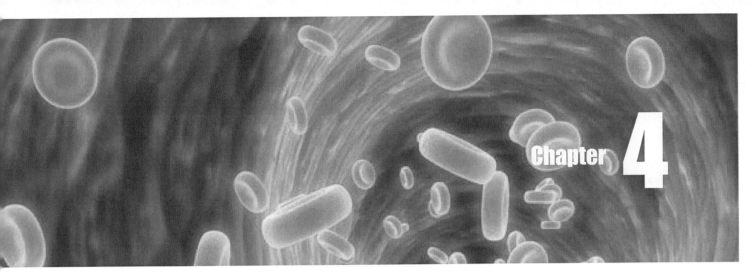

Chapter 4

Digestion and Absorption of Micronutrients

By Meghan Askew, Sharon Jackson, Eunice Kim, Melissa Loy, O Jesse Mendes, Catherine Mixon, Curtis Park, Yuting Qui, Rebecca Stanley and Jonathan Allen

Learning objectives: Students completing this chapter should be able to:

1. Explain the process and mechanisms by which water soluble and fat soluble vitamins are digested and absorbed.

2. Explain the process and mechanisms by which macrominerals, electrolytes, and trace minerals are digested and absorbed.

3. Identify which part of the digestive tract is involved with the absorption of each nutrient.

4. Compare and contrast different absorption methods such as passive diffusion and carrier mediated.

5. Describe what factors affect a nutrient for a constant or variable absorption rate in the body.

6. Recognize that foods or their components might inhibit or aid in absorption of different nutrients.

7. Apply what you have learned about digestion and absorption of each nutrient to other concepts such as transport, storage, and metabolism.

8. Recognize trends between similar nutrients and how they are absorbed.

9. Estimate the percent of intake that is absorbed and explain how changes in intake affect that percentage.

Introduction

Chapter 4 focuses on the digestion and absorption of water soluble and fat soluble vitamins, as well as macrominerals and trace minerals. Nutrient digestion by enzymes can occur in the lumen and brush border of the mouth, stomach, pancreas, and small intestine [1]. Absorption is a process that occurs after digestion and can start in the stomach with a few nutrients, but most nutrients are absorbed in the duodenum, jejunum, and ileum of the small intestine [1].

The following sections explain how each nutrient is digested and absorbed in the body. Section 4.1 covers the water-soluble vitamins, which include thiamine, riboflavin, niacin, biotin, pantothenic acid, vitamin B_6, folate, vitamin C, and vitamin B_{12}. Section

4.2 discusses the fat-soluble vitamins, which are vitamins A, D, E, and K. Section 4.3 covers macrominerals that include calcium, phosphorus, and magnesium, as well as electrolytes such as sodium, potassium, and chloride. Section 4.4 discusses important essential trace minerals, which are iron, zinc, copper, iodine, selenium, molybdenum, manganese, and chromium. The last section, 4.5, outlines the digestion and absorption of nonessential trace minerals, which are arsenic, boron, fluoride, nickel, silicon, and vanadium.

4.1. Digestion and Absorption of Water Soluble Vitamins

4.1.2. Digestion and Absorption of Thiamine (B1)

Because humans cannot synthesize thiamine they must obtain it from exogenous sources, either from their diet or from bacteria that can synthesize it [2]. When thiamine is not absorbed in adequate concentrations thiamine-responsive megaloblastic anemia may be the result. This has been shown to be caused by a genetic defect in the thiamine transporter SLC19A2 [3]. The most common form of dietary thiamine is thiamine pyrophosphate. Once thiamine has been ingested it is carried through the stomach to the jejunum where it is absorbed. The thiamine pyrophosphate has to be hydrolyzed by intestinal phosphatases in order to

be absorbed [4]. The rate of absorption of thiamine is variable depending on the concentration. In lower concentrations thiamin is absorbed through a carrier-mediated system that is dependent on Na^+ and pH [5]. At higher concentrations thiamin is absorbed by means of passive diffusion. When given a high dose of thiamine only a small fraction is absorbed [6]. The excess is excreted in the urine. The free thiamine is transported across the basolateral membrane in the blood [7].

The transporter proteins that are responsible for thiamine absorption are THTR-1 and THTR-2 [3]. These transporter proteins are expressed in both the small and large intestine but more abundantly in the small intestine [8]. The amount of thiamine that is absorbed is related to the level that is in the diet [8]. When there is an abundance of thiamine in the diet, less is absorbed; conversely, more is absorbed when there is a deficiency. Chronic alcohol use leads to a thiamine deficiency by inhibiting thiamine absorption in the small intestine, colon, and kidneys [9]. Infections with enteropathogenic *Escherichia coli* has also been shown to inhibit the absorption of thiamine by suppressing the expression of THTR-1 and THTR-2 [10]. Kidney disease also decreases the absorption of thiamine but it is unclear by what mechanism [11].

4.1.3. Digestion and Absorption of Riboflavin (B2)

Similar to thiamine, there are two sources of dietary riboflavin. Riboflavin is synthesized by plants and bacteria. Some animal foods, such as cows' milk, can concentrate riboflavin. Riboflavin exists as free riboflavin and in two coenzyme forms, FAD and FMN. Analogous to thiamine, the coenzyme forms found in food, FAD and FMN, must be hydrolyzed by intestinal phosphatases prior to being absorbed [12].

Riboflavin generally is consumed as a part of a food protein [13]. Hydrochloric acid in the stomach and enzymatic hydrolysis in the intestine frees riboflavin from the protein [1].

The mechanism of absorption of riboflavin uses a Na^+-dependent carrier. The transporter proteins are RFT-1 and RFT-2 [2]. Genetic mutations of these transporter proteins have been observed in the deficiency of riboflavin in patients with the rare Brown-Vialettlo- Van Laere syndrome [14]. Riboflavin absorption is regulated by the extracellular concentration [15]. Similar to thiamine, an abundance of riboflavin decreases the percentage of the vitamin absorbed and a deficiency of riboflavin increases the uptake. It appears that the uptake of riboflavin decreases after the early stages of life [16]. Pregnancy increases the amount of carrier proteins for riboflavin uptake [17]. It appears that the drug chlorpromazine inhibits riboflavin uptake due to its affinity for the carrier proteins [18].

4.1.4. Digestion and Absorption of Niacin (B_3)

Niacin is a precursor to the coenzymes NAD^+ and NADPH that are used in metabolic reactions [8]. Niacin can come from either endogenous or exogenous sources. It is a unique water soluble vitamin because humans do have the ability to synthesize it from the amino acid tryptophan. In order to synthesize 1 mg of niacin 60 mg of tryptophan, beyond that used for protein synthesis, are needed. The main exogenous source is dietary niacin. The absorption of niacin has been reported as being simple diffusion in the small intestine whereas others have reported it being a carrier-mediated mechanism [8]. The absorption of niacin is very rapid [13]. In the liver and intestines nicotinamide is released from NAD by glycohydrolases. The nicotinamide is then transported to tissues in order to produce NAD for metabolic reactions. NAD and NAHP are found inside the cell, with the inside of the cell having a higher concentration of NAD [1]. Excess niacin is converted to NAD in the liver and stored in small quantities which remain unbound to enzymes [1].

4.1.5. Digestion and Absorption of Biotin

Biotin is an important vitamin that is a cofactor to various carboxylases that are used in a variety of metabolic reactions [8]. In the diet biotin exists as free and protein- bound forms. The protein-bound form of biotin must first be digested by gastrointestinal proteases such as biocytin [8]. Absorption of biotin occurs mainly in the small intestine but also occurs in the colon [13]. The absorption of biotin is through a carrier-mediated mechanism that is Na^+ dependent. This carrier has also been found to be used in the absorption of pantothenic acid and lipoate [8]. The amount of biotin to be absorbed is regulated by the amount of the substrate in the diet [8].

4.1.6. Digestion and Absorption of Pantothenic Acid (Vitamin B5)

Pantothenic acid is usually bound in food to coenzyme A (CoA). CoA is hydrolyzed to pantetheine and then to pantothenic acid in the lumen of the gastrointestinal tract [1]. When concentrations of pantothenic acid in the body are high, it is absorbed in the jejunum of the small intestine by passive diffusion [1]. Another known pathway into the intestine is by a sodium-dependent multivitamin transporter (SMVT) that is also shared with biotin [1, 8].

4.1.7. Digestion and Absorption of Vitamin B_6

There are three forms of vitamin B6: pyridoxine, pyridoxal, and pyridoxamine.

Vitamin B_6 comes from dietary and bacterial sources. The phosphorylated forms of vitamin B_6 are commonly found in the diet and are hydrolyzed in the intestine by phosphatase enzymes prior to absorption [19]. In the past the mechanism for absorption has been regarded as passive diffusion and as being nonsaturable [13]. Recent studies have observed that vitamin B6 is absorbed through a pH dependent carrier-mediated mechanism [20]. Nothing is currently known regarding the identity of the protein transporter [8].

Regardless of the mechanism, vitamin B6 is absorbed very quickly [8]. Most of the absorbed free vitamin B6 goes to the liver where pyridoxine, pyridoxal, and pyridoxamine are phosphorylated by pyridoxal kinase [13]. From the liver the various forms of vitamin B6 can be transported through the plasma [13].

4.1.8. Digestion and Absorption of Folate

Folate is important for the metabolism of nucleic and amino acids. It is involved in the single-carbon transfers used in those reactions [13]. The forms of folate commonly found are folic acid and its derivatives. Folate is synthesized in both plants and bacteria [8]. Folate is absorbed in the small intestine. Dietary folate consists of mono and poly- glutamate forms with the latter being hydrolyzed to mono glutamates prior to absorption [8]. The enzyme involved in the digestion of folate is called folylpoly-gamma-glutamate carboxypeptidase [8]. This enzyme is also commonly referred to as folate conjugase [13].

Once the poly-glutamates have been hydrolyzed to mono-glutamates they are available for absorption through a carrier-mediated mechanism [21]. This mechanism is pH and Na^+ dependent [8]. Folate absorption in the small intestine is regulated by a variety of factors, both extracellular and intracellular. The activity of folate conjugase is increased when there is a folate deficiency [22]. A significant increase in carrier-mediated folate absorption was also observed when there was a folate deficiency [22]. Folate uptake decreases with increasing maturation by a decrease in the carrier-mediated mechanism and expression of the protein transporter [23]. Folate uptake is also regulated by the protein- tyrosine-kinase-mediated pathway [24].

Once the mono glutamates are absorbed in the small intestines they are transported throughout the blood. Much of the folate is taken up in the liver [13]. This folate is then metabolized to polyglutamate derivatives and released into the blood or bile or retained in the liver. Most of the folate (about two-thirds) is bound to protein with much of that being albumin [13]. Foods such as legumes, lentils, cabbage and oranges, as well as alcohol consumption can inhibit the absorption of folate [1]. Levels of folate in the body range from 11 to 28 mg with one-half of that amount stored in the liver [1].

4.1.9. Digestion and Absorption of Vitamin C

Vitamin C is exists in two forms, an oxidized form, dehydro-L-ascorbic acid, and a reduced form, ascorbic acid, or ascorbate at physiological pH ($pK_1 = 4.17$). Most mammals can synthesize ascorbate but humans lack the enzyme L-gulonolactone oxidase in the pathway that converts D-glucose to ascorbate [8]. Unlike other water soluble vitamins, there is no indication that intestinal bacteria synthesize this vitamin. Vitamin C does not need to be digested prior to being absorbed by the intestine. Intestinal absorption of ascorbate is through a carrier-mediated mechanism that is dependent on Na^+ [2]. When high concentrations of ascorbate are ingested, some of the ascorbate is absorbed through passive diffusion [13]. The proteins responsible are called SVCT-1 and SVCT-2 [8]. They both transport only ascorbic acid and not the oxidized form dehydro-L-ascorbic acid [8]. Some of the glucose transporters have been shown to transport dehydro-L-ascorbic acid [8]. Like many other water-soluble vitamins, the uptake of ascorbate varies with the dietary concentration. When intake exceeds 1 g/day the absorption falls from the usual 70 to 90 percent to 50 percent [25]. The bioavailability of ascorbate from foods is not significantly different than from supplements [13].

4.1.10. Digestion and Absorption of Vitamin B$_{12}$

Vitamin B12 is generally referred to as cobalamin. Cobalamin is a group of cobalt containing compounds with ribose, phosphate, and a base attached to a corrin ring [13]. The process of absorption of vitamin B12 is different from the other water-soluble vitamins because it is mediated by proteins in the saliva, gastric juice, and ileum [26]. In the saliva, the proteins classified as haptocorrins are the first to bind up free cobalamin [26]. Other than the possibility of preventing loss of free cobalamin, no specific function of haptocorrins has been discovered [26]. In the stomach the gastric secretions contain a protein called intrinsic factor. Intrinsic factor has the ability to bind 50-60 ng of cobalamin per mL of gastric juice [26]. Based on the average gastric juice production over 24 hours, 1-5 mg of intrinsic factor is produced to bind about 30-150 µg of cobalamin [27]. Intrinsic factor produced by the parietal cells usually exceeds the molar quantity of cobalamin to be absorbed. Haptocorrins have a much lower binding specificity for cobalamin than intrinsic factor [26]. Therefore, compounds that are similar to cobalamin, such as cobinamide, will react with haptocorrins but not with intrinsic factor [26]. In the small intestine there is an intrinsic factor receptor protein called cubilin that is associated with the membrane of the ileum. When the cobalamin is bound to the intrinsic factor there is

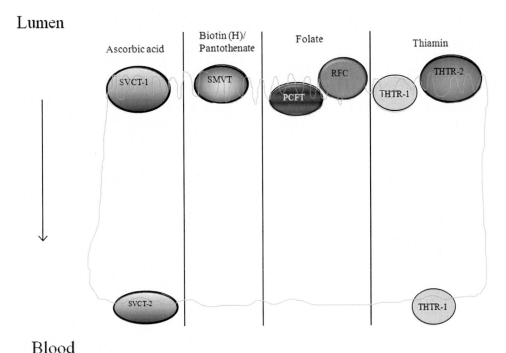

Figure 4.1-1: Schematic depiction of the membrane expression of well-characterized water-soluble vitamin transporters in polarized intestinal epithelial cells.

a change in its tertiary structure that allows it to bind to the cubilin [26]. There is another transmembrane protein called amnionless that aids in the absorption of the cobalamin bound to the intrinsic factor [26]. Once the cobalamin is absorbed into the enterocyte of the ileum it is released from intrinsic factor and becomes bound to transcobalamin. The mechanism for how this is done is still yet to be discovered [26]. Transcobalamin transports the cobalamin from the ileum to the rest of the tissues in the body where there is a receptor-mediated cellular uptake [28].

Absorption of cobalamin can be variable in certain cases. Binding of intrinsic factor to cobalamin may depend on Ca^{++} [25]. Decreased absorption of cobalamin can result from pernicious anemia, an autoimmune condition that destroys the parietal cells [29]. This would inhibit the production of intrinsic factor and reduce cobalamin absorption. Fractional cobalamin absorption decreases as the oral intake increases and the total amount absorbed increases with increasing intake [29]. Even in the absence of intrinsic factor about 1 percent of a large dose of crystalline cobalamin can be absorbed [30]. Intake of about 1.5

to 2.5 μg per meal of cobalamin saturates the protein receptors for absorption and limits further absorption [31].

4.2. Digestion and Absorption of Fat-Soluble Vitamins

4.2.1. Digestion and Absorption of Vitamin A

Vitamin A has three active forms: retinal, retinol and retinoic acid and a storage form retinyl ester. Vitamin A absorption comes from beta-carotene and retinyl esters in the intestine from the various food sources. Retinol, the most abundant form of vitamin A absorbed when eating animal food sources, is a yellow, fat-soluble substance. Carotenoids, such as alpha-carotene, beta-carotene and gamma-carotene, can be enzymatically converted to retinal in the enterocytes, then are converted completely to retinyl esters. These esters then travel through the lymph via chylomicrons to the liver, where they're either stored or immediately used [32].

Mechanisms involved in the digestion and absorption of dietary vitamin A require the participation of several proteins. Dietary retinyl esters are hydrolyzed in the intestine by the pancreatic enzyme, pancreatic triglyceride lipase, an intestinal brush border enzyme. Unesterified retinol is primarily bound to retinol-binding protein (RBP), and can enter and leave the liver several times per day in a process known as retinol recycling. Retinol bound to a cellular RBP can be esterified by the enzyme: retinol acyltransferase (LCAT). The retinyl esters are then incorporated into chylomicrons, and chylomicrons containing newly absorbed retinyl esters are then secreted into the lymph. Although under normal dietary condition much of the dietary vitamin A is absorbed via the chylomicron/lymphatic route, it is also clear that under some circumstances there is substantial absorption of unesterified retinol via the portal route [33, 34].

4.2.2. Digestion and Absorption of Vitamin D

Vitamin D is a group of fat-soluble vitamins. They are precursors to hormones, and are essential to endocrine health. There are several forms of vitamin D, but the most common are ergocalciferol (Vitamin D2) and cholecalciferol (Vitamin D3), which are known together as calciferol. Vitamin D2 is synthesized by plants. Vitamin D3 is synthesized by animals in the skin when it is exposed to ultraviolet-B (UV-B) rays from sunlight; it is also available from supplements and occurs naturally in a small range of foods. Certain foods may be fortified with vitamin D2 or D3. Dietary D2 and D3 digestion and absorption in the distal small intestine is similar to other sterols and lipids.

Enterocytes package vitamin D into chylomicrons that enter the lymphatic system and ultimately the blood stream (1). .

Vitamin D is carried in the bloodstream to the liver, where it is converted into the prohormone calcidiol (25-hydroxycholecalciferol). Calcidiol may then be converted into calcitriol (1,25-dihydroxycholecalciferol) in the kidney. Calcitriol or 1,25- dihydroxycholecalciferol (the biologically active form of vitamin D) is then released into the blood stream. By binding to vitamin D-binding protein (VDBP), a carrier protein in the plasma, calcitriol is transported to various target organs.

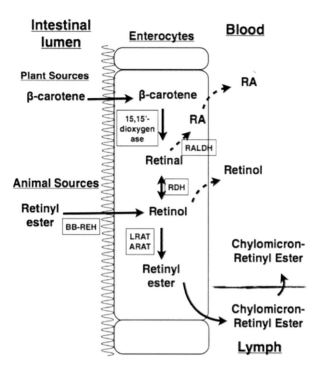

Figure 4.2-1: Overview of digestion and absorption of vitamin A.
From https://www.researchgate.net/figure/272645030_fig1_Figure-1-Schematic-representation-of-vitamin-A-VA-digestion-absorption-transport

Calcitriol mediates its biological effects by binding to the vitamin D receptor (VDR). Vitamin D compounds are catabolized primarily by oxidation of the side chain. The major catabolic enzyme is the vitamin D-24-hydroxylase. The oxidation of the side chain of 25(OH)D3 (calcidiol) and 1,25(OH)2D3 (calcitriol) is initiated at carbon C-24. Each oxidation step leads to progressive loss of biological activity. The final residual product 1,25(OH)2D3 is calcitroic acid which is biologically inert [35].

One of the most important roles of vitamin D is to maintain skeletal calcium balance by promoting calcium absorption in the intestines, promoting bone reapsorption by increasing osteoclast number, maintaining calcium and phosphate levels for bone formation, and allowing proper functioning of parathyroid hormone to maintain serum calcium levels. Calcitriol affects growth of normal cells and some cancer cells. Adequate vitamin D status has been

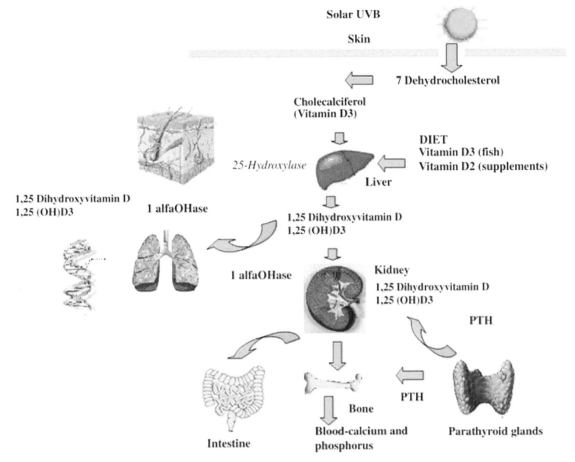

Figure 4.2-2: Activation of vitamin D. Creative Commons.
From http://www.vitamindwiki.com/tiki-download_wiki_attachment.php?attId=761

linked to a reduced risk of developing breast, colon, and prostate cancers [36].

4.2.3. Digestion and Absorption of Vitamin E

Vitamin E refers to several related compounds called tocopherols, of which alpha- tocopherol offers the highest bioavailability. While alpha-tocopherol seems to be the most active, beta-tocopherol, gamma-tocopherol and delta-tocopherol each play their complementary role. Vitamin E is stored mainly in adipose tissue, while some is stored in the muscle. The remaining vitamin E is found in cell membranes throughout the body.

Absorption of vitamin E is highly dependent upon the same processes that are utilized during dietary lipid digestion and metabolism. Both fat and vitamin E absorption are dependent on micelle and chylomicron formation. A lack of any component of these transporters will inhibit carrier formation and in turn will inhibit vitamin E absorption. Bile acids are considered essential for vitamin E separation from fat droplets. Conditions for absorption are efficient emulsification, solubilization within mixed bile salt, uptake by enterocytes, and secretion into the circulation via the lymphatic system. Emulsification takes place initially in the stomach and then in the small intestine in the presence of pancreatic and biliary secretions. The resulting mixed micelle aggregates the vitamin E molecules, solubilizes the vitamin E, and then transports it to the brush border membrane of the enterocyte. Within the enterocyte, tocopherol is incorporated into chylomicrons and secreted into the lymphatic system and subsequently into the blood stream [37].

Vitamin E is transported in the blood by the

plasma lipoproteins and erythrocytes. Chylomicrons carry tocopherol from the enterocyte to the liver. The catabolism of chylomicrons takes place in the systemic circulation through the action of cellular lipoprotein lipase (LPL). During this process some tocopherol can be transferred to high- density lipoproteins (HDLs), while some remains with the chylomicron remnants. The tocopherol in HDLs can transfer to other circulating lipoproteins, such as low-density lipoproteins (LDLs) and very low-density lipoproteins (VLDL) [38].

Vitamin E is an antioxidant and one of the body's primary defenders against oxidative damage caused by free radicals. Its activity is complemented by other antioxidants such as vitamin C and the mineral selenium. Vitamin E interrupts free-radical chain reactions by getting oxidized, thus protecting cell membranes from free-radical attack. So it can reduce the risk of chronic disease and cardiovascular disease [39].

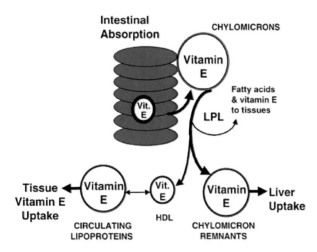

Figure 4.2-3: Overview of digestion and absorption of vitamin E.
From https://pt.slideshare.net/estherissaac/vitamins-46410133/5

4.2.4. Digestion and Absorption of Vitamin K

Vitamin K is a group of vitamers, mainly vitamin K1 and vitamin K2. Vitamin K1 and K2, like vitamins A, D, and E, are fat-soluble. Vitamin K1 and vitamin K2 are naturally occurring vitamins. In addition, there's a subset of vitamin K molecules that includes vitamin K_3,

K_4, and K_5, all of which are synthetic vitamins. Vitamin K participates in a series of reactions to form a clot that eventually stops the flow of blood. Vitamin K is also involved in the activation of bone proteins, which greatly enhances their calcium-binding properties. Low levels of circulating vitamin K have been associated with low bone- mineral density.

The absorption of Vitamin K1, known as phylloquinone and vitamin K2, known as the menaquinones (menaquinones are abbreviated MK-n, where M stands for menaquinone, the K stands for vitamin K, and the n represents the number of isoprenoid side chain residues) requires bile and pancreatic acids. Dietary vitamin K is absorbed in the small intestine, is incorporated into chylomicrons, and appears in the lymph which enters the bloods. Once in the circulation, phylloquinone is rapidly cleared at a rate consistent with its association with chylomicrons. These chylomicrons lose their triglyceride contents through the action of lipoprotein lipase and eventually become chylomicrons remnants.

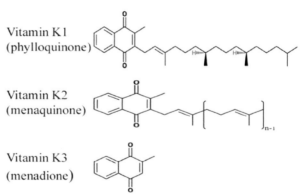

Figure 4.2-4: Structure of vitamers of vitamin K. Image from http://www.omjournal.org/images/images%20052014/R_vitk-f1.jpg

During this period, phylloquinone appears to be transferred from the chylomicron remnants to the liver, where it is incorporated into very low-density lipoproteins (VLDL) and ultimately distributed to tissues via low-density lipoproteins (LDL). Phylloquinone is the major circulating form of vitamin K but menaquinone is present in the plasma at lower concentrations. Menaquinone has a lipoprotein distribution similar to phylloquinone [40, 41].

Vitamin K is known as the clotting vitamin,

because without it blood would not clot. Some studies suggest that it helps maintain strong bones in the elderly. It is rare to have a vitamin K deficiency because vitamin K is found in leafy green vegetables and the bacteria in your intestines can make vitamin K. A deficiency occurs when the body can't properly absorb the vitamin from the intestinal tract. Vitamin K deficiency can also occur after long-term treatment with antibiotics.

4.2.5. Vitamin K, oxidative stress, cardiovascular disease

Vitamin K_2, also known as **menaquinone** (MK), is thought to reduce coronary heart disease. Bacteria produce MK; even though high amounts of MK are present in the gut, it cannot be absorbed there and is excreted in the feces. However, MK goes directly into blood vessel walls, bones, and tissues. MK, is found in animal products, whereas phylloquinone, or vitamin K_1, is found in vegetables. Vitamin K_2 was found to decrease coronary calcification; however, vitamin K_1 did not show the same effects [42]. The Rotterdam Study, one of the first studies to exhibit the beneficial effects of vitamin K_2 (MK), showed that people who consumed 45 µg/day of K_2 lived seven years longer than individuals that consumed only 12 µg/day of K_2 [43]. In the Prospect Study, 16,000 individuals were followed for 10 years to show similar beneficial evidence towards K_2 consumption. During this time, researchers found that for every additional 10 µg/daily of K_2 consumed, there were 9% fewer cardiac events. Vitamin K_1 failed to offer any significant heart benefits [44].

Vitamin K_2 interacts with vitamin D, possibly by directing calcium to the skeleton, therefore, preventing it from being deposited in organs, joints, and arteries [42]. MK does this by activating a protein called osteocalcin, which is produce by osteoblasts; this is needed to bind calcium into the bone matrix. Osteocalcin may prevent calcium from depositing into arteries, working very similarly to K_2 [45].

Individuals prone to exhibit CVD risk factors are urged to consume foods that contain high amounts of vitamin K. Vitamin K_2 is found in fats, oils, poultry, and meat products. K_1 is produced in dark green leafy vegetables, legumes, and nuts. Individuals who consume these types of foods may have lowered their risk of CVD and other heart and vascular illnesses. Vitamin K deficiencies are rare because both dark green leafy vegetables and the bacteria in human intestine can make vitamin K. However, there are several conditions that can lead to vitamin K deficiency, such as gallbladder or biliary disease, cystic fibrosis, celiac disease, Crohn's disease, liver disease, taking blood-thinners (warfarin or Coumadin), long-term hemodialysis, and serious burns.

4.3. Digestion and Absorption of Macrominerals

4.3.1. Digestion and Absorption of Calcium

Calcium is the most abundant divalent cation of the body and represents about two percent of total body weight. Ninety-nine percent of the body's calcium is found in the bones and teeth, while one percent is found on the intra- and extracellular fluids [1]. Calcium is ingested as insoluble salts and is then solubilized by the acidic environment in the stomach to free calcium ions that can be absorbed in the small intestine. Ingesting food or lactose with the calcium source improves the solubility of calcium.

The major pathway for calcium absorption occurs in the duodenum and jejunum and is saturable energy dependent [1]. Calcium moves through this saturable pathway against the concentration gradient from the lumen of the intestines across the brush border membrane, through the cytosol and into the plasma; this process is shown in figure 4.3.1. The first step in this pathway involves the uptake of Ca into the cell via the TRPV6 channel. The TRPV6 gene is regulated by 1,25-dihydroxyvitamin D_3 and there is evidence that this is not the only way that Ca enters the cell of the enterocyte, however other pathways are not as well understood at this time. Once Ca is in the cell it is bound to calbindin D and transported across the cell, an ATP dependent process then pumps Ca out of the cell and into the plasma [46].

The second major pathway for calcium absorption, paracellular, is diffusion through tight junctions. This occurs between cells instead of through them and when luminal concentrations of Ca are high. The cells are packed tightly together but become more permeable in response to certain signals that are not yet entirely understood. Suzuki and Hara found that four nondigestible saccharides increase paracellular absorption of calcium [47]. Fujita et al. found that claudins (the major transmembrane proteins) are responsible for the regulation of calcium paracellular absorption and are up-regulated by vitamin D [48]. The researchers noted that future studies should be performed to determine if the luminal concentration of calcium ions affects gene expression of claudins.

Calcium levels are regulated by the hormones PTH (parathyroid hormone), calcitriol, and calcitonin. When calcium levels are low the parathyroid gland releases PTH into the blood. PTH stimulates the kidney to increase synthesis of calcitriol, which improves calcium absorption in the intestines. Calcitonin works to lower serum calcium levels by turning off PTH production and by inhibiting osteoclasts [1].

Several factors inhibit calcium absorption including phytic acid, oxalic acid, divalent cations, unabsorbed dietary fatty acids, and proton pump inhibitors. Phytic acid, found in whole grains, binds to calcium and decreases its absorption. Oxalic acid, found in some fruits and vegetables, chelates calcium increasing its excretion from the digestive system. Magnesium and zinc can compete with calcium for absorption thus decreasing the amount of calcium absorbed from the diet. Fatty acids can interact with calcium forming insoluble soaps that are excreted. Proton pump inhibitors may hinder the production of gastric acid thus decreasing the solubilizing acids in the stomach [1]. As calcium intake decreases, efficiency of calcium absorption increases and vice versa. The increase of efficiency is not sufficient enough to offset the loss of absorbed calcium during periods of decreased dietary calcium intake. Calcium absorption declines with age in both men and woman [6]. Calcium absorption is enhanced by vitamin D, ingestion of food or lactose along with a calcium source (improving the solubility) and other sugars, sugar alcohol and protein. Foods high in calcium are milk, yogurt, cheese, calcium-fortified orange juice, kale and broccoli [6].

4.3.2. Digestion and Absorption of Phosphorous

Phosphorous is second to calcium in abundance in the body, inorganic elements. Phosphorus helps maintain a normal pH in the body, involved in metabolic processes, as well is a major component in teeth and bones. Dietary phosphorus supports tissue growth. Total body phosphorous breaks down to: 85 % in the skeleton, 1 % in the blood and body fluids, leaving 14% associated with soft tissues of muscle [6]. Phosphorous is found in a wide variety of foods in both organic and inorganic forms. The organic forms of phosphorous must be enzymatically digested before absorption. Many foods contain organic and inorganic phosphorous, although the ratios vary. The organic phosphorous contained in phytic acid it is less bioavailable than phosphorous that is bound to proteins, lipids, and carbohydrates. About 50 – 70 % of dietary phosphorous is absorbed [1].

Phosphorous is absorbed by the small intestine by two processes: saturable, carrier-mediated, active transport and by passive diffusion. Passive diffusion is thought to be the main mechanism of absorption when phosphate intake is high, the molecules will move into the cells along the concentration gradient. According to Marks, this passive transport mechanism seems to be unregulated [49]. When phosphate intake is low, active transport is needed. "Intestinal absorption of phosphate is mediated primarily via the type IIb sodium-phosphate transporter Npt2b. 1,25-Dihydroxyvitamin D3 and dietary phosphate depletion are thought to be the most important physiological stimuli of intestinal phosphate absorption and act by increasing the abundance of Npt2b protein" [50]. In other words, when our intake of phosphorus is low, active transport is needed, and when our intake is high, passive diffusion is sufficient to absorb the mineral. 1,25- Dihydroxyvitamin D3 (active vitamin D) helps intestinal cells absorb phosphorous when it is needed. Vitamin D as calcitriol stimulates phosphate absorption in both the duodenum and jejunum. Phosphorous is impaired by phytate and excessive intake of minerals, magnesium, calcium, and aluminum.

Phosphorus is found in nearly all food because of its important intracellular functions, and dairy is a rich source because of the calcium-phosphate complexes in the casein micelles [1]. Animal products that contain bone, such as sardines, also have abundant phosphorus. Increasing phosphorus intake is therefore accomplished by choosing higher phosphate foods. Body phosphorus content is influenced by both percentage of the intake that is absorbed and the amount that is excreted in urine

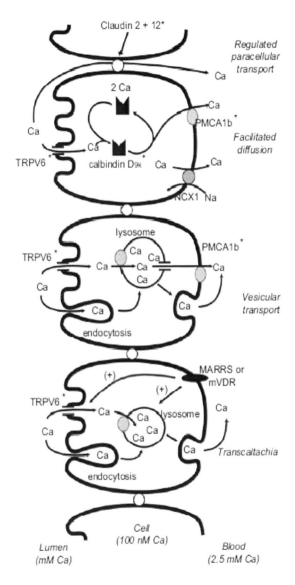

Figure 4.3-1: Absorption of Calcium.
From http://www.sciencedirect.com/topics/page/Calbindin

4.3.3. Digestion and Absorption of Magnesium

Magnesium is the second most abundant intracellular cation and is found in a wide variety of foods from nuts to whole grains. Magnesium does not require digestion before absorption which occurs in the distal end of small intestine (jejunum and ileum primarily). The large intestine is also capable of absorbing magnesium although this is less common [51].

The two predominant modes of absorption for magnesium are diffusion and saturable, carrier-mediated active transport (1). Diffusion through the tight junctions between enterocytes accounts for more than a third of total absorption [51], particularly at higher intakes, and is determined by the electrochemical gradient [52]. When intake is low, carrier-mediated diffusion of magnesium becomes more important and occurs through TRPM6 and TRPM7 protein channel molecules. TRPM6 is found throughout the length of the intestine, along the kidney nephron, and in lung tissue [53]. TRPM7 is found throughout the body in epithelial and nonepithelial tissues [54]. TRPM6 and TRPM7 are permeable to, Ca^{2+} and Mg^{2+} as well as other cations [54]. Once inside the enterocyte, magnesium can be actively transported out of the cell and into the plasma.

Magnesium does not appear to be as tightly regulated (hormonally) as other minerals [52]. A pure magnesium deficiency from low dietary intake has never been reported in humans, except for in a rare genetic disorder Gitelman-Bartter 104 sydrome [1]. Scientists have also been able to demonstrate Mg deficiency in laboratory experiments [1] and it occurs in some species of domestic animals. There are, however, dietary components that limit the absorption or bioavailability of magnesium. A high fiber diet reduces magnesium absorption by binding of magnesium to phytate [52].

4.3.4. Absorption and digestion of Sodium

Electrolytes are the ions distributed throughout the body to maintain electrical neutrality. The anion concentration must balance the cation concentration. The kidney is primarily responsible for the maintenance of electrolyte balance using both passive and active processes to achieve balance. Sodium, potassium, and chloride are important electrolytes, and the percentage absorbed from the gut is very high.

Sodium is the most abundant cation in the body and about 95% to 100% of ingested sodium is absorbed [1]. Three main pathways are important in the absorption of sodium: the Na+/glucose cotransport system, Na+ and Cl- cotransport system, and an electrogenic sodium absorption mechanism [1]. The Na+/glucose cotransport system is active throughout the small intestine and involves the binding of Na+ and glucose to a carrier molecule that brings the molecules into the cell. The second pathway involves the 1:1 exchange of Na+ with H+ and Cl- with HCO3- as illustrated in figure 4.3.1 and is electrically neutral [55]. The third known pathway is by electrogenic sodium absorption that occurs in the colon is not coupled with absorption or release of other ions.

4.3.5. Digestion and Absorption of Potassium

Potassium is very common in the diet but is particularly rich in certain fruits (bananas, avocados, mangoes) and vegetables (leafy greens, yams). Over 85% of all potassium consumed is absorbed [1]. High potassium diets can lead to lowered risk of high blood pressure. Absorption of potassium is not very well understood, more research is needed in this area. Similar to other macrominerals, it is likely that potassium is absorbed by a combination of passive and active processes including a K^+/H -ATPase pump. This type of pump exchanges H^+, which is inside the cell, for K^+ that is in the lumen of the intestine. It is similar to the absorption mechanism described for sodium ions [1]. Potassium affects water balance and the acid-base balance in the blood and tissues, along with sodium. Potassium is an important component of muscle and is essential for normal growth.

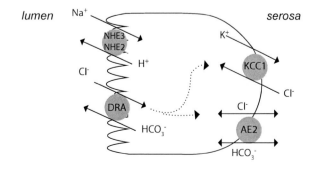

Figure 4.3-2: Absorption of electrolytes.

4.4.6. Digestion and Absorption of Chloride

About 85% of all chloride in the body is found in the extracellular fluid, making it the most plentiful anion found in the ECF [1]. Chloride is consumed in the form of salt (NaCl) and is absorbed in the small intestine. When sodium is taken into cells actively via the Na^+/glucose pathway, chloride passively flows through a paracellular pathway to maintain ion balance [1]. This newly absorbed Na+ creates an electrical gradient which enables paracelluar diffusion of Cl- in between the cells [1]. In addition, Cl/HCO3 exchange acts in concert with Na/H exchange to mediate electroneutral NaCl uptake by enterocytes [56]. Na^+ and Cl^- uptake in the colon aids in the absorption of water. Chloride is obtained primarily from salt, such as table or sea salt. It is contained in most foods, including vegetables. Examples of good sources are seaweeds, olives, rye, lettuce, tomatoes, and celery [1]. Chloride accompanies sodium and water to maintain electrical neutrality, and helps generate the osmotic pressure of body fluids. It is an important component of stomach hydrochloric acid (HCl), the key digestive acid. Chloride is needed to maintain the body's acid- base balance.

4.4. Digestion and Absorption of Trace Minerals

4.4.1. Digestion and Absorption of Iron

Iron functions in forming molecular complexes such as the **hemoglobin** and **myoglobin** to that bind and release oxygen in the blood and muscle. In addition to transport of oxygen, many other metabolic functions of iron include the production of energy. Since it serves as an electron donor or acceptor, iron is important in biological reactions that involve the oxidation of organic substrates by molecular oxygen. Iron exists in a variety of oxidation states varying from Fe^{6+} to Fe^{2-} depending on the chemical environment. However, the only states stable within the body are the ferric (Fe^{3+}) and the ferrous (Fe^{2+}) forms. Along with being a cofactor in the transport of oxygen and respiration, it is also an essential component in amino acid, lipid, alcohol, vitamin A, and sulfite metabolism [57].

Absorption of the various oxidation states of iron can be very limited unless they can be both solubilized and ionized in the intestine. Three pathways for the uptake of iron include one for heme-bound iron, one for ferrous iron through a divalent metal ion transporter, and one for ferric iron via the beta 3-integrin mobilferrin pathway [57]. Mobilferrin is a cytosolic iron-binding protein. The ferrous form of iron can be absorbed from the gastrointestinal tract, however the ferric compounds must be reduced by the gastric juice in order to be absorbed [58]. Heme-bound iron is first hydrolyzed from either hemoglobin or myoglobin. Digestion of heme-bound iron is done by both proteases in the stomach and small intestine and results in the release of heme iron from the globin. Non-heme-bound iron that is bound to food must be hydrolyzed before it can be absorbed also.

After its digestion, heme iron can be readily absorbed across the brush border of the enterocytes with help from the heme carrier protein 1 (HCP1). This protein is mainly found in the proximal small intestine (duodenum) where iron absorption occurs most efficiently. Iron is released from the enterocytes by a carrier called **ferroportin**-1. The amount of ferroportin in the basolateral membrane of these cells is down-regulated by the hormone **hepcidin**. Hepcidin secretion by hepatocytes increases when the liver has more iron stored. Thus, the hepcidin-ferroportin feedback loop can closely control iron stores in most people.

Absorption of iron in the small intestine requires the help from transferrin, which is a plasma iron-transport protein that carries ferric iron between the sites of its absorption and utilization. Ferrous iron is taken up through the divalent metal ion transporter 1 and transported across the brush border membrane of the duodenum [57]. Ferric iron has low solubility in the alkaline pH of the small intestine, so it must be reduced by ferrireductase before absorption [57].

Iron absorption can change with a person's need for iron [58]. For example, if iron levels are normal in the body then a typical person may absorb 10% from their diet. If a person is iron deficient their absorption may be increased to 35% [58]. Vitamin C, other organic acids, and sugars, are thought to enhance nonheme iron absorption by chelation and forming ligand complexes. Some inhibitors of nonheme iron absorption are polyphenols found in coffee and tea, oxalic acid,

phytic acid, and phosvitin. Divalent cations such as calcium, zinc, and manganese also inhibit absorption of nonheme iron [58].

4.4.2. Digestion and Absorption of Zinc

Zinc is a metallic element that is essential for the activation of many genes and acts as a cofactor for many enzyme reactions. Zinc is known for being a good reducing agent and can from stable complexes with many anions [58]. Zinc is an important element in the metabolism of RNA and DNA, signal transduction, and gene expression. It is also critical for normal functioning in the brain and central nervous system. Before it can be absorbed, zinc must be liberated from its binding sites in food by hydrolyzing the ligand by proteases and nucleases (DNAases, and RNAases) in the stomach and small intestine. Zinc forms complexes with histidine, cysteine, and nucleotides that are well-absorbed [57].

Zinc is absorbed by enterocytes in the jejunum through a carrier-mediated process, meaning that low intakes of zinc will be absorbed more efficiently than higher intakes. The protein carrier called ZIP4 is the main mechanism for zinc uptake in the intestine. Another transporter is the **divalent mineral transporter 1** (DMT1), which transports zinc into intestinal cells. Passive diffusion, and paracellular zinc absorption can be involved to a greater extent than carrier-mediated transport when zinc intake is high. Iron and chelating ligands can inhibit zinc uptake [1]. When dietary zinc is high, fractional absorption will be less; when dietary intake is low, the body may absorb up to 100% of the intake [58]. A dietary zinc deficiency increases the intestinal secretion of ZIP4 and decreases the synthesis of the cytosolic Zn-binding protein, **metallothionein** [58A]. Some inhibitors to zinc absorption include phytic acid, oxalic acid, and polyphenols. Some vitamins and minerals may also inhibit zinc absorption such as folate, iron, and calcium [58].

4.4.3. Digestion and Absorption of Copper

Copper is a transition metal that contains two oxidation states and is essential for energy metabolism, brain function, soft tissues and bone, nutrient metabolism, and antioxidant defense against free radicals [57]. In most living systems the biologically active form is cupric ion (Cu^{2+}). The richest dietary sources of copper are organ meats and shellfish [1]. Copper is also secreted daily in the gastrointestinal tract within the digestive juices. Most copper that enters the gastrointestinal tract is bound to a food component.

Hydrochloric acid and pepsin help to free the bound copper so that absorption can occur, as do proteolytic enzymes in the small intestine.

Copper absorption occurs mostly in the duodenum and a very small amount is thought to be absorbed in the stomach [57, 58]. Copper is transported into the enterocyte by copper transporter 1 (CTR 1). CTR 1 transports copper in its Cu 1+ state. Another way copper is absorbed is by the proton-coupled divalent metal transporter, which also binds iron and zinc. The amount of copper absorbed is dependent upon the food mixture consumed and the presence of other divalent minerals. Fractional absorption of copper decreases as intake of the mineral increases [58]. Because copper must compete for uptake with other divalent minerals, it is usually excreted in the feces, urine, skin, and hair. After it has been absorbed by enterocytes it passes to the blood and binds to albumin or transcupreien [58].

4.4.4. Digestion and Absorption of Iodine

Iodine is an essential component of the thyroid hormones, which function in the control of development, growth, and metabolism [57]. Iodine coming from the diet is either bound to amino acids or found free in two forms, iodate (IO_3^-) and iodide (I^-). Iodide is most efficiently absorbed, and iodate is usually reduced to iodide by glutathione in the stomach. Iodine that is organically bound is freed and absorbed in the stomach and small intestine [1]. Iodine has a very high absorption rate and because of this it is rarely found in the feces during excretion.

Iodine is absorbed rapidly in both the small intestine and stomach. In the stomach iodine is absorbed with the help of sodium/iodide symporter that is expressed by chief and parietal epithelial cells [57]. The thyroid gland sequesters iodide in a very efficient way by using a Na+/I- symporter in the thyroid gland's basolateral membrane [58, 59, 60].

4.4.5. Digestion and Absorption of Selenium

Selenium has three potential oxidation states (+6, +4, -2). It is a cofactor that is important in antioxidant defense, thyroid hormone and insulin function, regulation of cell growth, and maintenance of fertility [57]. Selenium is an essential element in a group of proteins called selenoproteins, some of which are particularly important in suppressing free radicals [58].

Selenium occurs primarily as selenomethionine and selenocysteine in most organic food compounds. Selenium is also found in inorganic forms including selenide (H_2Se), selenite (H_2SeO_3), and selenate (H_2SeO_4). Selenium in both forms does not need to be digested prior to being absorbed in the small intestine [61]. Selenium in its organic form is absorbed efficiently by amino acid transport systems. Organic forms of selenium presented as selenocysteine and selenomethione are readily taken up in the enterocytes, by amino acid transporter 1, neutral amino acid transporter and hydrogen ion peptide co- transporter [57]. Following absorption in the small intestine it travels through the blood to the liver and other tissues. In its inorganic form, selenate is absorbed by an active, sodium dependent transport, while selenite is absorbed by passive diffusion [58]. Selenate is absorbed in the small distal intestine, while selenite is absorbed in the jejunum [58, 62].

4.4.6. Digestion and Absorption of Molybdenum

Molybdenum is a transition element that functions in the metabolism of sulfite, nucleic acids, aldehydes and taurine. In excess molybdenum can interfere with copper and iron absorption. Molybdenum has also been linked to having a role in the function of glucocorticoid hormones and immune defenses. The digestion and absorption of molybdenum is not well understood, but may be passive and occur in both the stomach and proximal intestine. Sulfate is an inhibitor of its absorption. Molybdenum deficiency is rare in humans, but has occurred in patients receiving prolonged total parenteral nutrition with clinical signs characterized by tachycardia, headache, mental disturbances, and coma [59, 63, 64].

4.4.7. Digestion and Absorption of Manganese

The requirement for manganese is low relative to other essential elements, so little is known about manganese's absorption mechanism. Fractional absorption of Mn^{2+} tends to increase as intake decreases; still only about 5% of total Mn intake is absorbed [1]. Absorption may involve an active carrier protein [1].

4.4.8. Digestion and Absorption of Chromium

Chromium 3+, which is the most stable oxidation state and the metabolically active form in humans, is released from food when it enters the acidic environment of the stomach [1]. Chromium is absorbed in the jejunum of the small intestine, but its exact absorption mechanism remains unknown. Amino acids and some ligands enhance Cr absorption, while phytic acid and antacids can inhibit absorption [1].

4.5. Digestion and Absorption of Nonessential Trace Minerals

4.5.1. Digestion and Absorption of Arsenic

Arsenic has a reputation of being linked to toxicity. Its nutritional value to humans is minor, yet still present in everyday nutritional consumption. Trace amounts of organic and inorganic arsenic are found in substances such as fruit juices, meats, dairy products, cereal, and water [1]. The main existence of arsenic is in its trivalent and pentavalent oxidation states (As^{3+} and As^{5+} respectively) [1]. Like most nonessential trace elements, arsenic digestion and absorption varies with chemical form and solubility [1]. The most common forms of ingested arsenic include the inorganic forms of arsenate and arsenite, and the organic forms of arsenobetaine and arsenocholine [1]. Most of the absorption of organic and inorganic arsenic occurs through simple diffusion across enterocyte membranes [1]. Once in the intestine, arsenic is bound to transferrin and transported to the liver in the blood where it is further metabolized [1]. In the liver, the organic forms of arsenic (arsenobetaine and arsenocholine) experience little metabolism compared to the extreme metabolism of the inorganic forms of arsenic [1]. The arsenate, generally viewed as the more toxic type of arsenic, undergoes a reduction reaction to produce arsenite [1].

Next, a methylation reaction occurs dependent upon the methyl groups created from the catabolism of choline and methionine and the arsenite is converted to monomethylarsenic (MMA) [1,64]. As the reaction proceeds in the liver, MMA is converted to dimethylarsenic (DMA) [64]. In some cases, MMA fails to convert to DMA [64]. The build up of MMA becomes toxic to the human body and can lead to a variety of arsenic- related diseases [64].

4.5.2. Digestion and Absorption of Boron

Prior to the 1920's, boron was used as a major preservative in foods [1].

Contemporaneous beliefs of the 1920's led to a change in this practice; from then until the 1970's, boron was considered a dangerous element for human consumption and was therefore banned. However, over the last 30 years, popular opinion changed yet again, with the increasing volume of evidence that shows the importance of boron in an everyday diet.

Boron is primarily absorbed as boric acid through passive diffusion from the gastrointestinal track [1, 65]. After absorption, boron moves through the blood as both boric acid and as borate monovalent anion $B(OH)4^-$ [1, 65]. Some evidence suggests that a sodium-dependent borate transporter actively transports borate monovalent anion into cells for further usage, although the verity of this cannot yet be confirmed.

Although trace amounts of boron are expected to be beneficial for humans, boron has no clear biochemical function in humans [1]. Major sources of boron include legumes, nuts, fruits, and vegetables [1, 66, 67]. Some studies propose that boron's interactions with other nutrients are playing a regulatory role in the metabolism of calcium, in turn affecting bone metabolism [67]. However, further research is required prior to accepting boron as an essential trace nutrient [1, 65, 67].

4.5.3. Digestion and Absorption of Fluoride

When consumed in foods, fluoride is usually bound to a protein [1]. In order to hydrolyze and isolate the fluoride, pepsin and other protein proteases are required [1]. Once hydrolyzed, the fluoride can be absorbed by the stomach through passive diffusion, as fluoride absorption is pH dependent [1, 68]. The permeability of stomach lipid bilayer membranes to hydrofluoric acid is nearly one million times greater than that of fluorine in its anion form [68]. The low pH of the stomach and the high acidic nature of hydrofluoric acid correlate to a high gastric absorption rate [1]. When fluoride is ingested through water consumption, nearly 100% of the fluoride will be absorbed within 90 minutes of consumption [1]. Any excess fluoride will be absorbed in the small intestine [1, 68].

4.5.4. Digestion and Absorption of Nickel

Most individuals don't tend to associate nickel with having positive nutritional value to the human body. In fact, nickel is another nonessential trace mineral where no specific role has been identified in humans. On a daily basis, humans consume 70 to 260 µg of nickel [1, 69]. The body absorbs nickel more readily when it is consumed in liquids rather than in food form. Nickel absorption from solid foods is less than 10%, compared to nearly 50% absorption from liquids such as water, tea, coffee, and fruit juices [1]. The absorption process occurs by passive and carrier diffusion across the enterocyte's brush border membrane [1]. As it enters the blood stream, nickel competes with iron for the carrier transport on the divalent mineral transporter (DMT) 1 in the proximal intestine [1]. As iron deficiency occurs in a human, nickel absorption increases due to the lack of iron binding to DMT 1 [1]. Various methods of cellular uptake of the nonessential trace mineral includes association with amino acids, binding of transferrin, and through uptake in a divalent cation channel [1].

Although no specific role has been determined, nickel may play a minor role in the early stages of the metabolism of methionine [1]. Also, in most enzymes, nickel can substitute magnesium or zinc as a cofactor during an enzymatic reaction. Some evidence suggests nickel's role in the stability of an enzyme in the complement system, which generally requires magnesium for the enzyme's activity. The substitution for nickel actually enhances the enzymes stability and activity during the reaction [1, 70]. However, further research in this area is needed to conclude nickel's essential role in the metabolic process.

4.5.5. Digestion and Absorption of Silicon

Foods of plant origin generally have a higher silicon composition than foods of animal origin [1]. The dietary intake of silicon for an average adult is between 14-62 mg a day [1]. The overall estimates of silicon absorption in the human body range from 1% to 70% based on the type of silicon ingested [1]. The process by which silicon is absorbed is proven difficult to measure due to the multitude of ingested forms of silicone. These different forms of ingested silicon include silica, monosilicic acid, orthosilicic acid, and phytolithic silica [1]. Silicon absorption from fluids, mainly orthosilicic acid, is estimated at over 50%. Once orthosilicic acid is absorbed, it freely diffuses into the blood stream without the aid of proteins [1]. This mechanism explains the orthosilicic acid's quick involvement in urinary excretion [1].

The amount of fiber in a diet directly relates to the absorption of silicon [1]. In a high-fiber diet nearly all silicon is unabsorbed, as 97% of the dietary silicon is lost in fecal excretion. In a low-fiber diet however, 40% of the silicon is unabsorbed [1, 71]. Silicon's major function in the human body is its association between macromolecules that are chiefly involved in cartilage composition and calcification, as well as in bone growth and development [1, 72].

4.5.6. Digestion and Absorption of Vanadium

Vanadium is found in several oxidation states. In the human body, vanadium is most prevalent in its tetravalent state (V^{4+}) as vanadyl, and in its pentavalent oxidation state (V^{5+}) as vanadate or monovanadate [1]. To the body, the tetravalent oxidation state is less toxic than the pentavalent state [1].

Because vanadium content of food and liquids is generally very low, the average dietary intake is also low [73]. Vanadium intake ranges from 10 to 60 μg a day [1]. After vanadium is consumed the oxidation state of the mineral determines the pathway of absorption [73]. If the vanadium is consumed as vanadate it may be reduced to vanadyl in the stomach prior to being absorbed in the small intestine [1]. But, vanadate may also be directly absorbed using the same carrier system as phosphate, which increases it's likelihood to be absorbed more efficiently than the vanadyl form [1]. Yet, the yield for overall vanadium absorption is still low, with less than 10% [1].

4.6. Summary

The mechanism for absorption of most water-soluble vitamins have similar characteristics and kinetics, with a few exceptions. Thiamine, riboflavin, niacin, folate, vitamin C, biotin, and vitamin B6 are all absorbed through a carrier-mediated system involving a specific protein in the small intestine. These systems vary a little by their dependency on factors such as Na^+ concentration and pH. Vitamin B12 is different in that it requires intrinsic factor from the gastric juice of the stomach to be absorbed later in the small intestine by using a specific receptor. In general, absorption of the water-soluble vitamins increases with a deficiency of the vitamin and decreases when there is abundance.

Vitamins B6, thiamine, and riboflavin all must be hydrolyzed by phosphatases to be absorbed. Niacin and folate must both be hydrolyzed to be converted into forms of the vitamins acceptable for absorption. Niacin is released from NAD and the polyglutamate forms of folate are hydrolyzed to the monoglutamate form. A decrease in thiamine, riboflavin, and niacin absorption has been seen in individuals who are chronic alcoholics.

Each of the fat-soluble vitamin groups contains several related biologically active compounds. They are absorbed from the small intestines along with dietary fat. Poor absorption of these vitamins will result in various diseases. Fat-soluble vitamins are primarily stored in the liver and adipose tissues until they're needed (much like fat). They are found in the fats and oils of foods and require bile for absorption. They follow the same path of absorption as fat and any condition interfering with the absorption of fats would result in poor absorption of these vitamins as well. Once absorbed, these vitamins are stored in the liver and fatty tissues until the body needs them.

Macrominerals are important to the health and well-being of animals. Their jobs are varied and vital for normal cellular activity. After ingestion, macrominerals must be digested and absorbed into the blood stream for transport to individual cells and tissues. Absorption often depends on passive and active transport mechanisms as well as specific carrier proteins. Many of the minerals are regulated by hormones to ensure proper balance.

Sodium, potassium, and chloride are distributed throughout the body fluids maintaining electrical neutrality and osmolarity. The anion concentration must balance the cation concentration. The kidney is primarily responsible for the maintenance of electrolyte balance using both passive and active processes to achieve balance.

Trace minerals are very important to human metabolism. Although trace minerals are only required in small amounts they are fundamental in the growth and development of the body. Digestion and absorption of these minerals can have similar characteristics and sometimes the intake level of one affects the absorption of other minerals. The processes of digestion and absorption have been identified recently for the more important trace minerals like iron, zinc and iodine, but less is known about the digestion and absorption of selenium, molybdenum, and most other trace elements.

4.7. Literature Cited

1. Gropper, S. A. S., & Smith, J. L. *Advanced nutrition and human metabolism* (6th ed.). Belmont, CA: Wadsworth/Cengage Learning, 2013, print.

2. Said HM. 2004. Recent advances in carrier-mediated intestinal absorption of water-soluble vitamins. Annu. Rev. Physiol., 66 (2004), pp. 419–446.

3. Diaz GA, Banikazemai M, Oishi K, Desnick RJ, Gelb BD. 1999. Mutations in a new gene encoding a thiamine transporter cause thiamine-responsive megaloblastic anaemia syndrome. Nat. Genet. 22:309–12

4. Sklan D, Trostler N. 1977. Site and extent of thiamin absorption in the rat. J. Nutr. 107:353–56

5. Dudeja PK, Tyagi S, Kavilaveettil RJ, Gill R, Said HM. 2001. Mechanism of thiamine uptake by human jejunal brushborder membrane vesicles. Am. J. Physiol. Cell Physiol. 281:C786–92

6. Institute of Medicine. 1998. Dietary Reference Intakes: Thiamin, Riboflavin, Niacin, Vitamin B6, Folate, Vitamin B12, Pantothenic Acid, Biotin, and Choline. Standing Comm. on Sci. Eval. of Dietary Ref. Intakes, Inst. Med., Natl. Acad. Sci. Washington, DC: Natl. Acad. Press.

7. Rindi G. 1984. Thiamin absorption by small intestine. ActaVitaminol. Enzymol. 6:47–55

8. Said HM. Intestinal absorption of water-soluble vitamins in health and disease. 2011. Biochem J 437: 357–372

9. Subramanya, S. B., Subramanian, V. S. and Said, H. M. 2010. Chronic alcohol consumption and intestinal absorption: effects on physiological and molecular parameters of the uptake process.Am. J. Physiol. Gastrointest. Liver Physiol. 299, G23–G31

10. Ashokkumar, B., Kumar, J. S., Hecht, G. A. and Said, H. M. 2009. Enteropathogenic Escherichia coli inhibits intestinal vitamin B1 (thiamin) uptake: studies with human-derived intestinal epithelial Caco-2 cells. Am. J. Physiol. Gastrointest. Liver Physiol. 297, G825–G833

11. Bukhari, F. J., Moradi, H., Gollapudi, P., Kim, H. J., Vaziri, N. D. and Said, H. M. 2010. Effect of chronic kidney disease on the expression of thiamin and folic acid transporters. Nephrol. Dial. Transplant. 26, 2137–2144

12. Daniel, H., Binninger, E. and Rehner, G. 1983. Hydrolysis of FMN and FAD by alkaline phosphatase of the intestinal brush border membrane. Int. J. Vitam. Nutr. Res. 53, 109–114

13. Institute of Medicine. Dietary Reference Intakes for Thiamine, Rivoflavin, Niacin, Vitamin B6, Folate, Vitamin B12, Pantothenic Acid, Biotin and Choline. 1999. National Academy Press: Washington, DC.

14. Green, P., Wiseman, M., Crow, Y. J., Houlden, H., Riphagen, S., Lin, J.-P., Raymon, F. L., Childs, A.-M., Sheridan, E., Edwards, S. and Josifova, D. J. 2010. Brown–Vialetto–Van Laere syndrome, a ponto-bulbar palsy with deafness, is caused by mutations in C20orf54. Am. J. Hum. Genet. 86, 485–489

15. Said, H. M. and Ma, T. Y. 1994. Mechanism of riboflavin uptake by Caco-2 human intestinal epithelial cells. Am. J. Physiol. 266, G15–G21

16. Said, H. M., Ghishan, F. K., Greene, H. L. and Hollander, D. 1985 Developmental maturation of riboflavin intestinal transport in the rat. Pediatr. Res. 19, 1175–1178

17. Natraj U, George S, Kadam P. 1988. Isolation and partial characterisation of human riboflavin carrier protein and the estimation of its levels during human pregnancy. J Reprod Immunol 13:1– 16.

18. Yanagawa, N., Shih, R. N., Jo, O. D. and Said, H. M. 2000. Riboflavin transport by isolated perfused rabbit renal proximal tubules. Am. J. Physiol. Cell Physiol. 279, C1782–C1786

19. Hamm, M. W., Hehansho, H. and Henderson, L. M. 1979. Transport and metabolism of pyridoxamine and pyridoxamine phosphate in the small intestine. J. Nutr. 109:1552–1559

20. Said, H. M., Ortiz, A. and Ma, T. Y. 2003. A carrier-mediated mechanism for pyridoxine uptake by human intestinal epithelial Caco-2 cells: regulation by a PKA-mediated pathway. Am. J. Physiol. Cell Physiol. 285, C1219–C1225

21. Sirotnak, F. M. and Tolner, B. 1999. Carrier-mediated membrane transport of folates in mammalian cells. Annu. Rev. Nutr. 19, 91–122

22. Said, H. M., Chatterjee, H., Haq, R. U., Subramanian, V. S., Ortiz, A., Matherly, L. H., Sirotnak, F. M., Halsted, C. and Rubin, S. A. 2000. Adaptive regulation of intestinal folate uptake: effect of dietary folate deficiency. Am. J. Physiol. Cell Physiol. 279:1889–C1895

23. Balamurugan, K. and Said, H. M. 2003. Ontogenic regulation of folate transport across rat jejunal brush-border membrane. Am. J. Physiol. Gastrointest. Liver Physiol. 285:G1068–G1073

24. Kumar, C. K., Moyer, M. P., Dudeja, P. K. and Said, H. M. 1997. A protein-tyrosine kinase regulated, pH-dependent carrier-mediated uptake system for folate by human normal colonic epithelial cell line NCM 460. J. Biol. Chem. 272: 6226–6231

25. Kallner A, Hartmann D, Hornig D. 1979. Steady-state turnover and body pool of ascorbic acid in man. Am J Clin Nutr 32:530–539.

26. Quadros, E.V. 2010. Advances in the understanding of cobalamin assimilation and metabolism. British Journal of Haematology 148:195-204

27. Allen, R.H. 1975. Human vitamin B12 transport proteins. Progress in Hematology, 9, 57–84.

28. Rothenberg, S.P. & Quadros, E.V. 1995. Transcobalamin II and the membrane receptor for the transcobalamin II-cobalamin complex. Baillieres Clinical Haematology, 8, 499–514.

29. Chanarin, I. 1979. Megaloblastic Anemias. Blackwell Scientific Publications. UK.

30. Berlin H, Berlin R, Brante G. 1968. Oral treatment of pernicious anemia with high doses of vitamin B12 without intrinsic factor. Acta Med Scand184:247–258.

31. Scott JM. 1997. Bioavailability of vitamin B12. Eur J Clin Nutr 51 Suppl 1:S49-S53.

32. Blomhoff R, Green MH, Berg T, Norum KR. 1990. Transport and storage of vitamin A. Science 250:399–404.

33. E.H. Harrison, M.M. Hussain, Mechanisms involved in the intestinal digestion and absorption of dietary vitamin A, J. Nutr. 131 (2001) 1405–1408.

34. 33A. Chen W, Chen G. 2014. The roles of vitamin A in the regulation of carbohydrate, lipid, and protein metabolism. *J. Clin. Med.* 3(2), 453-479; doi:10.3390/jcm3020453

35. During A, Harrison EH. 2004. Intestinal absorption and metabolism of carotenoids: insights from cell culture. Arch. Biochem.Biophys. 430:77–88.

36. Holick MF, Schnoes HK, Deluca HF, Suda T, Cousins RJ (1971). "Isolation and identification of 1, 25-dihydroxycholecalciferol. A metabolite of vitamin D active in intestine". Biochemistry 10 (14): 2799–804. "Vitamin D and Calcium: Updated Dietary Reference Intakes". Nutrition and Healthy Eating. Health Canada. Retrieved 2012-06-13.

37. Johnson,P. & Pover,W. F. R. (1962) Intestinal absorption of α-tocopherol. Life Sei. l: 115-117.

38. Brigelius-Flohé; Traber, MG (1999). "Vitamin E: function and metabolism". The FASEB journal: official publication of the Federation of American Societies for Experimental Biology 13 (10): 1145–55.

39. Sies H, Stahl W, Sundquist AR. 1992. Antioxidant functions of vitamins (vitamins E and C, beta-carotene, and other carotenoids). Ann. N.Y. Acad. Sci. 669:7–20.

40. Bell, R. G., Sadowski, J. A., Matschiner, J. T. 1972. Mechanism of action of warfarin. Warfarin and the metabolism of vitamin K. Biochemistry I I: 1 959-66.

41. Shearer, M. J., McBurney, A., Barkhan, P. 1974. Studies on the absorption and metabolism of phylloquinone (vitamin K) in man. Vitam. Horm. 32: 5 1 3-42.

42. Beulens JW, Bots ML, Atsma F, Bartelink ML, Prokop M, Geleijnse JM, Witteman JC, Grobbee DE, van der Schouw YT. 2009. High dietary menaquinone intake is associated with reduced coronary calcification. Atherosclerosis. 203(2):489-93. doi:10.1016/j.atherosclerosis.2008.07.010.

43. Geleijnse JM, Launer LJ, van der Kuip DAM, Hofman A, and Witteman JCM. 2002. Inverse association of tea and flavonoid intakes with incident myocardial infarction: The Rotterdam Study." *The American Journal of Clinical Nutrition* 75(5): 880–886.

44. Gast GCM, de Roos NM, Sluijs I, Bots ML, Beulens JWJ, Geleijnse JM, Witteman JC, Grobbee DE, Peeters PHM, and van der Schouw YT. 2009. A high menaquinone intake reduces the incidence of coronary heart disease." *Nutrition, Metabolism, and Cardiovascular Diseases: NMCD* 19(7): 504–510. doi:10.1016/j.numecd.2008.10.004.

45. van den Heuvel EGHM, Van Schoor NM, Lips P, Magdeleyns EJP, Deeg DJH, Vermeer C, and

Martin den Heijer. "Circulating Uncarboxylated Matrix Gla Protein, a Marker of Vitamin K Status, as a Risk Factor of Cardiovascular Disease." *Maturitas*. Volume 77, Issue 2 , Pages 137-141, February 2014Accessed December 9, 2013. doi:10.1016/j.maturitas.2013.10.008.

46. Fleet, J. C., & Schoch, R. D. (2010). Molecular mechanisms for regulation of intestinal calcium absorption by vitamin D and other factors. Critical Reviews in Clinical Laboratory Sciences, 47(4), 181–195. doi:10.3109/10408363.2010.536429

47. Suzuki, T., & Hara, H. (2004). Various Nondigestible Saccharides Open a Paracellular Calcium Transport Pathway with the Induction of Intracellular Calcium Signaling in Human Intestinal Caco- 2 Cells. The Journal of Nutrition, 134(8), 1935–1941.

48. Fujita, H., Sugimoto, K., Inatomi, S., Maeda, T., Osanai, M., Uchiyama, Y., Chiba, H. (2008). Tight Junction Proteins Claudin-2 and -12 Are Critical for Vitamin D-dependent Ca2+ Absorption between Enterocytes. Molecular Biology of the Cell, 19(5), 1912–1921. doi:10.1091/mbc.E07-09- 0973

49. Marks, J., Debnam, E. S., & Unwin, R. J. (2010). Phosphate homeostasis and the renal-gastrointestinal axis. American Journal of Physiology - Renal Physiology, 299(2), F285–F296. doi:10.1152/ajprenal.00508.2009

50. Ohi, A., Hanabusa, E., Ueda, O., Segawa, H., Horiba, N., Kaneko, I., … Miyamoto, K. (2011). Inorganic phosphate homeostasis in sodium-dependent phosphate cotransporter Npt2b+/− mice. American Journal of Physiology - Renal Physiology, 301(5), F1105–F1113. doi:10.1152/ajprenal.00663.2010

51. Kohlmeier, M. (2003). Magnesium. In Nutrient Metabolism (pp. 708–712). London: Academic Press. Retrieved from http://www.sciencedirect.com/science/article/pii/B9780124177628501009

52. Vormann, J. (2003). Magnesium: nutrition and metabolism. Molecular Aspects of Medicine, 24(1–3), 27–37. doi:10.1016/S0098-2997(02)00089-4

53. Rondón, L. J., Groenestege, W. M. T., Rayssiguier, Y., & Mazur, A. (2008). Relationship between low magnesium status and TRPM6 expression in the kidney and large intestine. American Journalof Physiology - Regulatory, Integrative and Comparative Physiology, 294(6), R2001–R2007. doi:10.1152/ajpregu.00153.2007

54. Quamme, G. A. (2010). Molecular identification of ancient and modern mammalian magnesium transporters. American Journal of Physiology - Cell Physiology, 298(3), C407–C429. doi:10.1152/ajpcell.00124.2009

55. Gäbel, G., Vogler, S., & Martens, H. (1993). Mechanisms of sodium and chloride transport across isolated sheep reticulum. Comparative Biochemistry and Physiology Part A: Physiology, 105(1), 1– 10. doi:10.1016/0300-9629(93)90165-Z

56. Montrose, M. H., & Kere, J. (2000). Chapter 8 Anion absorption in the intestine: Anion transporters, short-chain fatty acids, and role of the DRA gene product. In M. D. Kim E. Barrett (Ed.), Current Topics in Membranes (Vol. Volume 50, pp. 301–328). Academic Press. Retrieved from http://www.sciencedirect.com/science/article/pii/S1063582300500106

57. Kohlmeier, Martin. Nutrient Metabolism. San Diego, California: Academic Press, 2003. Print.

58. Berdainier, Carolyn D. Advanced Nutrition and Micronutrients. San Diego, California: CRC Press, 1998. Print.

58A. Luizzi JP, Guo L, Chang SM, Cousins RJ. (2009) Krupple-like factor 4 regulates adaptive expression of the zinc transporter ZIP4 in mouse small intestine. Am J Physiol: Gastrointesinal and Liver Physiol. 296(3): G517-G523,

59. National Research Council. Dietary Reference Intakes: The Essential Guide to Nutrient Requirements. Washington, DC: The National Academies Press, 2006.

60. Mina, A., Favaloro, E.J., & Kouts, J. (2011). Iodine deficiency: Current aspects and future prospects. Lab Medicine, 42(12), 744-746.

61. Solomons, Noel W., and Irwin H. Rosenber, eds. Absorption and Malabsorption of Mineral Nutrients. New York, New York: Alan R. Liss, INC., 1984. Print.

62. Hardy, G., & Hardy, I. (2004). Selenieum: The se-xy neutraceutical. Nutrition, 20(6), 590-593.

63. Sardesai, V.M. (1993). Molybdenum: An essential trace element. Nutr Clin Pract., 8(6), 277-281. Doi:10.1177/0115426593008006277

64. Forbes, R.M., & Erdman, J.W. (1983). Bioavailability of trace minerals. Annu. Rev. Nutr, 3, 213- 231. Doi:10.1146/annurev.nu.03.070183.001241

65. Sutherland B., Woodhose L., Strong P., King J. 1999; Boron Balance in humans. J Trace Elm Exp Med. 12:271-84.

66. Boron Rich Foods – Sources of Boron. *AlgaeCal Plant Calcium*. AlgaeCal Inc., 2005. Web. 01 Dec. 2013. <http://www.algaecal.com/algaecal-ingredients/boron/boron-sources/>.

67. Naghii MR, and Samman S. 1993. "The Role of Boron in Nutrition and Metabolism." *Prog Food Nutr Sci* n. pag. *PubMed.gov*. Web. 22 Nov. 2013.

68. Buzalaf MA, and Whitford GM. "Fluoride Metabolism." *Monogr Oral Sci.* (2011): n. pag. *PubMed.gov*. Web. 22 Nov. 2013.

69. Food and Nutrition Board. *Dietary Reference Intakes for Vitamin A, Vitamin K, Arsenic, Boron, Chromium, Copper, Iodide, Iron, Manganese, Molybdenum, Nickel, Silicon, Vanadium, and Zinc*. Washington, DC:National Academy Press, 2001 pp.502-53.

70. Fishelson Z, Muller-Eberhard H. 1982; C3 convertase of human complement:enhanced formation and stability of the enzyme generated with nickel instead of magnesium. J Immunol, 129:2603-07.

71. Kelsay J, Behall K, Parther E. 1979; Effect of fiber from fruits and vegetables on etabolic responses of human subjects II: calcium, magnesium iron, and silicon balances. Am J Clin Nutr. 32:1876-80.

72. Nielsen, F. H. 1991. Nutritional Requirements for Boron, Silicon, Vanadium, Nickel, and Arsenic: Current Knowledge and Speculation." *The FASEB Journal* 5(12):2621

73. French, R. J. 1993. "Role of Vanadium in Nutrition: Metabolism, Essentiality and Dietary Considerations." *Life Sci* 52(4): 339-46.

74. Askew, M; Kim, E; Loy, M; Park, C; Yuting, Q; Stanley, R. *Advanced Nutrition and Metabolism-the Textbook*. Raleigh, NC: Jonathan Allen. Ebook, 2013.

4.8. Review Questions

1. List the water soluble vitamins

2. Describe the difference in thiamin absorption when the concentration is low versus high.

3. What transporter proteins are involved with Riboflavin absorption?

4. How much tryptophan is needed to synthesize 1 mg of niacin?

5. Fill in the blank: Biotin can be absorbed in the small intestine and the_.

6. True or False: Phosphorylated forms of vitamin B_6 are commonly found in the diet and are hydrolyzed in the intestine by phosphatase enzymes prior to absorption.

7. Which foods can inhibit the absorption of folate?

8. Which enzyme's activity increases when there is a folate deficiency?

9. Which proteins are responsible for transporting vitamin C?

10. What are the cells in the stomach called which release intrinsic factor for B_{12} absorption?

11. What are the three different forms of vitamin A?

12. What role do chylomicrons play in vitamin A absorption?

13. What is the difference between vitamin D_2 and D_3?

14. What is the name of the active form of vitamin D?

15. Name the precursor of 1,25-dihydroxycholecalciferol

16. Are bile acids needed for vitamin E absorption? Why?

17. True or False: Low levels of circulating vitamin K have been associated with low bone-mineral density.

18. Name two different forms of vitamin K.

19. Name the channel which intestinal enterocytes use for calcium absorption.

20. How does parathyroid hormone regulate calcium levels?

21. Describe the digestive and absorption process of phosphorus.

22. Which protein channels are permeable to magnesium?

23. Name the electrolytes.

24. True or False: Sodium is the most abundant cation in the body.

25. What are the two main absorption pathways for sodium?

26. Describe how the K^+/H ATPase pump works with potassium absorption.

27. Why is glucose an important part of choride absorption?

28. What is the difference between heme-bound iron and non-heme iron?

29. Explain how iron is digested and absorbed in the body.

30. Why might a person's need for iron change? How does the body respond to this change?

31. Does dietary intake impact zinc absorption?

32. How is copper transporter 1 involved with copper absorption?

33. How does the thyroid gland sequester iodide?

34. Describe organic and inorganic forms of selenium and how their absorption differs.

35. Fill in the blank: Molybdenum is thought be absorbed through_diffusion.

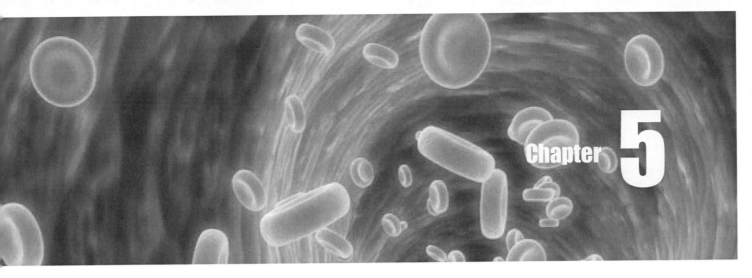

Chapter 5

Excretion: How do animals get rid of excess or unneeded molecules?

By Jonathan C. Allen, Shalimbala Chizonda, Caroline Dickson, Samantha Duxbury, Christian Johansson, Kayla Lawson, Danielle Lucas, and Larry Witt

Learning Objectives

Learning objectives: Students completing this chapter should be able to:

1. Describe the breakdown of the energy supplying macronutrients carbohydrates, lipids and protein, and explain how their end products are eliminated.

2. Define what dietary and functional fibers are and how they are related to carbohydrate excretion

3. Discuss how respiratory quotient (RQ) is used to calculate excretion of carbohydrates.

4. Describe the role of carbonic acid in carbohydrate excretion

5. Identify all pathways for vitamin and mineral excretion.

6. Identify the primary means of excretion for each water-soluble vitamin and the macrominerals calcium and magnesium.

5.1. Excretion of Carbohydrates

5.1.1. Excretion of Carbohydrates as Result of Malabsorption

Human beings require energy for metabolism and carbohydrates provide a good source. After digestion, the majority of carbohydrates are absorbed by the small intestines but impairment of digestion can allow carbohydrates to pass of into the colon without being absorbed. Quantitative estimation of fecal carbohydrates is done through established methods. This process involves collection and handling of stool for 24-72 hours, extraction and distillation [1].

Non-starchy polysaccharides (NSP) and undigested starch, called resistant starch (RS), are the major carbohydrates that reach the colon without being digested. These impact the function of the colon by increasing fecal weight that is a result of an increase of microbial mass that ferments the escaped carbohydrates. Infants exhibit small fecal losses of intact carbohydrates when fed a diet consisting of either 100% lactose or 50% lactose plus 50% glucose [2].

5.1.2. Fiber

TABLE 5.1-1: Characteristics of carbohydrates that do or do not comprise dietary fiber.

Characteristic	Dietary Fiber
Nondigestible animal carbohydrate	No
Carbohydrates not recovered by alcohol precipitation[a]	Yes
Nondigestible mono-and disaccharides and polyols	No
Lignin	Yes
Resistant starch	Some
Intact, naturally-occurring food source only	Yes
Resistant to human enzymes	Yes
Specifies physiological effect	No

a Includes inulin, oligosaccharides (3–10 degrees of polymerization), fructans, poly-dextrose, methylcellulose, resistant maltodextrins, and other related compounds, Reference [3].

Dietary Fiber consists of nondigestible carbohydrates intrinsic and intact in plants.

It described as a nutrient that includes **plant nonstarch poly- saccharides** (e.g., cellulose, pectin, gums, hemicellulose, β-glucans, and fibers contained in oat and **wheat bran**), **plant carbohydrates that are not recovered by alcohol precipitation** (e.g., inulin, oligosaccharides, and fructans), lignin, and some resistant starch [3].

Characteristics of dietary fiber include its ability to resist digestion by human enzymes (Table 5.1.1). Some

fibers that are soluble in water (Fig. 5.1.1) are found in foods like legumes, apples, pears and some vegetables. Some fibers have a water holding capacity that is independent of the fiber's solubility in water. These water holding fibers can have the effect of slowing movement of digesta, decreasing nutrient absorption, and reducing enzyme function [4]. Functional Fiber consists of isolated, nondigestible carbohydrates that have beneficial physiological effects in humans while Total Fiber is the sum of Dietary Fiber and Functional Fiber [5].

*Other fibers that are considered to be less soluble or insoluble in water and ability/inability to form viscous solutions [4].

5.1.3. Energy Balance and Expenditure

Low energy intake that causes a negative energy balance can result in loss of body tissue or weight while excessive energy intake with a large positive energy balance can lead to deposition in fat tissue and therefore, an increase in weight. This decrease or increase in weight depends on the energy requirements of the body and whether or not they being met.

Some of the components of energy expenditure are basal metabolic rate (BMR) or resting energy expenditure (REE). Basal metabolic rate is a measure of energy spent to sustain life processes and is measured after having fasted for at least 12 hours, in a motionless state and lying down.

Total daily expenditure can be calculated using a formula:

Total daily energy expenditure (TDEE) = RMR + TEF + PAEE

Thermic effect of food (TEF) is a measure of increase in energy expenditure after a consumption of a meal. There is a variation on the content of TEF depending on composition of diet. Thermic effect on food is also referred to as diet induced thermogenesis and represents approximately 10% of TDEE. RMR is resting metabolic rate and PAEE is the spontaneous physical activity or fidgeting and physical activity (Fig. 5.1.2).

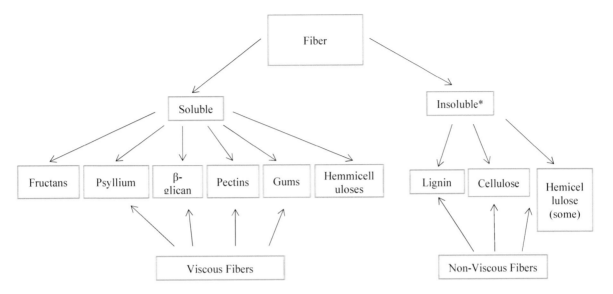

Figure 5.1-1: Fibers classified by solubility/insolubility in water and ability to form viscous solutions.

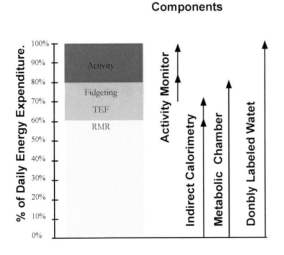

Figure 5.1-2: Components of daily energy expenditure.

The highest component of TDEE is resting metabolic weight, measured at in thermoneutral environment. Energy expenditure in humans can be measured through individual components, that is, heat, water and oxygen produced or macronutrient or oxygen consumption.

$$Macronutrients + O_2 \rightarrow Heat + CO_2 + H_2O$$

5.1.4. Respiratory quotient (RQ)

The respiratory quotient is the ratio of carbon dioxide expired to oxygen inhaled. It is also termed respiratory exchange ratio (RER). The ratio is an indicator of collective (not in individual organs and tissues) energy expenditure and carbohydrate or fat oxidation. For carbohydrates, a ratio of 1.0 is an indicator of oxidation since oxygen used up in glucose combustion is equal to carbon dioxide output as shown below:

$$C_6H_{12}O_6 + 6\,O_2 \rightarrow 6\,CO_2 + 6\,H_2O\ RQ= 6\,CO_2/6\,O_2 = 1.0$$

The RQ for fat and protein are 0.7 and 0.8 respectively. A mixed diet of the three energy nutrients is set at a ratio of 0.85. An RQ greater than 1 is an indication of acidosis. The total caloric value of the exchange is calculated using the respiratory quotient and tables providing the thermal equivalent of O_2 and CO_2 for nonprotein RQ [4].

5.1.5. Doubly Labeled Water

This method allows measurement of energy in free living human beings. It is an accurate measure of energy expenditure that has been validated by several studies.

Doubly labeled water is based on the principle that an oral dose of $^2H_2$ ^{18}O mixes with total body water, and the oxygen atoms in body water are in equilibrium with exhaled CO2. There is differential elimination of the two isotopes from the body and ^{18}O is eliminated as carbon dioxide and water, while deuterium is eliminated only as water. Carbon dioxide influx which is proportional to total energy expenditure is calculated through the difference between the elimination rates of oxygen and hydrogen from body water [5].

5.1.6. Direct calorimetry

The method is a measure of the total heat lost from the body. It has limited use because the process is expensive and unpleasant to test subjects [4]. Direct calorimetry employs the use of metabolic chambers. Also known as respiratory chambers, metabolic chambers are used in long duration studies that can go from 24 hour to several days, hence the discomfort for participants. The chamber measures concentration of carbon dioxide expired and oxygen and therefore requires accurate analyzers. Detectors in the chamber make it possible to assess energy expenditure due to activity. Sleeping energy expenditure is accurately measured as well as spontaneous activity or fidgeting which is a variable parameter. Respiratory quotient is calculated from oxygen consumption and carbon dioxide production measurements that are derived from concentration measurements and flow rate through the chamber [5].

5.1.7. Transport of Carbon Dioxide

Carbon dioxide is produced in tissues of the body by metabolism in the mitochondria and leaves the body through respiration in the lungs. To get there, there are several channels the body has developed as a transport system. Carbon dioxide is transported in three different forms: physically dissolved, buffered in water as carbonic acids (HCO_3^-), or bound to proteins as carbamate [6,7]. Hydration/dehydration reaction between CO_2, HCO_3^-, and H^+ is accelerated by carbonic anhydrase, which can be found in several organs of the body [7].

Being more soluble than oxygen (20 times), carbon dioxide obeys Henry's law (the number of molecules

in solution is proportional to the partial pressure at the liquid surface). In the skeletal muscle, carbon dioxide produced diffuses from the intracellular space into the plasma and erythrocytes in order to get to the lungs. Exercise has the effect of producing lactic acid which affects the relative contribution of the forms of carbon dioxide by contributing H^+ [6].

Carbonic acid formation

The following reaction is accelerated by carbonic anhydrase to form carbonic acid which can dissociate to make bicarbonate and hydrogen ions:

$$CO_2 + H_2O \leftrightarrow H_2CO_3 \leftrightarrow H^+ + HCO_3^-.$$

Bound to haemoglobin and other proteins

The terminal group of amino acids ($R\text{-}NH_2$) combines with carbon dioxide to form carbamino compounds while the combination with haemoglobin forms carbaminohemoglobin, which contributes to the exhalation of approximately 30% of carbon dioxide. The reduced hemoglobin has a buffering effect due to its high histidine content and reduced haemoglobin combines more effectively (3.5 times) with carbon dioxide than oxyhaemoglobin. Chloride ions move into red blood cells to maintain an electrically neutral environment as HCO_3^- is transported out [7]. In the lung, these processes are reversed, as CO2 diffuses into the air in the alveoli.

5.1.8. Excretion of Sugars

Early research found that rats exhibit sugar excretion in their feces at a ratio of 2- 5% (excreted : consumed sugar) when fed legume seeds. This was observed 20-24 hours after introducing the diet. The study attributed the presence of stachyose and verbascose metabolites in leguminous seeds as the cause of this occurrence [8].

There is minimal direct excretion of carbohydrates except for indigestible polysaccharides because carbohydrates are preferentially used for energy, or with very high carbohydrate diets, changed to fat and deposited in the adipose tissue for storage. Because carbohydrates should provide 45 to 65% of calories, in addition to a recommended 25 to 38 g of dietary fiber that is mostly made of unavailable carbohydrate, the two routes for carbohydrate excretion are fecal excretion of unabsorbed forms, and metabolic conversion to CO_2, transport to the lung, and respiratory loss. When blood glucose concentration is not under proper hormonal control and exceeds the threshold for renal reabsorption, glucose excretion in the urine also can occur.

5.2. Lipid Digestion, Absorption, and Excretion in the Body

5.2.1. Digestion of Lipids

The intake of dietary fat is important for human growth and development.

Fats are essential because they provide energy, form cell membranes, carry fat-soluble vitamins, and supply essential fatty acids [9]. Lipids found in the body that serve as sources of dietary energy or play a role as functional or structural components of the cell can be classified as either simple or complex lipids. Simple lipids include fatty acids, triacylglycerols, diacylglycerols, waxes, and monoacylglycerols, while complex fats include phospholipids, glycoproteins, and lipoproteins [4]. Digestion of lipids in the body begins mainly in the small intestine and ends with the emulsification of fats through the creation of micelles, a mixture of lipids and water. Lipid digestion is more complex than carbohydrate and protein digestion because lipids are not soluble in water; therefore, more components are involved in their digestion and absorption. The mechanism for lipid digestion and absorption were explained in Chapter 3.

5.2.2. Absorption of Lipids

The absorption of lipids takes place mainly in the duodenum and jejunum of the small intestine. Once fats are broken down by digestion, fat in the form of micelles are absorbed through the brush border. About 95% of dietary fat is absorbed [10]. Once taken in, short and medium chain fatty acids enter the cardiovascular system through the portal vein, while long chain fatty acids are re-esterifed into triglycerides in the enterocytes [11]. They eventually enter lymphatic circulation.

Fats are then stored in the body in adipose, muscle, or liver cells or used for other bodily functions. Fat malabsorption can occur in some cases. This is known as steatorrhea, or oily stools.

Steatorrhea can lead to a deficiency in the fat-soluble vitamins A, D, E, and K due to a decrease in the absorption of fat, and therefore a decrease in absorption of these vitamins. Causes of steatorrhea include: bacterial overgrowth, pancreatic insufficiency, and mucosal diseases [12].

The exact mechanism of fatty acid absorption is not fully understood. Studies have shown that a protein-independent diffusion model is used that consists of fatty acid transport proteins. A protein dependent model has also been suggested as a potential mechanism [13]. The proteins involved in this reaction are produced in the intestine and called FATP 1-4. FATP-4 has been shown to trap fatty acids rather than move them across the membrane [14]. No energy is used in the absorption of short and medium chain fatty acids due to their size. The absorption of bile salts takes place in the ileum. Once absorbed, they are returned to the liver through the portal vein where they can be reused as a component of bile. This process is called the enterohepatic circulation (figure 5.2.1). Because bile salts are synthesized from cholesterol, any break in this enterohepatic recirculation process drains cholesterol from the body. The cholesterol that the liver uses to make the bile salts could have come from either a dietary source or endogenous synthesis.

The absorption of dietary cholesterol occurs once it is hydrolyzed to free cholesterol from cholesterol ester. It makes up part of the intestinal micelle.

Transmembrane proteins help in free cholesterol absorption, which is an energy- independent process [15]. Once absorbed, cholesterol is taken to the endoplasmic reticulum and about 70-80% is esterifed by cholesterol acyltransferase 1 and 2 [16]. Overall, the absorbed lipids are made into chylomicrons for transport through exocytosis. The chylomicrons leave the enterocytes and enter the lymphatic system where they can be used in the body where needed. Cholesterol absorption from the gut can be reduced if it binds to dietary fiber or other indigestible material that leaves the body through fecal excretion.

5.2.3. *Transport of Dietary Lipids*

Due to the fact that fats are not water soluble, transportation of lipids occurs in the form of lipoproteins. Lipoproteins have a lipid core and an outer shell made of proteins, phospholipids, and cholesterol [10]. This structure makes it easier for fats to circulate the blood stream. Major lipoproteins that circulate the blood include chylomicrons, very low density lipoproteins, low density lipoproteins, and high density lipoproteins. Chylomicrons are used for transporting fat taken in from the diet. Once secreted from the intestinal cells into the lacteals, chylomicrons are transported to body tissues for use. When lipoprotein lipase, an enzyme attached to the inside of most cell walls, is activated by apo C-II, a protein portion of lipoprotein shell, triglycerides from the chylomicrons are transferred to cells where lipoprotein lipase is attached [4]. These transferred triglycerides are either used for energy immediately, or they are stored for later use. Muscle cells generally use triglycerides for energy while adipose cells are more inclined to store them. What is left of the chylomicron once the triglycerides are absorbed is called a chylomicron remnant. This is a smaller particle that is richer in cholesterol and cholesteryl esters. This remnant is removed from the bloodstream by hepatocyte endocytosis [4]. The other major lipoproteins in the body, VLDL, LDL, and HDL, are used for transporting endogenous fat rather than dietary fat. HDL also carries lipid, including cholesterol, from the periphery to the liver, where it can be used to synthesze bile acids and be excreted back into the gut.

5.2.4. *Excretion of Fats*

The excretion of lipids occurs through their breakdown and use of metabolites for energy. During lipolysis, triglycerides are broken down into free fatty acids and glycerol. Breakdown mainly occurs in the white or brown adipocytes, as well as in other tissues and cell types. The products of breakdown are used as energy substrates, precursors for the synthesis of new lipids and membranes, or mediators in cell signaling processes [17]. There are many enzymes involved in lipolysis, a few of which include a TAG hydrolase called adipose triglyceride lipase, hormone sensitive lipase and monoglyceride lipase. All of these enzymes work together to carry out lipolysis. Many factors can affect the rate of lipolysis, including exercise, cold, stress, caffeine and stimulant drugs [18].

Fatty acid oxidation further breaks down fats in order to generate energy for the body. During fatty acid oxidation, electrons from fatty acids are donated to oxygen in the mitochondria. When intake of calories is low, the enzyme hormone sensitive lipase, which is released from the blood, breaks down triglycerides in fat cells. Hormones such as glucagon, growth hormone and epinephrine increase the activity of hormone sensitive lipase while its activity is decreased by insulin [4]. Once broken down, the fatty acids are taken from the blood stream by cells throughout the body, primarily muscle, and carried into the mitochondria from the cell cytosol by carnitine. Mitochondria use beta-oxidation and the citric acid cycle to break the fatty acids into CO_2. Transport and excretion of CO_2 follows the pathway explained earlier.

5.2.5. *Formation of Ketone Bodies*

Ketone bodies are soluble compounds produced as by-products when fatty acids are broken down for energy (25). The formation of ketone bodies is called ketogenesis and generally occurs when excess acetyl-CoA is present or when there is a shortage of citric acid cycle intermediates due to a low intake of carbohydrates. The three ketone chemicals are acetoacetate, B-hydroxybutyrate, and acetone. Ketone body formation occurs in the mitochondria of the liver. Ketogenesis begins with the condensation of two acetyl-CoA molecules to form acetoacetyl-CoA. This molecule accepts another acetyl group, and is cleaved to form acetoacetate, which is further reduced to beta-hydroxybutyrate and acetone [19]. The reverse reaction leads to the generation of ketone bodies as a source of fuel for muscle, brain and other extrahepatic tissues [20]. The use for energy occurs when the ketones acetoacetate and beta-hydroxybutyrate are transported to the peripheral tissues through the blood; here, they are converted back to acetyl-CoA and oxidized through the citric acid cycle [21]. Ketone bodies are formed as another pathway for acetyl-CoA use. Overall, ketones are used for energy when carbohydrates are scarce, such as during times of fasting. If the ketone body concentration in blood exceeds the kidney's capacity for reabsorption, they are excreted in urine, creating another source for energy-yielding carbon compounds to be removed from the body. In times of ketoacidosis, ketones can be expelled through the respiratory tract and give a sweet odor to the breath.

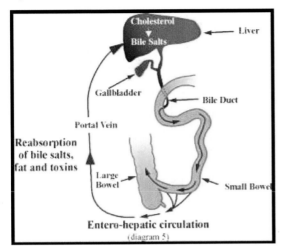

Figure 5.2-1: Enterohepatic Recirculation.

5.3. Excretion of Protein

5.3.1. Basics of Amino Acid Metabolism as Related to Excretion

The protein portion of the diet is broken down into amino acids, which are then metabolized by the body. Amino acid metabolism is complicated and the exact processes are generally dependent on the chemical structure of the individual amino acids. The specificity involved is related to the wide variety of functions that proteins have within the body and was covered in the section on metabolic uses of proteins. There are several reactions, however, that occur directly in relation to the catabolism, or break down, of amino acids in the liver and the excretion of the nitrogenous component in the form of urea.

5.3.2. Transamination

The majority of indispensible amino acid catabolic reactions occur in the periportal hepatocytes of the liver [4]. Generally, an amino acid will undergo either transamination or deamination, which involves the transfer or removal of the amino group, respectively.

Both types of reactions are important in maintaining proper amino acid balance. During transamination, enzymes called aminotransferases or transaminases, which require pyridoxal phosphate as a cofactor, catalyze the transfer of an amino group from one AA to an α-keto acid in order to form different amino acids [4]. An example of this group of enzymes includes alanine aminotransferase (ALT), which is found in a high concentration in the liver and is responsible for transferring an amino group from alanine to form another amino acid and pyruvate. All of the amino acids except lysine, histidine and threonine can undergo transamination [4].

5.3.3. Deamination

Deamination is generally catalyzed by classes of enzymes called lyases, dehydratases and dehydrogenases and result in the production of a α-keto acid and ammonia or ammonium ion. The amino acids glutamate, serine, glycine and histidine are preferentially deaminated [4]. Also, oxidative deamination by DOPA decarboxylase (DDC), a pyridoxal 5'-phosphate (PLP) dependent enzyme, can remove the amine group aromatic L-amino acids [23]. PLP is derived from vitamin B6 in the diet. The reaction involves the consumption of oxygen, the creation of quinonoid and ketimine intermediates and ultimately the production of either an aldehyde or ketoester and ammonia with byproducts of carbon dioxide, superoxide anion and hydrogen peroxide [23].

Both the ammonia and the α-keto acid must further be processed after being produced by the deamination reaction. High levels of free ammonia have detrimental effects on the body and thus the ammonium ions are generally used in reactions to produce more stable molecules. The α-keto acid, or amino acid carbon skeleton, is metabolized for various uses or used as a substrate for transamination reactions.

A portion of the resulting ammonia produced by deamination reactions is used in a chemical reaction that produces the amino acid glutamate. This is catalyzed by the enzyme glutamate dehydrogenase (1). Glutamate, in turn, can also consume ammonia in the ATP dependent production of glutamine, which is catalyzed by glutamine synthetase.

$$NH_4^+ + \alpha\text{-ketoglutarate} + NADPH <-> Glutamate + NADP^+ + H_2O$$

$$NH_4^+ + glutamate + ATP <-> Glutamine + ADP + P_i$$

Figure 5.3.1 Glutamine and Glutamate Synthesis Reactions

5.3.4. Basics of the Urea Cycle

Another fate of ammonia is its incorporation into urea using the urea cycle to capture or eliminate the excess nitrogen from amino acid catabolism [24]. The urea cycle consists of five reactions that occur in the liver and ultimately result in the sequestration of ammonia (See figure 5.3.2). The first two reactions occur within the mitochondria and the latter three take place in the cytosol. The resultant product, urea, receives one nitrogen from ammonia, one nitrogen from aspartate and a carbon from carbon dioxide or bicarbonate. The majority of the urea is then transported through the blood to the kidneys for urinary excretion. Some urea is also excreted into the intestinal lumen where it is degraded by bacteria in the gastrointestinal tract resulting in either microbial proteins or related compounds or ammonia that re-enters the body pool. However, most nitrogen from the protein that humans consume leaves the body as urea through urination. The amount and composition of urine produced by the kidneys is regulated by protein, water and sodium intakes [4].

5.3.5. The alpha-Keto Acid

The second product of deamination reactions, the α-keto acid or carbon skeleton, has many functions in the body. They can be used in the production of glucose, ketone bodies, cholesterol and fatty acids, depending on the metabolic state of the body. For example, when glucose stores are low due to either starvation or conditions such as diabetes, amino acids are converted to glucose in a process called gluconeogenesis. Thus, the complete oxidation of amino acids in the body ultimately generates energy, carbon dioxide or bicarbonate and ammonia or ammonium, all of which must be either used elsewhere in the body or excreted [4].

5.3.6. Urinary Protein Excretion Experiments

In most circumstances, urine contains very little intact protein. However, some dietary and physiological conditions can affect urinary protein excretion. For example, there may be a relationship between sodium intake levels and the amount of protein excreted. Proteomic analysis in rats showed that acute sodium loading had an effect on the excretion of as many as forty-five protein components through the urine [25]. For example, both ezrin and actin excretion were decreased, which supports the hypothesis of both proteins have a role in regulation of renal

1. $NH_3 + CO_2 (HCO_3) + 2ATP \rightarrow\rightarrow$ carbamoyl phosphate enzyme: mitochondrial carbamoyl phosphate synthetase (CPSI), cofactors: NAG, Mg

2. Cabamoyl phosphate + ornithine $\rightarrow\rightarrow$ citrulline enzyme: ornithine transcarbamoylase

3. Aspartate + citrulline $\rightarrow\rightarrow$ argininosuccinate enzyme: argininosuccinate synthetase

4. Argininosuccinate $\rightarrow\rightarrow$ fumarate and arginine enzyme: argininosuccinase

5. Arginine $\rightarrow\rightarrow$ urea + orninthine enzyme: arginase, cofactor: Mg

Figure 5.3-2: Urea cycle Reactions

sodium excretion. In general, the excretion of most proteins decreased in response to excessive levels of sodium, though a few, such as albumin and calbindin, experienced increased excretion [25]. This study demonstrates the interrelation of high sodium diets, hypertension, kidney disease and protein excretion, all of which impact nutritional homeostasis.

5.3.7. Disorders of Protein Excretion

The body's homeostatic mechanisms related to all aspects of nutrition are extremely complex and many are involved in disorders and diseases with severe clinical symptoms. Protein excretion is no exception. In relation to urea cycle disorders, the processing of the nitrogenous component of protein catabolism and thus the clinical symptoms are directly linked to the inability of the body to correctly excrete protein. In the case of the progression of renal disease, the amount of excreted urinary protein can serve as an indicator of severity.

5.3.7.1. Urea Cycle Disorders

There are many different metabolic abnormalities that can result in the malfunction of the urea cycle in the liver. The disorders are divided into mitochondrial disorders, which in include carbamoyl phosphate synthetase and ornithine transcarbamylase deficiencies, and cytoplasmic disorders, which include argininosuccinate synthetase, argininosuccinate lyase deficiencies and ornithine translocase defects [24]. The most common genetic disorder is ornithine carboamoyltransferase deficiency [25].

Hyperammonemia can occur from each of these disorders as well as increased serum concentrations of glutamine, since glutamine is readily synthesized from ammonia in the liver and other body tissues. These metabolic changes result from the body's inability to convert the nitrogenous byproducts of protein deamination to urea for excretion.

The metabolic disruption resulting from urea cycle defects can have serious effects on the nervous system such as encephalopathy. Symptoms can include brain edema, seizures, coma and death [24]. Both glutamine and ammonia may contribute to the neurological effects that can develop as a result of these disorders.

Glutamine is able to cross the blood brain barrier and is substantially increased in urea cycle defect patients, contributing to neurotoxicity.

Common management practices for urea cycle disorders include restriction of dietary protein, essential amino acid supplements, dialysis and nitrogen scavenging drugs [24]. The goal is to reduce the plasma ammonia levels, which rise in response to the inability of the body to convert protein byproducts into urea for excretion. Further research must now be done to find ways to lower plasma glutamine concentrations, as protein restriction seems to be fairly ineffectual [24].

5.3.7.2. Kidney Disease and Renal Failure

One important indicator of kidney malfunction is proteinuria, or increased levels of protein in the urine due to excess filtration of protein into the urine [28]. Proteinuria can be associated with hypertension, diabetes and obesity [29]. Thus, protein excretion through urine is clinically important to kidney disease as well as several metabolic diseases. Alterations of amino acid metabolism and the disruption of protein balance due to improper protein excretion can occur in both chronic and acute renal failure [30]. One important example is the decreased ability to convert phenylalanine to tyrosine, which is important for both the synthesis of various hormones and neurotransmitters [4]. In general, the overall balance of amino acids in the body is altered by renal disease, which in turn has effects on protein excretion. Providing the correct amino acid balance in diets consumed by patients with renal diseases can be important.

The level of proteinuria is both used to diagnose kidney disease and determine its state of progression. Common testing procedures for determining renal disease status involves the measurement of the excretion of the protein albumin in the urine and the determination of an albumin to creatine ratio of a first morning void sample [28]. In the cases of renal disease related to both diabetes and nephrophathy, albumin to creatinine ratio was most effective [28]. Another indicator of kidney disease is increased blood or plasma urea nitrogen concentration, as nitrogenous compounds normally excreted in urine accumulate in the blood.

5.4 The Excretion of Water Soluble Vitamins

5.4.1. Introduction

This section will explain the excretion of water soluble vitamins; specifically vitamin C, thiamin (vitamin B_1, riboflavin (vitamin B_2), niacin (vitamin B_3), pantothenic acid, biotin, folate, vitamin B_{12} (cobalamin), pyridoxine (vitamin B_6) and choline (a water-soluble nutrient). Choline is not a true vitamin but is often associated with the B-vitamins. A very small amount of the water-soluble vitamins are stored in the body for later use. The water- soluble vitamins are readily filtered by the kidneys and excreted in the urine for any excess amount that is consumed in the diet. The storage form for water-soluble vitamins is a result of their binding to transport proteins and enzymes. This is minimal for all of the water-soluble vitamins except for Vitamin B_{12} and as soon as the plasma levels are higher than the renal threshold, the vitamin is excreted in the urine.

5.4.2. Vitamin C

Vitamin C (Figure 5.4.1) is readily excreted in the urine through the kidneys. At intakes around 500 mg of vitamin C all of the additional intake is usually excreted. Maximum renal re-absorption of filtered vitamin C is reached

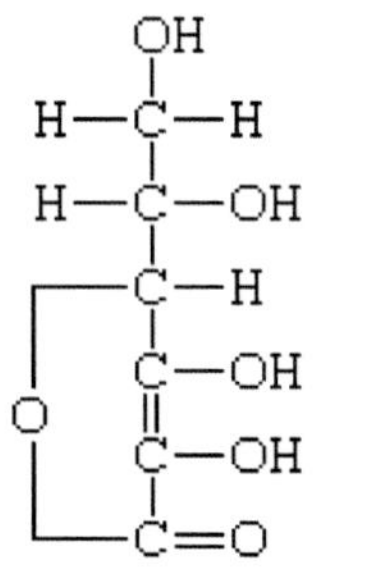

Figure 5.4-1: Structure of vitamin C.

when the plasma vitamin C concentration reaches a renal threshold or approximately 1.3 –1.8 mg/dL [4]. Renal excretion of vitamin C then increases proportionately if you consume higher amounts. These processes allow the body to excrete the vitamin when it is not needed and conserve it during periods of lower vitamin C intake.

Vitamin C is excreted both as the oxidized dehydroascorbic acid and as the reduced form, ascorbic acid. Further oxidation of dehydroascorbic acid yields 2,3- diketogulonic acid. The 2,3-diketogulonic acid can be either excreted or further hydrolyzed into threonic and oxalic acid or into a variety of five-carbon sugars. After this step the oxalic acid is then excreted through the urine, the five-carbon sugars are converted into cellular compounds or they can be excreted in the urine as CO_2 and water after oxidation.

5.4.3. Thiamin

Excess thiamin (**Figure 5.4.2**) is quickly excreted in the urine after being filtered by the kidneys. The vitamin can be catabolized before being excreted in the urine or it can be excreted as an intact molecule. This occurs when either thiamin, thiamin monophosphate (TMP) and thiamin diphosphate (TDP) are in higher concentrations than the storage capacity, or if the tissue no longer needs the vitamin for normal functioning. When the vitamin is degraded it is cleaved into a pyrimidine and the thiazole molecules. After being further catabolized 20 or more metabolites are generated. The RDI for thiamin is based on the urinary excretion of the vitamin along with thiamin intake data and erythrocyte **transketolase** activity [4]. Transketolase is a thiamin-dependent enzyme, so its activity decreases when thiamin status is low, and adding more thiamin into an in vitro test increases the enzyme activity.

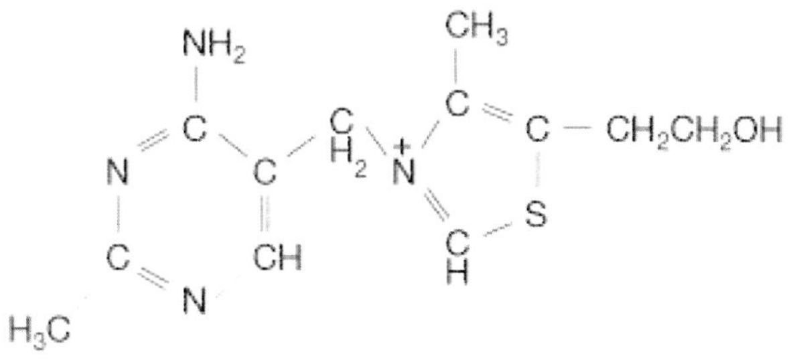

Thiamin

Figure 5.4-2: Structure of Thiamin.

When the ingested dose of thiamin is very high there is only a small fraction that is reabsorbed and the remainder is excreted in the urine in response to elevated serum values [31].

5.4.4. Riboflavin

Riboflavin excretion occurs primarily in the urine. The glomerulus filters the riboflavin (**Figure 5.4.3.**) that is not bound to any proteins in the plasma. 7α- and 8α- hydroxymethyl riboflavin, 8α-sulfonyl riboflavin, 10-hydroxyethyl flavin and riboflavinyl peptide ester are the predominant metabolites in the urine. Some riboflavin is bound to cysteine and histidine when it is excreted in the urine if it has been absorbed in these forms in the GI tract. Sometimes it can also be generated by the degradation of flavoenzymes in body cells. Most of the riboflavin is however excreted intact through the urine.

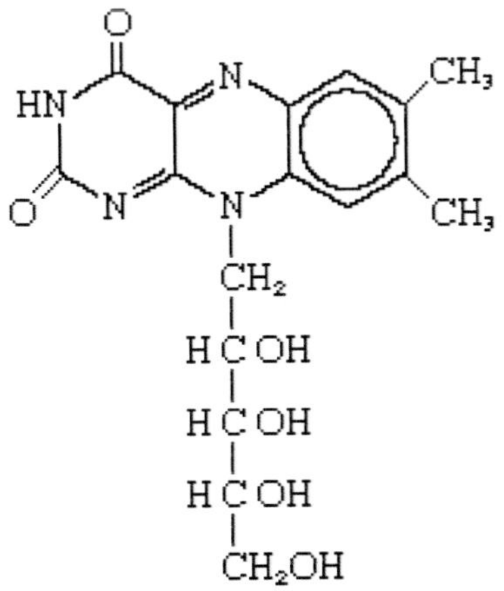

Figure 5.4-3: Structure of riboflavin.

The excretory process is fast for riboflavin. You can often notice the urinary excretion within a couple of hours from oral ingestion. When this vitamin is ingested in a quantity greater than 1.7 mg/L the urine turns into a brighter orangish yellow color. If you shine a black light on the urine it will glow in the dark because of the fluorescent characteristic. Riboflavin excreted in the feces is in very small amounts and is a product of the catabolism of riboflavin by intestinal bacteria.

Very little riboflavin is stored in the body. The urinary excretion varies with intake, age and metabolic events. Among healthy adults consuming a well-balanced diet the excretion of riboflavin accounts for about 60 to 70 percent. For newborns this excretory process is slow but the net product is similar to that of an older infant [31].

5.4.5. Niacin (Vitamin B3)

Most of the niacin (**Figure 5.4.4.**) consumed in the diet is absorbed from the stomach and the small intestine in the forms of nicotinic acid and nicotinamide. Because of the good absorption very little niacin is excreted in feces. However, if there is any excess niacin it will be excreted through the urine [10]. NAD and NADP are degraded to nicotinamide and ADP-ribose. The liver then oxidizes and methylates the nicotinamide and various metabolites are excreted in the urine, including N' methyl nicotinamide and N' methyl 2-pyridone 5-carboxamide.

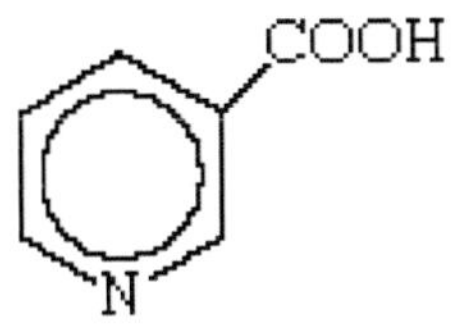

Figure 5.4-4: Structure of niacin, vitamin B3.

5.4.6. Pantothenic Acid

Pantothenic acid does not undergo any metabolism before it is excreted. It is excreted both in urine and in the feces, but primarily in the urine. The daily urinary excretion ranges from about 1 to 8 mg [4].

5.4.7. Biotin

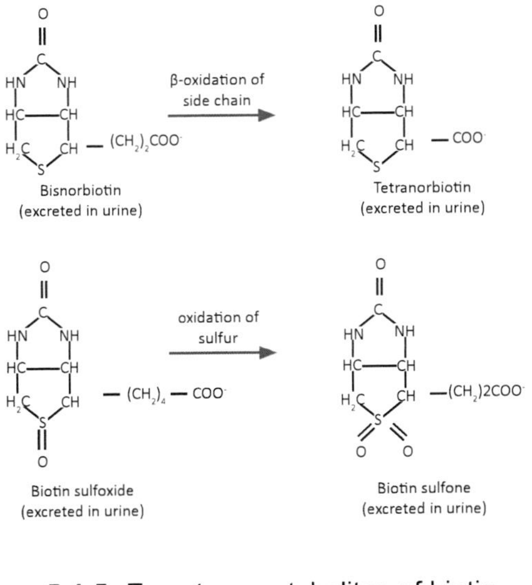

Figure 5.4-5: Excretory metabolites of biotin.

Biotin is mainly excreted through the urine with a minimal amount being excreted in the bile and feces. Very small amounts of intact biotin and biocytin usually appear in the urine. Biotin holocarboxylases are catabolized by proteases giving biotin oligopeptides and finally biocytin. From the biocytin the body then generates lysine and free biotin from the degradation by biotinidase. Biotin sulfone and biotin sulfoxide **(Figure 5.4.5.)** are metabolites of formed from the oxidation of sulfur on the biotin's ring. The valeric side chain on biotin is degraded by β-oxidation and yields mainly bisnorbiotin and tetraorbiotin. Bisnorbiotin methyl ketone and tetraorbiotin methyl ketone come from the catabolism but these metabolites are present to a lesser degree. The biotin that is excreted in the feces has been synthesized by intestinal bacteria. Dietary biotin that has been absorbed has not been shown to be excreted in the feces to a significant amount [4].

5.4.8. Folate

Folate is excreted in both the urine and the in feces. The body retains needed folate by folate-binding proteins. In the kidneys these proteins are present in the renal brush border and coupled with tubular re-absorption.

Folate is excreted in the urine both as the intact substance and also as a catabolized product. It is believed that the oxidative cleavage of folate occurs between C9 and N10 of polyglutamate. Para-aminobenzoyl poly-glutamate and pteridine are all generated by this cleavage process. This process will form N-acetyl para-aminobenzoyl glutamate which is the major metabolite in the urine. A smaller amount of folate is also secreted by the liver into the bile. Most of this is re-absorbed through enterohepatic circulation, so there is not much folate excreted through the feces [4].

5.4.9. Vitamin B12 (Cobalamin)

The excretion of vitamin B12 is minimal. Minute amounts are excreted through the bile, urine and dermal losses. Unlike any other water-soluble vitamin, vitamin B12 can be stored in the liver in amounts that could potentially last us for several years. Most of the vitamin B12 is excreted through the bile but because of

enterohepatic circulation it is very efficiently recycled and re-absorbed by the body [10]. The excretion of vitamin B12 is proportional to the amount the body has stored.

There are cases where a deficiency in certain substances or an illness can lead to vitamin B12 deficiency, due to lack of the intrinsic factors needed for absorption in an efficient enterohepatic circulation process. For individuals who are deficient in intrinsic factor all the vitamin B12 excreted in the bile will proceed to the stool and be excreted in the feces instead of being re-absorbed. A deficiency stemming from the lack of intrinsic factor is more acute than a deficiency from a poor diet because of the non-functioning re-absorptive process [31].

5.4.10. Vitamin B6

The primary excretory route for pyridoxine is through the urine with small amounts being excreted in the feces. The major metabolite is 4-pyridoxic acid which results from the oxidation of pyridoxal (aldehyde form) by FAD-dependent aldehyde oxidases or NAD-dependent aldehyde dehydrogenase. These substances can be found in the liver and kidneys and in all tissues respectively. When 4-pyridoxic acid is found in the urine it is an indicator of recent vitamin intake as opposed to vitamin stores. Ingestion of a large dose of vitamin B6 as pyridoxine (alcohol form) will result in the excretion of intact 5-pyridoxic acid and pyridoxine and a decreased urinary excretion of 4-pyridoxic acid.

5.4.11. Choline

Although choline cannot yet be classified as a B-vitamin it is often associated with this nutrient class. This water-soluble nutrient is important in synthesizing phospholipid components of cell membranes and plasma lipoproteins. Only a small amount is excreted in the urine because most excess choline is converted to a related donor of single-carbon groups [32].

5.4.12. Water-Soluble Vitamins in the Literature – Recent Research

Imae and colleagues [33] hypothesized that water-soluble vitamins are lower in diabetic patients because of large amounts of vitamins being excreted in the urine. They experimented with rats and found that the urinary excretion was higher in diabetic rats than in a control group. The study also found that the liver and blood concentrations were maintained despite the increased urinary output.

Fukuwatari and colleagues [34] investigated whether excretion of water-soluble vitamins can be used as a nutritional index. Urinary thiamin content drastically decreased after one day of fasting and riboflavin significantly increased its urinary excretion whereas the other water-soluble vitamins did not change much from fasting. Some vitamin concentrations in liver and skeletal muscle decreased. The results suggest that during fasting the body takes vitamins from the liver stores and supplies the peripheral tissues to maintain adequate metabolic functions.

Tsuji and colleagues [35] studied free living elderly females and hypothesized that the 24-hours urinary excretion of water-soluble vitamins would be correlated to the dietary intake. The study showed that urinary excretion was a good measure of water-soluble vitamins, except vitamin B12, and can be used to measure the recent intake in these vitamins

5.5. FAT- SOLUBLE VITAMIN EXCRETION: Vitamin A, D, E, and K

5.5.1. Introduction

Fat soluble vitamins are found in fats and oils and are insoluble in water. Excess fat soluble vitamins can be stored in the adipose tissue of the body and the liver. Nutrients can be excreted from the body in a number of different ways. Most unabsorbed material is excreted through fecal matter. Other ways include, the renal, dermal, and respiratory excretion. The rate of nutrient absorption can be impacted by the dietary material that it associates with in the gut. Fiber has a positive effect on how much fat excretion occurs in our feces, [36]. Inhibitors such as, oxalic acid, phytic acid, tannins and phytosterols can also effect the rate of absorption and excretion of fat-soluble vitamins.

The kidney is responsible for the processes involved in renal excretion. Most of the body's waste products are water-soluble and easily extracted through the kidney and pass out with urine. Compounds that are fat-soluble, such as vitamins A, D, E, and K, can be converted into water-soluble compounds in the liver. A smaller amount of vitamin excretion occurs through the skin when the body is not sweating. When fat-soluble vitamins are converted to be soluble by water in the liver, they can undergo this excretion mechanism as well, regardless of whether the animal has sweat glands. This type of perspiration is the result of passive diffusion of water from the sub dermal tissues to the skins surface [37]. The deposits are then evaporated from the surface of the skin.

5.5.2. Vitamin A

The first fat soluble vitamin identified was vitamin A. This vitamin is derived from a class of compounds together known as retinoids. The two sources of vitamin A are retinoids and carotenoids. Retinols come from animal products while carotenoids are obtained from dark green and yellow vegetables and fruits. Vitamin A is important for growth and reproduction, vision, immunity, and cell differentiation. If taken in excess, vitamin A is the most likely vitamin to cause toxicity. It is important to discuss how the body gets rid of vitamin A after use, and when it is obtained in excess.

The majority of vitamin A metabolites are excreted in the urine, [38]. If not excreted in the urine, the vitamin A metabolites are excreted in the feces or from breathing. In the event that too much vitamin A is consumed, vitamin A metabolites are excreted from the body in order to protect the body from excess storage of the vitamin in the liver [38]. In times of higher intake the excess vitamin A is generally excreted through the feces rather than urine. In order to be excreted through the urine, vitamin A molecules are oxidized and conjugated into water-soluble metabolites. Figure 5.5.1. shows the metabolism of vitamin A, with the focus on the excreted products that leave the body through bile.

In some instances, vitamins can be excreted at faster rates than usual. That can change the dynamic of the reactions shown above. The body may require more or less of the nutrient in order for the body to sustain normal activity. When patients have serious infections,

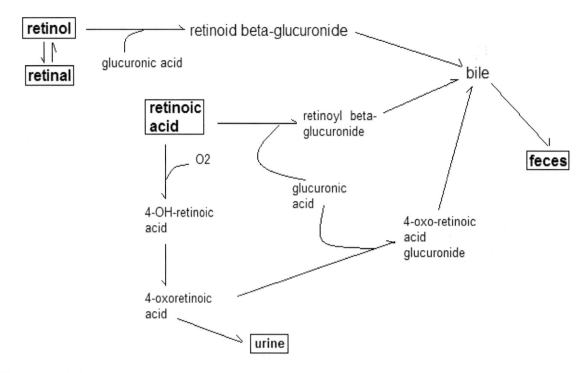

Figure 5.5-1: Vitamin A metabolism.

significant amounts of retinol-binding protein are excreted from the body through urine [39]. Normally, in a healthy individual, only a small amount of RBP is found in the urine. Vitamin A requirements increase substantially for people who have acute infections.

5.5.3. Vitamin D

Unlike other vitamins, vitamin D can be synthesized through the help of sunlight. Also, vitamin D acts like a hormone in that it can effect changes in cells via changes its concentration in blood. Vitamin D can enhance immune cell function, inhibit tumor growth and increase blood calcium levels.

The majority of vitamin D metabolites are excreted through feces, but leave the body through urine. Calcitriol hydroxylation forms the metabolites of vitamin D that will eventually be excreted [4]. At the same time, side chains of the molecules are modified to yield calcitroic acid, which, along with other metabolites of vitamin D, is then excreted in bile through the feces. About 70% of vitamin D is excreted via feces, leaving only a little to leave through urine [4].

5.5.4. Vitamin E

Vitamin E was discovered as a cause for an increase in fetal death for the pregnant female rats during dietary deficiency. There are two forms of the vitamin; tocopherols and tocotrienols. The most active form of the vitamin is the alpha form of a tocopherol.

Vitamin E is an antioxidant, so it protects other compounds in the body from free radicals. It minimizes free radical damage to the body tissues in cooperation with selenium, ascorbic acid, and other antioxidant molecules.

When humans take in excessive doses of supplemental vitamin E, the body creates metabolites that can be eliminated through urinary excretion. This process starts with hydroxylation that requires cytochrome P-450 in order to make hydroxychromanol [4].

Then a process similar to beta-oxidation occurs so that the phytyl side chain of vitamin E is cleaved. The product of that reaction gives a group of carboxyethyl hydroxychromans, (CEHC). These products are bound to sulfate or glucuronic acid right before excretion.

Sometimes having too much of a vitamin can cause problems with other processes in the body, such as the vitamin E metabolite gamma-CEHC. That metabolite has been shown to inhibit the potassium channel and increase the urinary sodium excretion [38]. In addition to urinary excretion, dietary vitamin E is also regularly excreted through the feces, since the absorption rate of vitamin E is fairly low [38]. Certain forms of vitamin E that are not used by the body, as well as excess tocopherol, are excreted in bile, even with high dose supplements.

Vitamin E presents low risk of toxicity, possibly because of the rate of biliary secretion, [40]. Another reason for a high level of fecal excretion is that there are benefits for the gastrointestinal tract when the amount of vitamin E present helps to scavenge reactive oxidant species resulting from digestion and bacterial metabolism.

5.5.5. Vitamin K

Vitamin K can be found in two different forms. There is a synthetic form called menadione and naturally occurring vitamin K that can be either phylloquinone or menaquinone. In the blood clotting cascade, there are 13 different proteins along with calcium that complete the process. Vitamin K is involved in the synthesis or post- translational modification of 4 out of those 13 proteins. Therefore, without vitamin K blood cannot clot properly. Vitamin K can be obtained either from leafy vegetables or made from bacteria in the large intestine or in food fermentation.

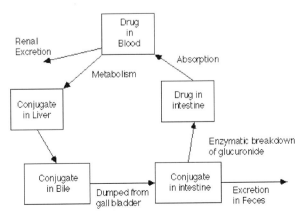

Figure 5.5-2: Excretion and enterohepatic pathways for lipid soluble vitamins.

After being catabolized, vitamin K is excreted from the liver into bile. A less prevalent route of vitamin K excretion is through the urine. Before the vitamin K metabolites are excreted within bile, the phylloquinone's metabolites are joined with glucuronic acid. The excretion of menadione follows reaction with phosphate and sulfate to form menadiol phosphate and menadiol sulfate, which are the end products excreted from the body [4]. The molecular weight or metabolic need of a compound can determine the possibility for the metabolite to be reabsorbed for an additional function. Vitamins in the bile can be either excreted in feces or reabsorbed into the body to be modified again and perhaps excreted through the urine. This somewhat circular process is shown in figure 5.5.2. [41].

From reference [41].

5.6. Excretion of Minerals: Calcium, Magnesium, and Iron

5.6.1. Introduction: Renal macromineral excretion

Minerals are important to the body's health and maintenance. They can support bone structure, participate in acid-base balance, and be involved in enzymatic reactions. There are two classes of minerals, trace minerals and macro minerals. This somewhat arbitrary distinction is based on the quantity needed in the diet, or the quantity stored in the human body. There are six main macro minerals: calcium, phosphorus magnesium, sodium, potassium, and chlorine. Most calcium and magnesium is found in bones and teeth, although nearly half of the body's magnesium may be inside soft tissues [42].

Macro minerals found in a variety food sources are digested and absorbed primarily in the small intestine. Excretion of minerals occurs through urine, feces, and sweat losses. The kidney and renal system are responsible for the excretion of a large portion of the body's metabolic waste to maintain a homeostasis of mineral content (Figure 5.6.1.).

Urinary excretion begins with blood from an arteriole entering the glomerulus, which is a dense ball of capillaries, to be filtered. The filtered blood then

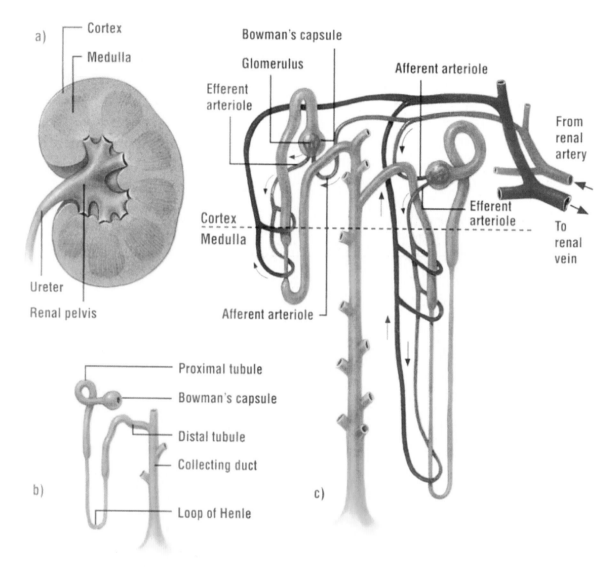

Figure 5.5-3: Renal Structure. a) cross section of kidney; b) general structure of a nephron; c) relation of nephron to vascular system and collecting duct.

enters Bowman's capsule of the renal tubule. The renal tubule reabsorbs some minerals, nutrients, water, and ions, while also secreting solutes and waste products into the glomerular filtrate. The reabsorbed substances are returned to the blood.

The renal tubule consists of several parts. It begins with the Bowman's Capsule which encompasses the glomerulus. The blood filtered by the glomerulus first enters the tubule at the capsule. The proximal convoluted tubule is the next segment of the renal tubule connected to the descending limb that begins

to descend into the medulla of the kidney. From there, the tubule begins to ascend to the cortex, which completes the Loop of Henle. The glomerular filtrate moves up the ascending limb into the distal convoluted tubule [43].

The filtrate, now called urine, still contains the excess ions and waste products, like urea, that were filtered in the glomerulus. The urine of the many nephrons of the kidney enters the collecting duct from the nephrons' distal convoluted tubules. The urine travels to the a common duct to leave the kidney to be stored in the urinary bladder and to be later excreted through the urethra [43]. As the collecting ducts pass through the renal medulla to the renal pelvis, the high concentration of salt and urea allows water to leave the urine osmotically, resulting in excretion of urine that is much more concentrated in salts and waste products than the blood serum or glomerular filtrate.

The specific substances, the amounts of these substances that are reabsorbed, and the amount of solutes secreted are determined by the concentration of protein, sodium, water, and a variety of other substances present in the body. Further discussion of two macrominerals, calcium and magnesium, will focus on how they are excreted and factors influencing these mineral's excretion. These two macrominerals are not classically thought to be important regulators of each other's balance but we will see how they can have effects on one another's excretion.

5.6.2. Calcium

5.6.2.1. Function

Calcium is the predominant divalent cation found in the body, contributing to 2% of the body's weight. Approximately 99% of the body calcium is stored in bone and teeth as hydroxyapatite [44]. Calcium can also be found in the soft tissues and extracellular space [45], and plays a role in muscle contractions, blood clotting, and enzyme activation.

5.6.2.2. Sources and Recommended Dietary Allowance

Dietary sources of calcium include dairy products and dietary supplements. Foods such as milk, yogurt and cheese are rich in calcium. Other good sources of calcium include tofu, kale, broccoli, and cabbage. In the United States, many fruit and vegetable juices are fortified with calcium [31].

The calcium requirement for the average adult is 1000 to 1200 mg/day. For children 9 to 18 years of age, the recommended calcium intake is 1300 mg/day [46]. Children and adolescents require a higher intake of calcium because of their greater need for growth and skeletal development.

Inadequate intakes or excess excretion of calcium can cause bone loss, or osteoporosis, and increased risk of bone fractures. On the other hand, excess calcium intake can cause adverse effects. Some problems associated with excessive intake, primarily from calcium supplements, are kidney stones and hypercalcemia. When calcium intake increases, balance is maintained by a combination of lower fractional absorption and increased renal excretion. Additionally, excess calcium can alter the absorption and/or excretion of other minerals and nutrients, such as magnesium, phosphorus, iron, protein, and other substances.

5.6.2.3. Excretion of Calcium

Excess calcium, not stored in the bones or used by the body's cells, is excreted in the urine, feces, or sweat. Calcium is filtered through the renal system and most of the calcium is reabsorbed. Calcium-sensing receptor proteins, in the ascending loop of Henle, sense the calcium concentrations in the blood and adjust the amount of calcium absorbed by the distal tubule [4].

5.6.2.4. Factors Affecting Calcium Excretion

The amount of calcium the body ingests and absorbs obviously affects the amount of calcium the body excretes. Other factors that influence urinary excretion of calcium include caffeine, protein, and sodium. Protein's effect on calcium excretion is somewhat controversial, due to the high protein diet consumed by many Americans. Cao, et al [47] observed that high protein diets increased calcium absorption and urinary excretion of calcium. The increase in protein intake may increase the acid load on the kidneys due to the ammonium nitrogen excretion associated with protein. This could result in increased renal filtration and loss of calcium. However, the increased urinary calcium loss that accompanies high protein diets may not have a negative impact on bone strength or density [48].

Another factor that can affect calcium excretion is caffeine. Caffeine is a non-essential substance that is commonly consumed in American Diets. It is found primarily in coffee and soft drinks. Caffeine can increase urinary excretion of calcium as well as decrease calcium absorption. Since caffeine is often consumed in the United States, it can lead to accelerated bone loss especially in older women, who are already at risk for calcium deficiency [31].

Sodium, in the form of sodium chloride, can also increase the amount of calcium excreted in the urine. A high salt diet can lead to decrease bone density due to excess amounts of calcium excreted. Inversely, less sodium intake reduced calcium excretion and markers of bone turnover in a study of postmenopausal women [49].

An additional factor affecting calcium excretion and balance is magnesium.

Magnesium deficiency is related to a decrease in blood calcium. The increased excretion and decreased re-absorption of calcium in the renal tubule brought on by insufficient magnesium can cause hypocalcaemia [42].

5.6.3. Magnesium

5.6.3.1. Function

Approximately 60-50% of the body's magnesium is stored in bones with calcium and other minerals. The crystal lattice form of bone magnesium helps with bone formation while the surface layer of bone magnesium, an amorphous form, is used to maintain magnesium concentrations in the blood [4].

The other 50% to 40% is found in the body's cells and tissues with about 1% found in the blood. Magnesium is essential to about 300 of the body's enzymatic reactions.

Intracellular magnesium is used in the hydrolysis of adenosine-5'-triphosphate, or ATP, which is a vital energy source for the body. Some of the pathways that require magnesium include glycolysis, the TCA cycle, pentose phosphate pathway, nucleic acid synthesis, DNA replication, RNA transcription, beta oxidation, and ion channel regulation of potassium and calcium [4].

5.6.3.2. Sources and Recommended Dietary Allowance

Magnesium is found in a variety of vegetables such as spinach, nuts, beans, and grains. The RDA for healthy

adults vary with age, gender, and states of pregnancy or lactation. The RDA for healthy males between 19 and 30 years is 400 mg/day. Above the age of 30, the RDA for men increases to 420 mg/day.

For healthy women between the ages of 19 and 30, the RDA is 310 mg/day, and 320 mg/day after the age of 30. RDAs are not increased for breastfeeding, but pregnant, women between the ages of 19 and 30, need 350 mg/day, and pregnant women 31 to 50 need a daily intake of 360 mg of magnesium [4]. There is no RDA established for infants but an AI for infants up to six months is 30 mg/day and for infants 7 to 12 months have an AI of 75 mg/day [31].

5.6.3.3. Digestion, Absorption, and Transport

Magnesium is absorbed mainly in the jejunum and ileum of the small intestine [31]. Magnesium uptake uses active transport through a "transient receptor potential melastatin divalent cation-permeable channel protein called TRPM6" found on the brush boarder membrane of the enterocytes [4]. Active transport is used mainly for low magnesium intake. As more magnesium is consumed, less magnesium is absorbed.

Approximately 50% of the magnesium that is ingested is absorbed [31]. The other form of transport, passive diffusion, is used mainly when there is high level of magnesium present in the small intestine. High levels of magnesium are absorbed from paracellular absorption. Once absorbed, magnesium is transported through the body either bound to a protein or transported as a cation [4].

5.6.3.4. Excretion of Magnesium

Magnesium that is not stored in bone or used in enzymatic reactions is excreted through the kidneys with some fecal excretion and magnesium lost via sweat.

Approximately 10% to 15% of filtered magnesium is reabsorbed in the proximal convoluted tubule. About 70% is reabsorbed in the loop of Henle and the remainder is reabsorbed in the distal convoluted tubule. Serum magnesium concentrations alter the amount absorbed in the distal convoluted tubule [4].

Factors that can alter the excretion of magnesium also affect the excretion of calcium in similar ways, such as protein and caffeine. High protein intake may increase magnesium excretion due to the increased kidney function associated with high protein diets. The kidney has an increased acid load with the high amount of nitrogen, phosphate, and sulfate removed from the protein. This increases the amount of magnesium as well as other macronutrients excreted through the urine [31]. Another factor increasing magnesium excretion is calcium intakes exceeding the UL of 2,500 mg per day.

Dlugaszek et al. [50] found significantly higher concentrations of magnesium in the urine in subjects with hypercalciuria.

5.6.4. Sodium and Potassium

The major electrolytes in blood and tissues, sodium, potassium and chloride, are mostly excreted in urine. Urine volume is determined by the sodium, potassium and water intake. Decreasing protein or sodium intake will limit the urine volume, which may be a recommended treatment for some kidney diseases. The typical volume of urine secreted daily is 1 to 2 liters. If urine volume falls below 600 mL due to low water intake, kidney stone formation for the concentrated urine may result.

Sodium retention is achieved when the juxtaglomerular apparatus in the kidney cortex senses a drop in blood pressure. The juxtaglomerular cells release the hormone renin into the blood stream. Renin cleaves a peptide fragment from the protein angiotensinogen that was secreted from the liver into the blood, forming angiotensin I. The enzyme, angiotensin converting enzyme (ACE), secreted in the lung, further processes angiotensin I to form angiotensin II. Angiotensin II acts on the hypothalamus and pituitary to release antidiuretic hormone (ADH, also called vasopressin) into the blood, and also causes the adrenal gland to release aldosterone. Antidiuretic hormone causes the collecting ducts in the kidney to allow water transport into the concentrated salt environment of the renal medulla for water retention. The aldosterone also causes the sodium retention and potassium excretion by the kidney. The net effect is that the sodium and water retention cause an increase in blood pressure.

Other hormones affecting blood pressure and the balance of sodium and potassium include natriuretic hormone and B-type natriuretic hormone (ANP and BNP). The actions of these hormones secreted by specialized cells in the heart in response to blood pressures changes include: additional sodium and water loss (**natriuresis** and **diuresis**); decreases in renin, aldosterone, and arginine vasopressin; constriction or dilation of vasculature in certain tissues; activation of nerves from heart to brain; and a shift in fluid from blood into cells, which increases red blood cell concentration (**hematocrit**) and reduces cardiac output [51].

Changes in the relative, sodium, potassium and chloride concentration can also be caused by changes in blood pH. Because higher concentration of the cations Na^+ and K^+, relative to the concentration of anions like Cl^-, result in increased pH, or alkaline conditions, and the reverse causes lower pH or acidosis, changes in the retention of these ions may occur to compensate for metabolic or respiratory alkalosis or acidosis [52].

5.6.5. Iron

5.6.5.1. Function

Iron is an essential part of many proteins and enzymes that are responsible for regulating cellular growth and differentiation. Iron has unusual properties which allow it to be flexible and to serve as both an electron donor and acceptor. The majority of iron in the body is attached to the heme group in oxygen-carrying and oxygen-storing proteins hemoglobin and myoglobin. Hemoglobin is found in red blood cells and myoglobin is found in muscles. Iron acts as a cofactor, cosubstrate, or a prosthetic group for many proteins and enzymes in life sustaining pathways to include: glycolysis, gluconeogenesis, the citric acid (TCA) cycle and oxidative phosphorylation. Almost two-thirds of iron in the body is found in hemoglobin [53,55,56].

5.6.5.2. Sources and Recommended Dietary Allowance

Food sources with high iron content include: dried beans, dried fruits, eggs (especially egg yolks), iron-fortified cereals, liver, lean red meat (especially beef), oysters, poultry, salmon, tuna, and whole grains [56].

The RDA values for iron consistently change from adolescence throughout adulthood due to physiological changes that include growth, development, and reproduction (**Table 5.6.4.2.**) [57].

5.6.5.3. Digestion, Absorption, Transport, and Recycling

The amount of iron absorbed compared to the amount ingested is typically low, but may range from 5% to as much as 35% depending on the circumstances and the type of iron [53]. Dietary iron is obtained from eating inorganic sources or animal sources. Iron from meat, poultry, and fish are absorbed two to three times more efficiently than iron from plants. Like most mineral nutrients, the majority of the iron absorbed from digested food or supplements is absorbed in the duodenum by enterocytes of the duodenal lining. These cells have special transporters that allow them to move iron into the body. To be absorbed, dietary iron can be absorbed as part of a protein such as heme protein or must be in its ferrous Fe^{2+} form.

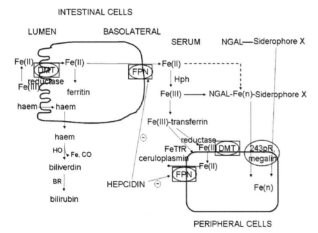

Figure 5.6-1: Schematic overview of the main elements considered to participate in mammalian iron metabolism. Kell BMC Medical Genomics 2009 2:2 doi:10.1186/1755-8794-2-2.

A ferric reductase enzyme on the enterocytes' brush border, Dcytb, reduces ferric Fe^{3+} to Fe^{2+}. A protein called divalent metal transporter 1 (DMT1), which transports different kinds of divalent metals into the body, then transports the iron across the cell membrane and into the cell. The absorbed iron can then

be used by the cell, store as ferritin for use at another time, or can be transferred to the blood plasma for use by other cells (**Figure 5.6.4.3**) [53,54,55].

Plasma transfer of iron from enterocytes to the transport protein, apotransferrin, occurs through specific iron channels, called ferroportins, and is facilitated by a protein called **hephaestin**. When apotransferrin binds iron, it is called transferrin.

Hephaestin contains copper, so copper deficiency will decrease iron absorption [53].Ferroportin iron channels are reabsorbed from the cell membrane into intracellular vesicles when plasma levels of the hormone, **hepcidin**, are elevated.

RDA for iron by age and sex.		
Age/Group	Life Stage	Iron (mg/day)
Infants	0–6 months	0.27*
	7–12 months	11
Children	1–3 years	7
	4–8 years	10
Males	9–13 years	8
	14–18 years	11
	19–30 years	8
	31–50 years	8
	51–70 years	8
	>70 years	8
Females	9–13 years	8
	14–18 years	15
	19–30 years	18
	31–50 years	18
	51–70 years	8
	>70 years	8
Pregnant Women	14–18 years	27
	19–30 years	27
	31–50 years	27
Lactating Women	14–18 years	10
	19–30 years	9
	31–50 years	9

Most of the iron used for red blood cell hemoglobin production is obtained from hemoglobin breakdown of senescent RBCs (called recycling).

When red blood cells reach the end of their lifespan (senescent), they are phagocytized by macrophages (in the spleen, liver, bone marrow). Hydrolytic enzymes in macrophages degrade the ingested RBCs and release hemoglobin. Proteolytic digestion of hemoglobin liberates heme and globins.

Globins are broken down to amino acids, which can be used for protein synthesis. The iron is released from heme, leaving a porphyrin ring that is converted to bilirubin [53]. The **reticuloendothelial system** in the liver, which consists of Kupfer cells and other phagocytes, is responsible for capture the iron so it can be excreted in the bile. The iron excretion in bile is variable, and is sometimes inadequate based on genetics and iron intake.

5.6.5.4. Iron Toxicity and Deficiency

Iron can be potentially toxic. Its ability to donate and accept electrons means that if iron is free within the cell, it can catalyze the conversion of hydrogen peroxide into free radicals. Free radicals can cause damage to a wide variety of cellular structures, and ultimately kill the cell. To prevent that kind of damage, all life forms that use iron bind the iron atoms to proteins. That allows the cells to use the benefits of iron, but also limit its ability to do harm [55].

Iron deficiency can result from a variety of causes, these causes can be grouped into several categories [55]:

- Increased demand for iron, which the diet cannot accommodate.

- Increased loss of iron (usually through loss of blood).

- Nutritional deficiency. This can result due to a lack of dietary iron or consumption of foods that inhibit iron absorption, including calcium, phytates and tannins. For example, black tea steeped for long times has high levels of tannins.

- Inability to absorb iron because of damage to the intestinal lining. Examples of causes of this kind of damage include surgery involving the duodenum, or intestinal diseases.

Review questions:

1. Question: What is the function of iron that gives it a toxic effect?

2. Question: What is the name of the transport protein that transfers iron from the enterocytes?

3. Question: What source of iron, either inorganic or animal source, is absorbed at a greater rate than that of the other.

5.7. Chapter 5 Summary and Conclusion

The digestion, absorption and excretion of nutrients plays a major role in keeping the body in a homeostatic state. These processes involve many enzymes and hormones that work together in an efficient manner to get the job done. Humans do not excrete carbohydrates in the same manner as other macronutrients. Quantification of carbohydrate excretion is through carbon dioxide and water produced as byproducts in the metabolism of carbohydrates. Carbon dioxide moves out of the body through the lungs and is transported from the cells in three forms, that is, physically dissolved, buffered in water as carbonic acids (HCO_3^-), or bound to proteins as carbamate. Quantification of carbohydrate lost is used as a measure of energy expenditure through the use of respiratory quotient, of oxygen inhaled and carbon dioxide exhaled. Carbohydrates are also excreted through dietary fiber or digestive malabsorption. Some studies have indicated fecal excretion of nonfiber carbohydrates by neonates and rats.

Digestion breaks down lipid particles into easily absorbed forms. Bile acids and phospholipids act as emulsifiers to allow lipid molecules to move away from lipid droplets for absorption through enterocyte cell membranes. Absorption involves a large surface area to make sure as many nutrients as possible are taken in for transport and storage. Excretion of lipid is usually in the form of metabolic breakdown products, carbon dioxide and water.

Protein metabolism is extremely important in maintaining amino acid balance to support the many metabolic processes that depend upon proteins. Part of this process involves the excretion or conversion of generated waste products when an amino acid is broken down, particularly ammonia, which is used for the synthesis of glutamine and glutamate or is converted to urea. Disruptions in this process, such as urea cycle disorders, can cause serious clinical symptoms. Furthermore, increased urinary secretion of proteins can be a powerful tool in both research and medical fields.

All water-soluble vitamins with the exception of vitamin B12 (Cobalamin) are readily excreted through the urine. Secondary pathways for water-soluble vitamin excretion are through the bile and feces, and a trace amount through dermal losses. The water-soluble vitamins are readily excreted through the urine because the body does not store any significant amounts in tissue or organs; an exception to this is vitamin B12 where larger amounts, relative to daily requirements, are stored in the liver. Most of the water- soluble vitamins, with the exception of pantothenic acid, undergo some form of metabolism prior to being excreted. Choline, a water-soluble nutrient, is not considered to be part of the water-soluble vitamins, but can be considered to be a conditionally essential nutrient with some functions analogous to the vitamins.

Excretion is an essential process for all living things. After metabolism occurs, the waste products and unused metabolites have to leave the body. Organs that specialize in excretion processes include the kidney and the liver. Fat-soluble vitamins can be extracted from the body in the feces, urine, or through the skin. In order to leave through the urine vitamin A, D, E, and K rely on conversion to a water-soluble metabolite, usually by the liver. Since fat-soluble vitamins are stored in the liver and fatty tissues, they are excreted at a much slower rate than water soluble vitamins. The excretory process is very important since these vitamins can stay in the body for such a long time and could pose a higher risk of toxicity. A healthy individual who has an adequate intake of nutrients should have no trouble excreting fat-soluble vitamin metabolites, whether it is through the feces, urine or skin.

Excretion of minerals, and excretion in general, is a vital mechanism to the human body. Many factors can alter the excretion of macrominerals and macrominerals can affect the excretion of other minerals and nutrients. Calcium and magnesium can affect the body's balance of other substances. Other dietary factors contribute to the body's homeostatic state. It is important to try to maintain proper balance to keep the healthy body operating efficiently.

5.8. References Cited

1. Stein J, Purschian B, Zeuzem S, Lembcke B, Caspary WF. Quantification of fecal carbohydrates by near-infrared reflectance analysis. Clin. Chem. 1996 Feb 1;42(2):309– 12.

2. Ameen VZ, Powell GK. Quantitative fecal carbohydrate excretion in premature infants. Am J Clin Nutr. 1989 Jun 1;49(6):1238–42.

3. Food and Nutrition Board. Dietary Reference Intakes for Energy, Carbohydrate, Fiber, Fat, Fatty Acids, Cholesterol, Protein, and Amino Acids (Macronutrients). Washington DC: National Academies Press, 2005.

4. Gropper SS, Smith JL. Advanced nutrition and human metabolism. 6th Ed. Belmont (CA) Cengage Learning;2013

5. DeLany JP. Measurement of energy expenditure. Pediatric Blood & Cancer. 2012;58(1):129–34.

6. Geers C, Gros G. Carbon Dioxide Transport and Carbonic Anhydrase in Blood and Muscle. Physiol Rev. 2000 Jan 4;80(2):681–715.

7. Arthurs GJ, Sudhakar M. Carbon dioxide transport. Contin Educ Anaesth Crit Care Pain. 2005 Dec 1;5(6):207–10.

8. Jacórzyński B, Filutowicz H. [Excretion of carbohydrates by rats fed legume seeds]. Nahrung. 1982;26(10):875–85.

9. Dutchen S. "What Do Fats Do in the Body?." National Institute of Health. N.p., 15 2010. Web. 20 Nov 2012. <http://publications.nigms.nih.gov/insidelifescience/fats_do.html>.

10. Byrd-Bredbenner C , Beshgetoor D, and Berning J. Wardlaw's Perspectives in Nutrition. 9th. New York, NY, 2013. 205

11. Ramirez M, Amate L, Gil A. Absorption and distribution of dietary fatty acids from different sources. Early American Development. 2001; 96-99.

12. Bailen L. Pathophysiology of Diarrhea. Tufts University. 2007; 21.

13. Jan F, Glatz C, Joost J, Luiken P, Bonen Arend. Membrane Fatty Acid Transporters as Regulators of Lipid Metabolism: Implications for Metabolic Disease. Physiological Reviews. 90; 2010: 379-417.

14. Universal Protein Resource (UniProt). Long Chain Fatty Acid Transport Protein 1. Cited: 20 Nov 2012. Web. http://www.uniprot.org/uniprot/Q6PCB7#section_ref

15. Iqbal J, Hussain MM. Intestinal lipid absorption. Am J Physiol Endocrinol Metab. 2009; 296:1183-1194

16. Christie W. Plasma lipoproteins: composition, structure and biochemistry. LipidLibrary. 2012; 1-11. http://lipidlibrary.aocs.org/lipids/lipoprot/index.htm

17. Lass A, Zimmermann R, Oberer M, Zechner R. Lipolysis- A highly regulated multi- enzyme complex mediated the catabolism of cellular fat stores. Prog Lipid Res. 2011; 50: 14-27.

18. Kraemer F, Shen WJ. Hormone-sensitive lipase control of intracellular tria-(di-) acylglycerol and cholesteryl ester hydrolysis. J Lipid Res. 2002; 43: 1585-1594

19. Laffel L. Ketone bodies: a review of physiology, pathophysiology and application of monitoring to diabetes. Diabetes Metab Res Rev. 1999 Nov-Dec;15(6):412-26.

20. Numba, S. Fatty acid metabolism and its regulation. Netherlands, 1984. 127

21. Berg JM, Tymoczko JL, Stryer L. Section 22.3, certain fatty acids require additional steps for degradation. In: Biochemistry. 5th edition. New York: W H   Freeman; 2002. Available from: http://www.ncbi.nlm.nih.gov/books/NBK22387/

22. Isaacson D. Enterohepatic Recirculation. N.d. Drawing. n.p. Web. 30 Nov 2012. <http://isaacsondianaphysiology.wikispaces.com/18 Digestion>.

23. Bertoldi M, Cellini B, Montoli R, Volattorni CB. Insights into the mechanism of oxidative deamination catalyzed by DOPA decarboxylase. Biochemistry 2008 June; 47(27):7187-7195

24. Serrano M et al. Assessment of plasma ammonia and glutamine concentrations in urea cycle disorders. Clinical Biochemistry 2011 April; 44:742-744

25. Thongboonkerd V, Klein J, Pierce W, Jevans A, Arthur J. Sodium loading changes urinary protein excretion: a proteomic analysis. American Journal of Physiology-Renal Physiology 2003 June; 284(6):1155-1163

26. Nicolaides P, Liebasch D, Dale N, Leaonard J, Surtees R. Neurological outcome of patients with ornithine carbamoyltransferase deficiency. Arch Dis Child 2002; 86:54-56

27. Singh, R H. Nutritional management of patients with urea cycle disorders. J Inherit Metab Dis 2007 July; 30:880-887

28. Heerspink HJ, Gansevoort R, Brenner B, Cooper M, Parving H, Shahinfar S, de Zeeuw D. Comparison of different measures of urinary protein excretion for prediction of renal events. J Am Soc Nephrol 2010 Aug; 21(8):1355-1360

29. Torpy, Janet M; Lynm, Cassio; Glass, Richard M. Proteinuria. JAMA 2010 Feb; 303(5)

30. Druml W, Fischer M, Liebisch B, Lenz, K. Roth E. Elimination of amino acids in kidney failure. Am J Clin Nutr 1994; 60: 418-423

31. Otten J, Hellwig J, Meyers L. (2006). Dietary Reference Intakes: The Essential Guide to Nutrient Requirements. The National Academies Press, Washington, DC.

32. Hollenbeck CB. An introduction to the nutrition and metabolism of choline. Cent Nerv Syst Agents Med Chem. 2012;12(2):100-13.

33. Imai E, Sano M, Fukuwatari T, Shibata K. Urinary excretion of water-soluble vitamins increases in streptozotocin-induced diabetic rats without decreases in liver or blood vitamin content. J Nutr Sci Vitaminol (Tokyo). 2012;58(1):54-8

34. Fukuwatari T, Yoshida E, Takahashi K, Shibata K. Effect of fasting on the urinary excretion of water-soluble vitamins in humans and rats. J Nutr Sci Vitaminol (Tokyo). 2010;56(1):19-26.

35. Tsuji T, Fukuwatari T, Sasaki S, Shibata K. Urinary excretion of vitamin B1, B2, B6, niacin, pantothenic acid, folate, and vitamin C correlates with dietary intakes of free-living elderly, female Japanese. Nutr Res. 2010 Mar;30(3):171-8.

36. Stephensen, C B., Mette Kerstensen, Morten G. Jensen, Julie Aarestrup, Kristina E. Petersen, Lise Sondergaard, Mette S. Mickelsen, and Arne Astrup. "Flaxseed Dietary Fibers Lower Cholesterol and Increase Fecal Fat Excretion, but Magnitude of Effect Depend on Food Type." Nutrition and Metabolism 9.8 (2012): N. pag. Web.

37. Mitchell, H H., and T S. Hamilton. "THE DERMAL EXCRETION UNDER CONTROLLED ENVIRON- MENTAL CONDITIONS OF NITROGEN AND MINERALS IN HUMAN SUBJECTS." The Journal of Biological Chemistry (1948): N. pag. Web.

38. Institute Of Medicine. Dietary Reference Intakes for Vitamin A, Vitamin K, Arsenic, Boron, Chromium, Copper, Iodine, Iron, Manganese, Molybdenum, Nickel, Silicon, Vanadium and Zinc. Washington, D.C.: The National Academies Press, Web.

39. Stephensen, C B., J O. Alvarez, J Kohatsu, R Hardmeier, J I. Kennedy, and R B. Gammon. "The American Journal of Clinical Nutrition." Vitamin a Is Excreted in the Urine During Acute Infection. 60.3 (1994): 388-392. Web.

40. Wu, J H., and K D. Croft. "Vitamin E Metabolism." Molecular Aspects of Medicine 28.5-6 (2007): 437-452. Web.

41. Bourne, David W. "Biliary Excretion." A First Course In Pharmacokinetics And Biopharmaceutics. N.p., 12 Feb. 2001. Web. <A First Course in Pharmacokinetics and Biopharmaceutics>.

42. Magnesium (2012). Besthesda, MD: National Institutes of Health: Office of Dietary Supplements. doi: http://ods.od.nih.gov/factsheets/Magnesium-HealthProfessional/#ref

43. Sadeva, D., Heller, H., Orians, G., Purves, W., & Hillis, D. (2008). Life: The Science of Biology (8ed). Sunderland, MA: Sinauer Associates, Inc.

44. Ross, A., Taylor, C., Yaktine, A., & Del Valle, H. (Eds.). (2011). Dietary Reference Intakes for Calcium and Vitamin D. Washington, DC: The National Academies Press.

45. Topal, C., Algun, E., Sayarlioglu, H., Erkoc, R., Soyoral, Y., Dogan, E., Sekeroglu, R., Cekici, S. (2008) Diurnal Rhythm of Urinary Calcium Excretion in Adults. Renal Failure. 30:499-501. doi: http://jn.nutrition.org/content/141/3/391.full

46. Calcium (2012). Besthesda, MD: National Institutes of Health: Office of Dietary Supplements. doi: http://ods.od.nih.gov/factsheets/Calcium-QuickFacts/

47. Cao, J., Johnson, L., Hunt, J. (2011). A diet high in meat protein and potential renal acid load increases fractional calcium absorption and urinary calcium excretion without affecting markers of bone resorption or formation in postmenopausal women. J. Nutr. 141 (3): 391-397. doi: http://jn.nutrition.org/content/141/3/391.full

48. Kerstetter, J.E., (2009) Dietary protein and bone: a new approach to an old question. Am J Clin Nutr 90: 1451-1452; doi:10.3945/ajcn.2009.28812

49. Dickinson, B., & Havas, S., (2008, Feb). Cardiovascular disease, sodium intake, and urinary calcium loss— Reply. Arch Intern Med. 2008;168(3):332-333. doi:10.1001/archinternmed.2007.90.

50. Dlugaszek, M., Kaszczuk, M., & Mularezyk-Oliwa, M. (2011). Magnesium, calcium, and trace elements excretion in 24-h urine. Biol Trace Element Res, 142 (1): 1 – 10.

51. Woods RL. (2004) Cardioprotective functions of atrial natriuretic peptide. Clin Exper Pharmacol Physiol. 31: 791-794.

52. Ring T, Frische S, Nielsen S. (2005) Clinical review: renal tubular acidosis - a physicochemical approach. Critical Care 9: 573-580.

53. "Basic Iron Metabolism." Basic Iron Metabolism. N.p., n.d. Web. 03 Dec. 2013. <https://ahdc.vet.cornell.edu/clinpath/modules/chem/femetb.htm>.

54. "Dietary Supplement Fact Sheet: Iron." Office of Dietary Supplements. N.p., n.d. Web. 3 Dec. 2013. <http://ods.od.nih.gov/factsheets/Iron-HealthProfessional/>.

55. "Human Iron Metabolism." Wikipedia. Wikimedia Foundation, 24 Nov. 2013. Web. 03 Dec. 2013. <http://en.wikipedia.org/wiki/Human_iron_metabolism>.

56. "Iron and Iron Deficiency." Centers for Disease Control and Prevention. Centers for Disease Control and Prevention, 23 Feb. 2011. Web. 01 Dec. 2013. <http://www.cdc.gov/nutrition/everyone/basics/vitamins/iron.html>.

57. "Iron in Diet." The New York Times. N.p., 02 Mar. 2011. Web. 02 Dec. 2013. <http://www.nytimes.com/health/guides/nutrition/iron-in-diet/overview.html>

SECTION 2

Storage and Functions of Nutrients in Organ Systems: If intake is not constant, how are nutrients stored?

Authors:

Jonathan C. Allen, Sarah Brown, Raven Canady, Briana Massey, Rini Triani, Hind Sadis, Phillip Vaughn, Sopani R. Neba, Kimberly Palatini, Maryanne T. Perrin, Tierra Pressley, Jennifer Cole, Julie Chytka, Kristen Glossen, Eunice Kim, and Beverly Neffa, Kyle Craver, Mary Craver, Annie Lassiter, Neel Shah, George Stoforos, Stephanie Dill, Nazish Durrani Natalia Smith, Annita Wilborn, Christina Inserillo, Kyle Emery, Charles Giamberadino, Katie Shiraishi, Meaghan Bethea, and Weston Bussler

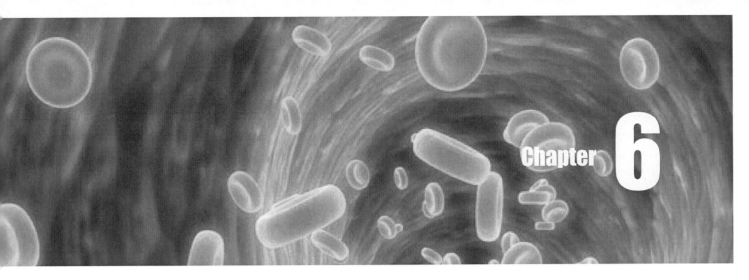

Chapter 6

Bone as a Storage Site Associated with Minerals and Vitamins

By Jonathan C. Allen, Shalimbala Chizonda, Caroline Dickson, Samantha Duxbury, Christian Johansson, Kayla Lawson, Danielle Lucas, and Larry Witt

Learning Objectives

Learning objectives: Students completing this chapter should be able to:

1. List food sources of vitamins and minerals associated with bone development.

2. Describe vitamin and mineral roles for nutrient storage in bones and teeth.

3. Recognize and explain the symptoms experienced by someone suffering from a deficiency of one or more of the vitamins and minerals associated with bone development.

4. Explain the physiological processes that allow minerals to be stored in and retrieved from bone.

6.1. Introduction: Functions and storage of nutrient in bone

Macrominerals are the major minerals found in the body, which are essential for life. Major minerals contribute to the hardness of bone and teeth, may serve as cofactors for metalloenzymes, and supply four percent of the total body weight [1].

The minerals that fall into the class of macrominerals are calcium, sodium, potassium, phosphorus, chloride and magnesium. Some of these minerals share similar roles in the body but each is independently important. All of these macrominerals must be taken in from the diet and then can be stored. Storage of these minerals is essential to provide an abundant supply for bone remodeling, cellular signaling, and muscle contraction.

6.2. Calcium

Calcium is the main mineral that makes up the human skeletal structure. It also plays a role in muscle contraction, blood clot formation, signal transduction and nerve transmission. Over ninety nine percent of calcium is stored in teeth and bones [2]. The remaining one percent is found in blood, muscle, tissue and extracellular fluid. Collectively, there are approximately 1,000 to 1,400 grams of calcium present within the human body [3]. Calcium flows through the body as a free divalent cation. It can be easily absorbed in the duodenum and jejunum in this free Ca^{2+} form [1]. The major source of calcium for human consumption is milk and dairy products. The average human receives approximately seventy three percent of consumed calcium from milk, nine percent from fruits and vegetables, and five percent from grains.

6.2.1 Regulation

Calcium homeostasis is monitored and regulated by parathyroid hormone, calcitriol and calcitonin. Low blood calcium signals to parathyroid gland to release parathyroid hormone into the blood. Parathyroid hormone binds to a receptor on the cell surface of bone cells and triggers the re-absorption of bone mineral. Parathyroid hormone also acts on the kidneys and signals the synthesis of calcitriol. These two molecules will cause re-absorption of calcium from the kidney to the blood.

6.2.2. *Storage*

The main function that calcium provides in the body is bone mineralization. It makes up the hydroxyapatite, which is structurally the hardest part of the bone, as it incorporates minerals and proteins that make up the bone matrix. This brings structure and rigidity to the skeleton. Osteoblasts are the cells responsible for the actual building of the bone [3]. These cells will eventually be absorbed into the bone matrix as osteocytes, furthering the stability of the bone. The building of the bone begins when the osteoblast cells set down a layer of phosphorus, followed by calcium that binds to the phosphorus. Together they form $Ca_3(PO_4)_2$, the binding agent that stiffens a network of collagen and other structural proteins. Magnesium and carbonate are also found bound within the bone matrix [1]. The other structural proteins included in the bone composition are glycoproteins and proteoglycans [3]. Figure 6.2.1 illustrates the location of the osteoblasts and osteocytes for more detail.

As we age, our bones do not mineralize as fast as they are broken down. Our bones display more activity by osteoclasts, which are the cells of the bone that exhibit the 'breaking-down' activity. This leads to osteoporosis, especially in older women. However, research shows that an increase in physical activity and a balanced diet at a young age will help to increase

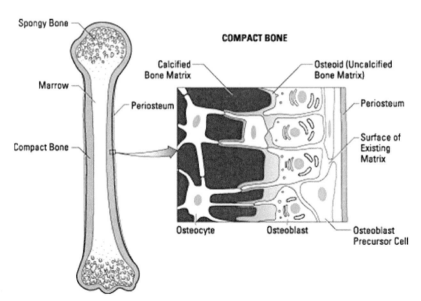

Figure 6.2-1: Osteoblast activity during bone mineralization. From http://player.slideplayer.com/23/6894269/#

bone strength. This increase in bone density early in the early stages of life has shown to have beneficial effects as an individual ages and bone formation is not as efficient [4].

The other functions of calcium include mineral homeostasis, signaling, and blood clotting. One percent of calcium in the human body is found circulating within the blood. This can be attributed to the continuous turnover consisting of degradation and rebuilding of our bone. This ionized calcium in the serum plays a major role in the signaling of nerve communication and muscle contraction. Calcium may also bind to lipids and proteins when clotting is necessary [3].

In order to replenish serum calcium concentrations, sodium and potassium increase calcium excretion, which leads to an accelerated bone resorption. In addition to sodium and potassium, caffeine has also been shown to increase calcium excretion. Conversely, protein in the diet has been shown to possibly enhance calcium absorption during digestion due to the increased acid content in the digest. However, protein increases urinary excretion of the calcium as well [3].

Calcium is primarily stored as the hydroxyapatite of bone. The hydroxyapatite is a crystal latticelike substance found in bone bound to protein and ground substance [1]. A small percentage of calcium is also stored within the endoplasmic reticulum in cells throughout the body. These calcium stores are released in response to depolarization, neurotransmitter signaling or hormonal signaling. Calcium is sequestered in the endoplasmic reticulum and released upon signaling as a second messenger. These intracellular stores are no longer just considered a place for storage. The endoplasmic reticulum and the mitochondria calcium stores can have regulatory functions [5]. The endoplasmic reticulum and its derived organelles (sarcoplasmic reticulum in muscle) release calcium upon the binding of inositol triphosphate to inositol triphosphate gated receptors on the endoplasmic reticulum surface. The calcium release is augmented by the binding of calcium to ryanodine receptors on the cytoplasmic side of the endoplasmic reticulum. This is pathway is activated by ionotropic glutamate receptors or voltage gated calcium channels in the cell membrane [5]. Calcium within the cell serves an extremely important function for gene regulation and expression or neuronal signaling [6].

6.2.3. Deficiency

Because of the essential role calcium plays in bone formation and regeneration, and intracellular signaling, adequate calcium intake is essential. Osteoporosis is the reduction of bone mass, increased fragility of bone, and an increased risk of having a bone fracture [2]. With decreased calcium intake, intracellular storage takes precedence and there is less calcium stored in the bone, resulting in the decreased bone mass.

6.3. Phosphorus

Phosphorus is the body's second most abundant mineral. Approximately eighty five percent of phosphorus in the body is found in bones. The remaining fifteen percent is stored in soft tissues [2]. The human body holds an average of 650 grams of phosphate at one time. It is largely in the form of calcium phosphate ($Ca(H_2PO_4)_2$), or the more complex mineral, hydroxyapatite, which is found in bones and teeth. The functions of phosphorus include: bone mineralization, energy transfer and storage, nucleic acid formation, and cell membrane structure. Phosphorus is an important part of adenosine triphosphate (ATP) and also an intricate portion of our cell membranes in the form of phospholipids [7].

Calcium phosphate in the form of hydroxyapatite is the main constituent of bone that is responsible for its structure and rigidity. Phosphorus is the first layer of the hydroxyapatite, followed by calcium. Inadequate levels of phosphorus inhibit osteoblast activity and therefore hinder bone formation [2].

Phosphorus is essential for life because it provides the phosphate groups for nucleic acids, nucleotides, and phospholipids, which make up biological membranes. Functionally, phosphorus serves as a buffer to maintain normal pH throughout the body. It also acts to transfer energy from metabolic fuels. The hydrolysis of the high energy bond in adenosine triphosphate provides metabolic energy [1].

Phosphorus is an important structural part of DNA, RNA and cell membranes. When examining DNA and RNA, phosphorus is the main structural component within each molecule. Phosphorous in cell membranes combine with lipids to form phospholipids. These bring fluidity and structure to the cell membrane, acting as a buffer between the cell and the extracellular fluid. Phospholipids are made up of a glycerol, two fatty acids, and a phosphate group [1].

Calcium phosphate has been identified as a possible carrier of antibodies, proteins, and other substances into the cell. Without such a carrier, the cell takes up substantially lesser amounts of these substances. This is an area that warrants further research and can be beneficial for future work relating to proteins and genes inside of the cell [8].

Phosphorus is found in pentavalent form attached to oxygen in the body [2] but is absorbed in the gastrointestinal tract as inorganic phosphate. Because phosphate groups are constantly being added and removed from molecules, phosphorus can be recycled indefinitely [2]. Phosphorus is found in meat, poultry, fish, eggs, milk, and dairy foods. It can also be used as a food additive in the form of phosphate salts.

Phosphorus is another macromineral that has a crucial role in the cell as a second messenger. Cyclic adenosine monophosphate (cAMP) is a second messenger for G- protein coupled receptor activated cells [1]. Cyclic adenosine monophosphate affects cellular metabolism by activating protein kinases. Cyclic guanosine monophosphate (cGMP) also serves a second messenger and can activate protein kinases that regulate gene expression. Lastly, phosphorus is a component of inositol triphosphate (IP3), another second messenger. Inositol triphosphate is a product of the cleavage of phosphotidylinositol 4,5, bisphosphate (PIP2) by phospholipase C [9]. As mentioned above, inositol triphosphate triggers the opening of intracellular calcium channels within the endoplasmic reticulum [6].

6.4. Magnesium

Magnesium is another important element involved in the makeup of bone. There are approximately 25 grams of magnesium found within the body, with over half of the body's store of magnesium found in bone. A reservoir of magnesium is found in skeletal muscle as well [2]. Bone and skeletal muscle provide all the available magnesium in the body. Magnesium can be released from these stores in times of deficiency. Magnesium is least abundant of the six macrominerals, but is nonetheless important. Magnesium is found in

unpolished grains, nuts, legumes, water, and leafy green vegetables [1].

Magnesium is yet another key element that makes up the hydroxyapatite, in addition to the phosphorus and calcium. It is deposited within the bone during bone formation and can also be found on the surface of the bone. The magnesium found on the bone surface can be utilized in cases of low serum levels of magnesium [1]. Over half of the magnesium found in bone is $Mg(OH)_2$ or $Mg_3(PO_4)_2$. A deficiency in magnesium can result in bone degradation, much like the deficiency calcium would cause. Lower serum levels of calcium and magnesium are observed succeeding a broken bone, demonstrating the importance of magnesium formation of new bone [10].

Magnesium found within the cell is used for the generation of ATP. It acts to stabilize the phosphate groups of ATP, aiding in oxidative phosphorylation located within the mitochondria. Magnesium is also utilized in the activation of proteins during DNA and RNA synthesis and repair. Synthesis of DNA and RNA is hindered during times of magnesium deficiency [11]. The sodium potassium ATPase pump is also magnesium dependent. More specifically, it promotes the movement of potassium out of the cells. This may explain the link between higher intakes of magnesium and a reduction in hypertension and risks of stroke. Although studies have shown mixed results, magnesium is thought to play a role in the regulation and lowering of blood pressure due to the promotion of potassium absorption and as a consequence, excretion of sodium. This is an area of research that warrants further study [2].

Hypomagnesemia has been shown in individuals with type II diabetes. Magnesium plays an important role in the metabolism of glucose. Low levels will impede the ability of insulin receptors and increase blood calcium levels promoting insulin resistance. Martini et al, [12] suggested that magnesium supplements may help to reduce insulin resistance and better manage an individual's diabetes.

Magnesium is absorbed as a divalent cation from the small intestine. It circulates free in plasma or bound to proteins. Magnesium has a high concentration within the cells, second behind potassium [1].

Magnesium is involved in over 300 enzymatic reactions including any reaction that results in the generation of ATP [2]]. Moreover, magnesium has a role in the synthesis of DNA, regulation of blood pressure, and glucose metabolism. Magnesium couples to adenosine triphosphate (ATP) or adenosine diphosphate (ADP) and plays a role in anaerobic and aerobic energy generation. The mitochondria require magnesium to complete oxidative phosphorylation. Lastly, magnesium acts a "naturally occurring physiological calcium channel blocker" [2]. With excess magnesium present, calcium channels cannot open. In states of magnesium depletion, calcium channels can open and intracellular calcium channels will rise. Magnesium is also associated with beta oxidation, glycolysis, the citric acid cycle, DNA synthesis and degradation, replication, and transcription. With so many different responsibilities, it is easy to see how important magnesium is to the human life [1].

6.5. Sodium

Thirty percent of sodium is located on the bone surface and the rest is found in extracellular fluid, interstitial fluid, and intracellular fluid in nerves and muscle tissue [1]. The major dietary source of sodium is salt. The average American receives more than enough sodium, due to processed food and excess salt consumption.

6.6 Fluoride

Fluoride is not essential for proper functioning of the body, however, it has an important role in the prevention of dental caries. When it combines with calcium and phosphate complexes to form hydroxyflouroappatite, it hardens bones and teeth. In the United States, the most abundant source of fluoride is fluoridated water. Fluoride can also be obtained through consumption of seafood, seaweed, teas, and the use of fluoridated toothpastes. The AI is currently set at 3 mg/day and 4 mg/day for adult women and men, respectively [2]. The AI for infants less than six months old is 0.01 mg/day, 0.5 mg/day for infants between six and twelve months old and 0.7-3 mg/day for young children and teens. The AI was established based on the average amount of fluoride needed to protect against dental caries without causing fluorosis.

After ingestion, absorption occurs very rapidly by passive diffusion in the stomach.

Fluoride then leaves the blood in a rapid manner, is distributed throughout the body, and stored primarily in the bones and teeth. The fluoride associated with bone is found either in the amorphous or crystalline state. In the crystalline state, fluoride is sequestered by apatite. Storage within the body increases in relation to the amount of fluoride ingested and absorbed, however, when large amounts are absorbed, urinary excretion increases [13]. Young individuals experiencing skeletal growth utilize more fluoride and excrete less than older individuals who are not experiencing growth [1].

Low fluoride intakes have been linked to a greater number of dental caries, however, there have been no specific diseases or conditions reported as a result of fluoride deficiency. Alternatively, overdose and toxicity is a dangerous threat, especially to young children. The most common toxicity incidents involve the ingestion of large amounts of fluoride toothpaste or tablets. Acute toxicity is uncommon but indications include nausea, vomiting, diarrhea, convulsions, and death. Furthermore, long term excessive fluoride intake during tooth development can result in fluorosis [14]. For this reason, an Upper Level of 0.1 mg/kg of body weight/day has been set for infants and kids less than eight years old. The UL for individuals over the age of eight is set at 10 mg/day [2].

6.7 Role of Vitamin D in maintaining body calcium stores

In all ages, vitamin D is associated with skeletal growth and strong bones. Children especially have to ingest an adequate amount of vitamin D to develop strong bones and healthy teeth. Vitamin D works by increasing the amount of calcium absorbed and aids to form and maintain bones. Vitamin D, (also known as calciferol and recognized as a prohormone) is a group of fat-soluble steroids and it is classified as a seco-steroid. It has several different forms (**Figure 6.7.1**), but ergocalciferol (Vitamin D2) and cholecalciferol (vitamin D3) are the most important in humans. Vitamin D2 (ergocalciferol) is found in certain plants and is chemically synthesized, and vitamin D3(cholecalciferol) is synthesized by animals and is found in animal-based foods.

6.7.1. Functions of Vitamin D

Vitamin D enhances calcium absorption in the gut and maintains adequate serum calcium and phosphate to support normal growth and mineralization of bone. It is also necessary for bone growth and bone remodeling by osteoblasts and osteoclasts. Without an adequate amount of vitamin D, bones can become thin, fragile, and malformed.

Vitamin D adequacy prevents rickets in children and osteomalacia in adults. Vitamin D plus calcium can help protect older adults from osteoporosis. It is also has an important roles in modification of cell growth, neuromuscular, and immune function, and reduction of inflammation. Vitamin D also has role in genes encoding proteins that regulate cell proliferation, differentiation, and apoptosis. Many cells have vitamin D receptors and some convert 25(OH)-D (calcidiol) to 1,25(OH)-D (calcitriol). Serum concentration on 25(OH)-D is the best indicator of Vitamin D status.

6.7.2. Metabolism

Vitamin D can be absorbed into the body either via the skin (endogenous source) or via the digestive tract. Endogenous sources of vitamin D is started with exposure of skin to ultraviolet light with wavelengths between 290 and 315 nm (UV-B) which converts some of the cholesterol precursor to provitamins D3, which then rearranges spontaneously to vitamin D3. A dose that does not cause sunburn or suberythemal irradiation of skin with UV-B was found to convert about one-

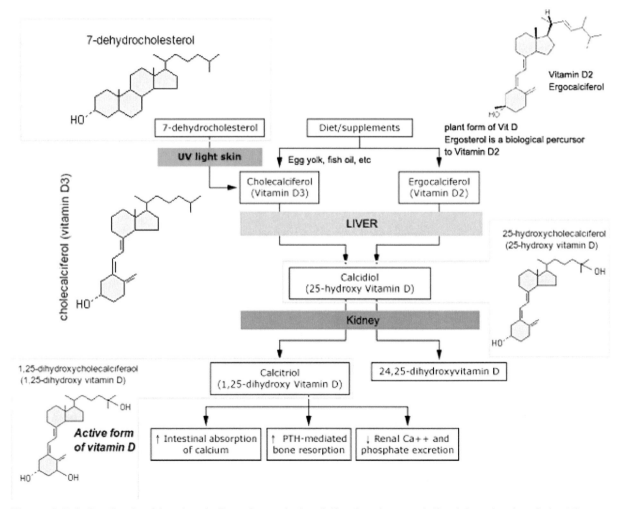

Figure 6.7-1: Synthesis of the vitamin D analogs, cholecalciferol and ergocalciferol, in animal and plant tissues. From http://www.globalrph.com/vitamin_d.htm

third of endogenous cholesterol precursor to vitamin D3. UV-B inactivates some of the newly generated vitamin D and its unstable precursors [15].

The amount of sun exposure an individual needs to produce vitamin D varies based on skin color, age, time of day, season, and geographical location. It is recommended that people sun bath their hands, feet, arms, and face 2-3 times per week for a period of 30-50% the time it takes to sunburn.

Vitamin D is highly fat-soluble and becomes part of the mixed micelles (consisting mainly of bile acids, phospholipids, fatty acids and mono- and diglycerides) during fat digestion. Nearly all the ingested vitamin D is absorbed. The vitamin enters the small intestinal cell along with fatty acids and other lipid. Chylomicrons then carry vitamin D into lymph vessels and eventually into blood circulation. The liver takes up about half of the triglyceride-depleted chylomicrons. Bone marrow and bone take up about 20% and other extrahepatic tissues clear the remainder. Vitamin D and all its normal metabolites in blood are bound to vitamin D-binding protein (DBP). Almost all of the vitamin D in circulation is 25-hydroxy-vitamin D; much smaller amounts are in the forms of 1,25-dihydroxy-vitamin D. It has been known that because of their high fat solubility, most of vitamin D metabolites can cross plasma membranes by simple diffusion.

Vitamin D is metabolized extensively in liver and kidneys. The first hydroxylation of vitamin D3 (cholecalciferol) occurs primarily in the liver. The active compound of vitamin D is 1,25-(OH)2 D3, which is formed in kidney tubules through the action of 25- OH-D3-1-α-hydroxylase, a mitochondrial mixed-function oxidase. This hydroxylation requires NADPH as a coenzyme. 1,25-(OH)2 D3 is believed to function like a steroid hormone, and this hormone has many target tissues, including intestine, bone, kidney and the heart. Upon reaching its target tissues, the hormone is easily released from DBP and quickly bound by its receptor. The primary function of 1,25-(OH)2 D3 in the intestine is increased absorption of calcium and phosphorous, the vitamin acts as a steroid hormone that initiates synthesis and translation of a protein in intestinal mucosa called calbindin-D. In addition to its genomic actions, 1,25-(OH)2 D3 also appears to produce a very rapid nongenomic stimulation of Ca transport.

In bone and kidney, the principal function of the vitamin appears to be the stimulation of transcellular transport of calcium across cell membranes. Vitamin D plays a major role in the parathyroid-directed mobilization of calcium from bone and is involved in the parathyroid stimulation of calcium absorption in the distal renal tubule. Vitamin D exerts its influence on bone mineralization primarily through supersaturating the plasma with calcium and phosphorous. Vitamin D also is required for the modeling and remodeling of bone because of its stimulation of osteoclast-mediated bone resorption. The more rapid, short term effect of the hormone probably is to release osteoblast-derived resorption factors, which stimulates osteoclast activity. The production of 1,25-(OH)2 D3 by the kidney is carefully regulated by the body's need for calcium [16].

When the blood calcium level drops, it triggers the secretion of parathyroid hormone from chief cells of parathyroid gland. Parathyroid hormone increases the levels of calcitriol in the body by stimulating the enzyme 1- hydroxylase, which converts 25-hydroxycholecalciferol into 1,25 dihydroxy-cholecalciferol, or calcitriol (the active form of vitamin D). Parathyroid hormone and calcitriol together increase calcium absorption from the intestinal lumen, increase calcium reabsorption from the kidneys while decreasing its excretion in the urine, and promote resorption of calcium and phosphate from bone. All these metabolic effects of parathyroid hormone and vitamin D cumulatively increase blood calcium concentration (**Figure 6.7.2**).

Calcitriol interacts with vitamin D receptors in the cell membrane and nucleus of various tissues. The mechanism of action is best elucidated in the intestine. The process begins with interaction of vitamin D with vitamin D receptors present in the enterocytes. Vitamin D binds with these high affinity receptors, vitamin D binding receptors (VDR) and makes a VDR-calcitriol complex. The complex travels to the nucleus where it up-regulates the genes responsible for the production of calcium transport proteins. Calcitriol-VDR complex makes a heterodimer complex with the retinoic acid receptor RXR that then binds to the promoter region of DNA on a specific gene (**Figure 6.7.3**) [17]. One such gene codes for a protein called Calbindin D9K, a protein responsible for increasing enterocyte calcium absorption and also transporting calcium across the intestinal mucosal cells towards the basolateral membrane. Calcium channels, such as TRPV6 in the brush border of enterocytes, are also up-regulated [1].

Current model for the control of vitamin D receptor (VDR)-mediated actions of 1,25(OH)2D3. The bioactivated vitamin D hormone 1,25(OH)2D3, circulates bound to the DBP. 1,25(OH)2D3 taken up by target cells is either targeted by IDBPs to mitochondrial 24-hydroxylase or the VDR. The 1,25(OH)2D3-VDR complex heterodimerizes with RXR, and the VDR/RXR heterodimer binds specific sequences in the promoter regions of the target gene. The DNA-bound heterodimer attracts components of the RNA polymerase II (Pol II) preinitiation complex and nuclear transcription regulators, thereby altering the rate of gene transcription. The 1,25(OH)2D3-VDR complex interaction with SUG1 targets the VDR for proteasomal degradation. Calreticulin interaction with the DNA-binding domain of the VDR sequesters the VDR, preventing transactivation.

In the kidney, another calcium transport protein may be synthesized in response to calcitriol to increase reabsorption of calcium. In the bone, calcitriol stimulates osteoblasts to produce a receptor activator that in turn increases production and maturation of osteoclasts. Osteoclasts then increase their activity to break down bone and release calcium and phosphorous into the blood [1].

6.7.3 Storage

Dietary vitamin D (D2 or D3) (**Fig. 6.7.1.**) is absorbed with other dietary fats in the small intestine. About 40% of vitamin D is transported into the blood by chylomicrons.

Some of vitamin D may transferred from the chylomicron to vitamin D- binding protein. Adipose tissues, muscle, and other tissues take the vitamin from the chylomicrons and the rest of it is delivered to the liver. Overweight or obese people store more of the vitamin in adipose tissue than people who have a normal weight. Thus, overweight people with low vitamin D status need larger doses of the vitamin to reach appropriate serum concentrations than people

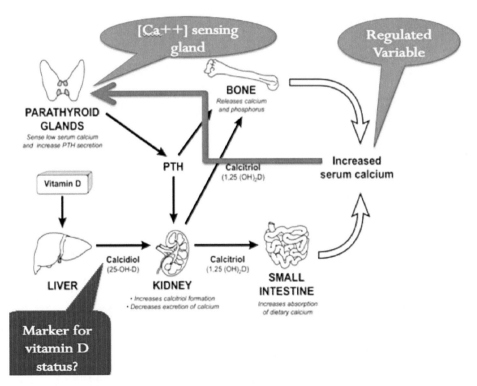

Figure 6.7-2: Calcitriol and parathyroid hormone increase blood calcium.
Modified from http://lpi.oregonstate.edu/infocenter/minerals/calcium/capth.html.

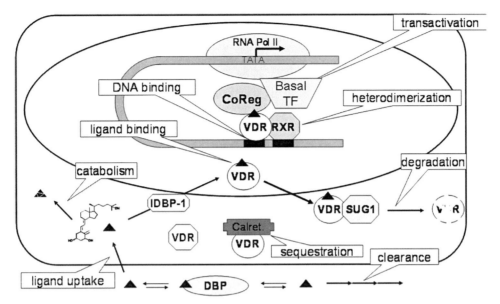

Figure 6.7-3: Calcitriol's effects on gene expression. From: Vitamin D, Amer J Physiol, Renal Physiology, Adriana S. Dusso, Alex J. Brown, and Eduardo Slatopolsky, doi: 10.1152/ajprenal.00336.2004AJP - Renal Physiol 2005 vol. 289 no. 1 F8-F28
From http://ajprenal.physiology.org/content/289/1/F8

with normal weight. Vitamin D3 that is made in the skin slowly extends from the skin into the blood and is transported by the hepatically synthesized vitamin D-binding protein (DBP). About half of plasma vitamin D is complexed with DBP and can be picked up by muscle adipose tissue, liver, and other tissues on its way to being hydroxylated by cytochrome P-450 related hydroxylases, which generate vitamin D's active form. Calcidiol can be converted into calcitriol, which is the biologically active form of vitamin D in the kidneys or monocyte macrophages of the immune system. Calcidiol acts as defense against microbial invaders when monocytes/macrophages convert it to calcitriol, which stimulates release of an antibacterial peptide. Calcitriol circulates as a hormone when synthesized in the kidneys. Vitamin D is excreted through the bile into the feces and, to a lesser extent, water-soluble metabolites are excreted via the urine.

6.7.4 Sources of Vitamin D

There is not much food in nature that contains vitamin D. A small number of foods of animal origin provide vitamin D such as, beef liver, eggs, cheese, and butter, but the last two contain small amounts of vitamin D3, which is the form that is found in all these sources, because milk is a poor source of vitamin D. Some plant-origin foods, such as mushrooms, provide vitamin D2. Since few foods contain vitamin D, fortified foods provide most of our intake. For example, milk, yogurt, margarine, some orange juice, breads, and breakfast cereals are fortified. Most vitamin D supplements contain vitamin D3.

6.7.5. RDA and Deficiency of Vitamin D

Recommended Dietary Allowances (RDA) for vitamin D (**Table 6.1.2**) suggest for adolescents and adults, including women who are pregnant and lactating, and children age 1 year and older an intake of 600 IU (15 µg) of vitamin D per day. The RDA increases to 800 IU (20 µg) of vitamin D for adults older than 70 years.

Deficiency is usually the result of inadequate intake when exposure to sunlight is limited. Milk allergy, and lactose intolerance are risk factors for vitamin D- deficient diets. Rickets and osteomalacia are the common vitamin D deficiency diseases. Rickets is a disease characterized by a failure of bone tissue to properly mineralize resulting in soft bone and skeletal deformities. Exclusive breast-feeding for

TABLE 6.7-1: Vitamin D RDAs [5].

Recommended Dietary Allowance (RDA) for Vitamin D Set by the Institute of Medicine			
Life Stage	Age	Males mcg/day (IU/day)	Females mcg/day (IU/day)
Infants	0-6 months	10 mcg (400 IU) (AI)	10 mcg (400 IU) (AI)
Infants	6-12 months	10 mcg (400 IU) (AI)	10 mcg (400 IU) (AI)
Children	1-3 years	15 mcg (600 IU)	15 mcg (600 IU)
Children	4-8 years	15 mcg (600 IU)	15 mcg (600 IU)
Children	9-13 years	15 mcg (600 IU)	15 mcg (600 IU)
Adolescents	14-18 years	15 mcg (600 IU)	15 mcg (600 IU)
Adults	19-50 years	15 mcg (600 IU)	15 mcg (600 IU)
Adults	51-70 years	15 mcg (600 IU)	15 mcg (600 IU)
Adults	71 years and older	20 mcg (800 IU)	20 mcg (800 IU)
Pregnancy	all ages	-	15 mcg (600 IU)
Breast-feeding	all ages	-	15 mcg (600 IU)

long periods without vitamin D supplementation is a significant cause of rickets. The extensive use of sunscreens is a contributing factor for rickets. Vitamin D deficiency can lead to ostemalacia in adults. Weak bone, bone pain, and muscle weakness are symptoms of osteomalacia.

6.7.5.1 Toxicity

Excessive ingestion of vitamin D can result in Vitamin D toxicity which is when large amounts, such as 10,000 IU or more per day over a long time is consumed. Toxicity seems related to increased oxidation of membranes and deposition of calcium in soft tissues. The Tolerable Upper Intake Level for vitamin D is 4,000 IU (100 μg) for children age 9 years and older, adolescents, and adults. Excessive exposure to sunlight may be a cause of skin cancer, but not hypervitaminosis D. Hyperkalemia and calcinosis, the associated calcification of soft tissues in organs such as the kidneys, heart, lungs, and blood vessels, are symptoms of vitamin D toxicity. Toxicity can also cause hypophosphatemia, anorexia, nausea, weakness, headache, renal dysfunction, and sometimes death.

6.7.6 Assessment

The level of the vitamin (25-OH D_3) provides reasonable index. Normal plasma concentration of 25-OH D_3 ranges from 10-80 ng/ml. A level less than 5 ng/ml is regarded as an indicator for vitamin D

theraphy. Because endogenous cholecalciferol can be stored in extrahepatic tissues such as fat and muscles, the circulating 25-OH D_3 does not fully reflect the extent of storage [16].

6.8 Vitamin K

Vitamin K exists in three main forms: phylloquinone from plants, menaquinone from bacteria, and synthetic menadiones (**Figure 6.8.1**). Vitamin K is most known for its role in blood clotting, but it also has a major role in the mineralization of bone. Both of these functions result from vitamin K's ability to carboxylate glutamic acid in proteins. Other lesser defined roles for vitamin K include apoptosis, arterial calcification, signal transduction, and growth control [1].

6.8.1 Vitamin K in bone, cartilage, and dentineets k

Vitamin K is required for the function of two proteins found in bone, cartilage, and dentine. Vitamin K plays a role in carboxylation of glutamic acid to form γ-carboxyglutamate in proteins that form the structure matrix for bone. Oxidized vitamin K quinone is reduced by reductases to vitamin KH_2, which can carboxylate glutamic acid with the addition of carbon dioxide and oxygen. This reaction also produces a vitamin K epoxide, which is then reduced back to a quinone, and the cycle can start again (**Figure 6.8.2**) [1]. Osteocalcin

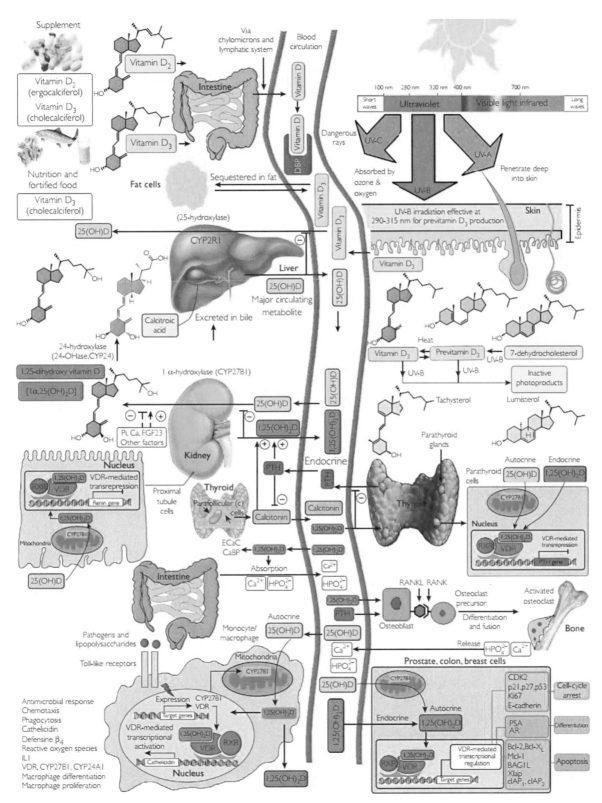

Figure 6.8-1: Inter-organ metabolic pathways for vitamin D.
From http://www.vitamindwiki.com/dl2610&display

is a major protein found in bone and is secreted by osteoblasts during bone formation. Matrix Gla protein is found in bone, dentine, and cartilage and is involved in the mobilization of bone calcium and prevention of calcification of soft tissues [1]. The carboxylic acid side chains on these proteins form a crystallization point that begins the precipitation of calcium phosphate that later matures into the mineral component of bone.

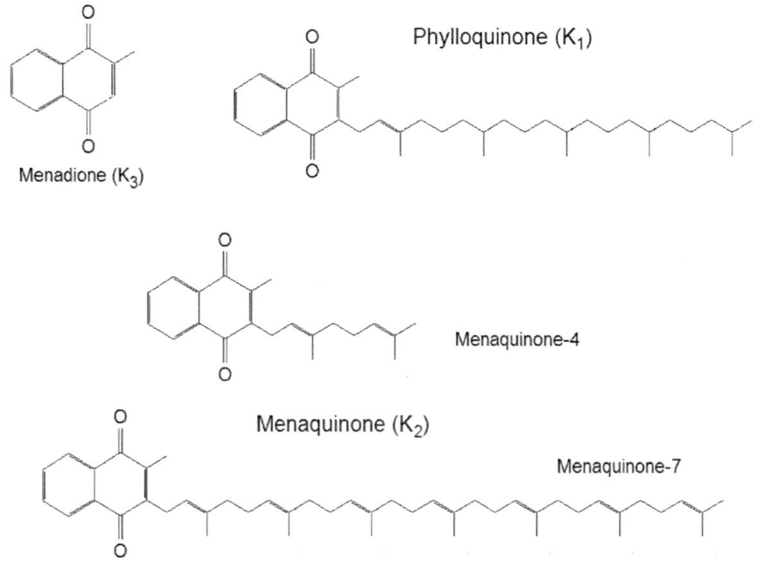

Figure 6.8-2: Structures of phylloquinone, menadione, and menaquinones.
Source: www.robertbarrington.net

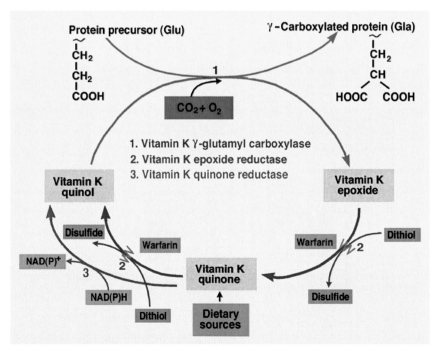

Figure 6.8-3: The vitamin K cycle results in the carboxylation of glutamate residues.
From http://www.bloodjournal.org/content/108/6/1795?sso-checked=true

6.8.2 *Vitamin K imbalance*

The AI for vitamin K is 120 μg/day for men and 90 μg/day for women. Deficiency is uncommon, occurring most often in people with fat malabsorptive disorders or those taking antibiotics over a long term. There is no UL for vitamin K, as there are no symptoms associated with high dietary intake [1].

6.9. References

1. Gropper S, Smith J, Groff J. Microminerals. In: Advanced nutrition and human metabolism. 5th ed. Belmont, CA: Wadsworth: 2009: 469-535.

2. Standing Committee on the Scientific Evaluation of Dietary Reference Intakes, Food and Nutrition Board, Institute of Medicine. Dietary Reference Intakes for Calcium, Phosphorus, Magnesium, Vitamin D, and Fluoride. Washington, DC: The National Academies Press, 1997. <http://www.nap.edu/openbook.php?record_id=5776>

3. Ross, A., Manson, J. E., Abrams, S. A., Aloia, J. F., Brannon, P. M., Clinton, S. K., &... Shapses, S. A. (2011). The 2011 Dietary Reference Intakes for Calcium and Vitamin D: What Dietetics Practitioners Need to Know [*] [*]

4. Czeczelewski, J. J., Dugoecka, B. B., & Raczyn´ska, B. B. (2011). Intake of calcium and phosphorus and levels of bone mineralization (BMC) and mineral bone density (BMD) of female swimmers in the pubescence period. Polish Journal of Food and Nutrition Sciences, 61(2), 137-142.

5. Rose, Christine R., and Arthur Konnerth. (2001) Stores not just for storage: Intracellular calcium release and synaptic plasticity. Neuron 31: 519-522. Web. 05 Dec. 2012.

6. Putney, JW. Signaling pathways between the plasma membrane and endoplasmic reticulum calcium stores."Cellular and Molecular Life Sciences 57.8-9 (2000): 1272-1286. Web. 05 Dec. 2012.

7. Childers, D. L., Corman, J., Edwards, M., & Elser, J. J. (2011). Sustainability challenges of phosphorus and food: solutions from closing the human phosphorus cycle. Bioscience, 61(2), 117-124. doi:10.1525/bio.2011.61.2.6

8. Sokolova, V., Rotan, O., Klesing, J., Nalbant, P., Buer, J., Knuschke, T., & ... Epple, M. (2012). Calcium phosphate nanoparticles as versatile carrier for small and large molecules across cell membranes. Journal of Nanoparticle Research, 14(6), 1-10. doi:10.1007/s11051-012-0910-9

9. Boron, Walter F., and Emile L. Boulpaep. Medical Physiology. Philadelphia, PA: Saunders, 2012. Print.

10. Bacher, M. M., Sztanke, M. M., Sztanke, K. K., & Pasternak, K. K. (2010). Plasma calcium and magnesium concentrations in patients with fractures of long bones treated surgically. Journal of Elementology, 15(1), 5-17.

11. Pasternak, K. K., Kocot, J. J., & Horecka, A. A. (2010). Biochemistry of magnesium. Journal of Elementology, 15(3), 601-616.

12. Martini, L. A., Catania, A. S., & Ferreira, S. G. (2010). Role of vitamins and minerals in prevention and management of type 2 diabetes mellitus. Nutrition Reviews, 68(6), 341-354. doi:10.1111/j.1753-4887.2010.00296.x

13. Whitford G, Williams J. (1986) Fluoride absorption: Independence from plasma fluoride levels. Proc Soc Exp Biol Med. 181:550-54.

14. Byrd-Bredbenner C, Moe G, Beshgetoor D, Berning J. Trace Minerals. In: Wardlaw's perspectives in nutrition. 8th ed. New York, NY: Mc-Graw-Hill: 2009: 534-571.

15. Kohlmeier, M. (2003) Fat-soluble vitamins and non-nutrients. In: Nutrient Metabolism. 1st ed. San Diego, CA. Academic Press: 464-501

16. Hunt, S.M. & Groff, J. L. (1990) The Vitamins Part 2: The Fat-soluble vitamins. In: Advanced Nutrition and Human Metabolism. 8th ed. St. Paul, MN. West Publishing Company: 226-252

17. Dusso AS, Brown AJ, Slatopolsky E. (2005) Vitamin D. American Journal of Physiology - Renal Physiology, 289(1): 8 - 28

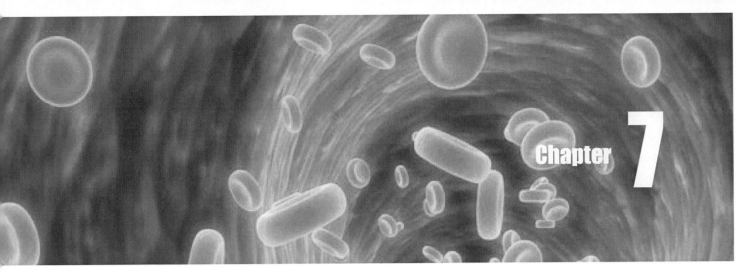

Chapter 7

Storage of Nutrients in Visceral Organs and Muscle.

Learning Objectives

After reading this chapter, you will be able to:

1. Identify tissues containing high concentration of various vitamins and minerals that have short and long term storage in internal organs.

2. Briefly describe functions vitamin A and carotenoids, vitamin E, vitamin C, thiamin, niacin, cobalamin, iron, zinc, copper, manganese, iodine, selenium, chromium, molybdenum and ultratrace minerals in metabolic processes in internal organs.

3. Describe the role of protein in building the contractile apparatus of muscle.

4. Describe the concept of whole body protein turnover and explain its role in protein storage.

5. List other nutrients or metabolites that have important role in muscle protein turnover, muscle growth, or sarcopenia.

7.1. Introduction: Visceral Tissue Distributions and Fat-Soluble Vitamins

When various tissues in the body are analyzed for their content of minerals and vitamins, the highest concentrations frequently occur in internal organs such as kidney, liver, adrenal, or thyroid glands. This concentration might be due to the physiological need for these micronutrients as cofactors in biochemical pathways that help these tissues carry out their specialized functions. In contrast, tissues that make up a larger share of the total body mass, may represent the greater share to the total quantity of these micronutrients ion the body, even though the amount of nutrient per gram of tissue is lower than in some other organs. The reference 54 kg female and 70 kg male are comprised of tissues in the decreasing order of muscle, adipose, blood, skin or bone marrow, and liver. Individuals with greater obesity have an increasing proportion of the body made up of adipose tissue, whereas the fractional weight of muscle, blood, liver, kidney, and brain decline with increasing body mass (or body mass index) [1]. Storage of nutrients in bone was discussed in the previous section. The nutrients discussed in this section are largely stored in internal organs such as adipose, liver, and kidney. Muscle will be discussed in the next section, with emphasis on the function, synthesis and turnover of muscle protein, along with micronutrients that have significant concentrations in muscle, and hence, in muscle foods. The following chapter will then describe the functions of particular micronutrients that are important for maintaining the appropriate concentrations of cells, and other functional constituents of blood. Some nutrients have relevance to each of these tissue-based sections.

Fat-soluble vitamins (A, D, E, and K) are vitamins that dissolve in fat and oils and are excluded from the aqueous phase of tissues, except when bound to a soluble agent, such as a protein. Fat-soluble vitamins are retained in the body for a longer period of time than water-soluble vitamins and can be stored in fatty tissue and liver in varying amounts. They are eliminated much more slowly than water-soluble vitamins. Health problems related to absorption of fat have a direct impact in the absorption of fat – soluble vitamins. As with dietary lipid, optimal absorption of these vitamins requires bile salts.

Vitamins in the diet are essential for maintaining normal metabolism because the body can't produce them. However, they are required in small amounts because many of the vitamins are stored in the body and are used as cofactors and not substrates that are consumed in reactions. Vitamin D is an exception to the rule because it can be synthesized in the body.

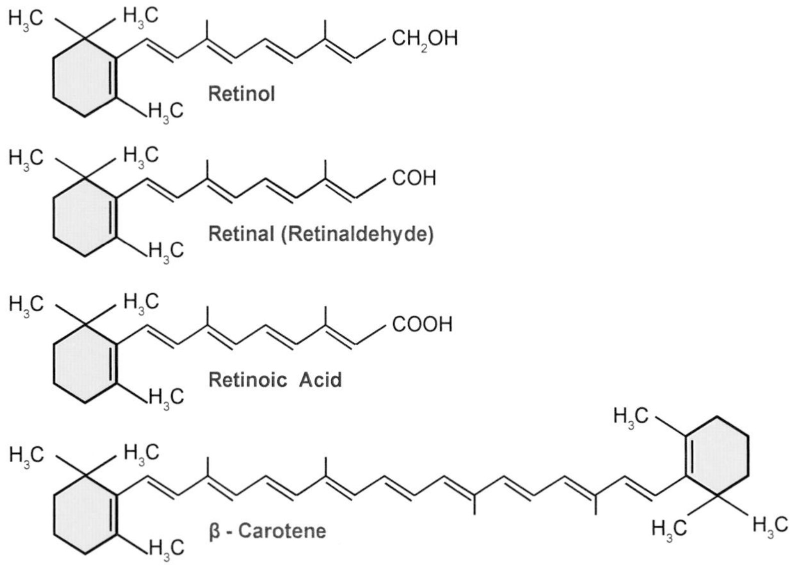

Figure 7.1-1: Structures of retinoids.

7.1.1. Vitamin A and Carotenoids

Vitamin A, the first fat-soluble vitamin discovered, was identified by McCollum and Davis about 1915. Vitamin A is part of a family of molecules called retinoids. Retinoids contain a β-ionone ring and polyunsaturated side chain. The vitamers in the group, retinol (containing an alcohol group), retinal (an aldehyde group), retinoic acid (carboxylic acid), and retinyl ester (linked to a fatty acid side chain), are structurally similar. Carotenoids consist of an expanded carbon chain containing conjugated double bonds, sometimes with an unsubstituted β-ionone ring at one or both ends of the chain.

7.1.1.1. Metabolism and Excretion

Both retinol derivatives and carotenoids are absorbed from the proximal small intestine in a process that requires the formation of mixed micelles and concurrent fat absorption. Retinylesters are cleaved by lipase and sterol esterase from pancreas and at least one other brush border esterase. Retinol is only absorbed efficiently when it is incorporated into mixed micelles along with lipase-digested fat (fatty acids and monoglycerides), bile acids, and phospholipids. Retinol binding protein 2 (RBP2) is needed for retinol metabolism and trafficking across the enterocyte. Retinol and retinylesters exit enterocytes as integral components of chylomicrons. Retinoic acid is exported through an unknown pathway into portal blood and taken up by the liver.

Digestion by the various proteases and peptidases releases carotenoids, if they are attached to proteins. Since carotenoids in plants are embedded in the thylakoid matrix within cells with digestion-resistant walls, cooking or extensive mechanical grinding (chewing) is usually necessary. Carotenoids have to be incorporated into mixed micelles before they can be absorbed. Carotenoids are incorporated into chylomicrons and exported into lymph.

Retinol and its provitamin A precursors are converted into active metabolites in tissue-specific patterns. Conversion of retinol to retinoic acid requires two successive oxidation reactions. The first oxidation is done by alcohol dehydrogenases, which contain zinc, in the cytoplasm of epithelial cells of the gut. The second oxidation is done by retinal dehydrogenase 2 using FAD as an electron acceptor, and this will complete the retinoic acid synthesis. Beta-carotene may also be converted directly into retinoic acid [2].

Retinoic acid and other metabolites can be conjugated to glucuronide and excreted with bile, thus being able to exit the body in the feces. Most of these products are highly polar and can be absorbed and returned to the liver [3]. The relatively high efficiency of intestinal absorption for most retinoids minimizes losses, and maintains extensive enterohepatic cycling [2].

7.1.1.2. Functions

Vitamin A is recognized as being essential for vision, growth, cellular differentiation, reproduction, and integrity of the immune system [3].

Role in visual sensing and communication: Rhodopsin is a biological pigment in photoreceptor cells of the retina that is responsible for the first events in the perception of light and thus, vision. The retinal form of vitamin A is needed in the retina of the eye to turn visual light into nerve signals to the brain. In the visual cycle, transformation of the protein opsin to active rhodopsin is associated with binding of 11-*cis*-retinal followed by cis-trans rearrangement to all-*trans* retinal, which allows for uncoupling of the vitamin from the protein. This cis-trans rearrangement modifies the shape of rhodopsin to cause a change in permeability (hyperpolarization) of the photoreceptors and initiate a signal to the nerve cells to communicate with the central cortex of the brain, so that vision occurs [4].

Vitamin A also combines with opsin to form rhodopsin in the rod cells of the retina. Thus, inadequate amount of vitamin A results in a lack of rhodopsin, consequently, the difficulty of vision in faint light for the person who is suffering from lack of vitamin A. The retinoic acid form of vitamin A is needed to maintain normal differentiation of cells that make up structural components, such as cornea and rod cells

Role in Growth and diffentiation: Vitamin A is also essential for immunity functions and its deficiency is associated with decreased resistance to infections. Vitamin A and retinoic acid play a central role in the development and differentiation of white blood cells, for example lymphocytes, which play critical roles in the immune response. Retinol is required to maintain the integrity and function of the epithelial and mucosal cells [4]. The intensity of infections, such as diarrheal diseases and measles, is reduced by vitamin A supplementation among those who suffer from vitamin A deficiency. In growth and development, vitamin A is involved in normal cell differentiation, a process through which embryonic cells transform into mature tissue cells with highly specific functions. In addition, vitamin A is important in gene expression leading to embryonic development and growth.

7.1.1.3. Storage

Vitamin A requires some digestion before it can be absorbed into the body because it is bound to other food components. Retinoids are converted to retinol in the intestines and transported with dietary fat to the liver where it is stored. After that, retinol is transported from the liver to other tissues by a special transport protein (retinol binding protein). The vitamin A in liver resides mainly as retinyl palmitate in lipid globules of hepatocytes and of stellate cells. The stored esters are released through the action of all- trans-retinyl-palmitate hydrolase. High alcohol intakes can mobilize vitamin A and deplete stores [2].

Carotenoids are present in a number of human tissues including adipose, liver, kidney, and adrenal. Adipose tissues and liver are the main storage sites. Thirty four carotenoids were identified in human serum and milk. One third of these carotenoids were geometrical isomers of their all-trans parent structure and eight were metabolites. In contrast to this finding, up to 50 carotenoids that have been identified in the U.S. diet and more than 600 found in nature. Beta-carotene, lycopene, and lutein are the most prevalent carotenoids in human serum. Cis-isomers of lycopene are commonly found in human serum, unlike cis-isomers of beta-carotene, which are less common in serum than the trans-isomers. The concentrations of various carotenoids in human serum and tissues are highly changeable and likely rely on a number of factors, such as food sources, efficiency of absorption and amount of fat in the diet. It has been suggested that beta-carotene and other carotenoids (also called phytochemicals) may function as antioxidants by neutralizing free radicals.

7.1.1.4. Sources

Retinoids and carotenoids are found naturally in foods. Vitamin A is found primarily in foods of animal origin especially liver, although, the current U.S. and international guidelines encourage plant based diets with less emphasis on foods of animal origin. Vitamin A is also found in dairy products, such as milk, cheese, and butter, in addition to eggs, and oily fish like tuna, sardines and, herring. Some products, such as margarine and breakfast cereal, may be enriched with vitamin A. Some foods of plant origin contain the antioxidant, beta-carotene, which converts to vitamin A in the body. Generally, carotenoids are found in red, orange, dark green, and yellow vegetables, and orange fruits.

7.1.1.5. RDA and Deficiency

Recommended Dietary Allowances (RDA) for vitamin A (**Table 7.1.1**) suggests for adolescents and adult women an intake of 2,300 IU (700 µg) of vitamin A per day.

Vitamin A deficiency is more rare in the U.S. than in developing countries, where children under 5 years of age are the predominant group of people suffering from inadequate vitamin A intake. People with alcoholism or liver diseases, and those with fat absorption disorders, and newborn, premature infants, and older adults are all at increased risk. Lack of vitamin A results in night blindness, which is a temporary condition, but it can lead to permanent blindness if it untreated. In addition to very dry, rough skin, and follicular hyperkeratosis, condition which hair follicles over-express keratin, giving the appearance of ragged hair. Decreased resistance to infection, slower bone growth, and faulty tooth development are other symptoms of possible vitamin A deficiency. It may take a long time for symptoms of vitamin A deficiency to appear because it is stored in the body. To avoid vitamin A deficiency, adequate intake of vitamin A sources is the most important long-term solution. Developing countries are now promoting increased production and consumption of fruits and vegetables rich in the vitamin A precursor, beta-carotene.

TABLE 7.1-1: Vitamin A RDAs.

Recommended Dietary Allowance (RDA) for Vitamin A as Preformed Vitamin A (Retinol Activity Equivalents)			
Life Stage	Age	Males: mcg/day (IU/day)	Females: mcg/day (IU/day)
Infants (AI)	0-6 months	400 (1,333 IU)	400 (1,333 IU)
Infants (AI)	7-12 months	500 (1,667 IU)	500 (1,667 IU)
Children	1-3 years	300 (1,000 IU)	300 (1,000 IU)
Children	4-8 years	400 (1,333 IU)	400 (1,333 IU)
Children	9-13 years	600 (2,000 IU)	600 (2,000 IU)
Adolescents	14-18 years	900 (3,000 IU)	700 (2,333 IU)
Adults	19 years and older	900 (3,000 IU)	700 (2,333 IU)
Pregnancy	18 years and younger	-	750 (2,500 IU)
Pregnancy	19 years and older	-	770 (2,567 IU)
Breast-feeding	18 years and younger	-	1,200 (4,000 IU)
Breast-feeding	19 years and older	-	1,300 (4,333 IU)

The earliest evidence of vitamin A deficiency is impaired dark adaptation or night blindness. Mild vitamin A deficiency may result in changes in the conjunctiva called Bitot's spots. Bitot's spots are drying of the eye and hardened epithelial cells. Severe or prolonged vitamin A deficiency causes a condition called xeropthalmia (dry eye), characterized by changes in the cells of the cornea (clear covering of the eye) that ultimately result in corneal ulcers, scarring, and blindness [4].

7.1.1.6. Toxicity

Toxicity can result from an excessive intake of vitamin A by teratogenic effects of 13-cis-retinoic acid, which is used extensively in the treatment of acne. Use of this compound with women in the early months of their pregnancy has resulted in a number of birth defects among the infants born to these women. A chronic intake of vitamin A in amounts ten times greater than the RDA can result in hypervitaminosis manifested by a veriety of maladies. Manifestations of toxicity (e.g., anorexia; dry, itchy and desquamanting skin, alopecia and coarsening of the hair) subside gradually once excessive intake of the vitamin is discontinued. But there is some evidence that any liver damage that may have occurred is irreversible [3].

On the other hand, chronically ingesting amounts larger than the Upper Intake Level (UL), which is 3,000 μg RAE (10,000 IU) of vitamin A per day, may cause severe hypervitaminosis A. Nausea, vomiting, blurred vision, increased intracranial pressure, headache, dizziness, skin peeling, and muscle discordance are all sign of acute hypervitaminosis A. Oral ingestion of more than 4,500 μg daily by pregnant women can increase risk of fetal malformation.

7.1.1.7. Assessment

Serum retinol concentration is used to assess vitamin A status in humans. Liver concentration gives a more complete assessment in animal research [6]. Human serum retinol levels are relatively constant unless there is severe deficiency and liver stores exhausted or unless intake is excessive to the point that the vitamin can no longer be complexed for storage in the liver [3].

7.1.2. Vitamin E

Vitamin E is a family of eight naturally occurring vitamers with distinctive antioxidant activities. Each of these compounds contains a phenolic functional group. The eight compounds are divided into two groups. The tocopherols have saturated side chains with 16 carbons, and the tocotrienols have unsaturated side chains with 16 carbons (**Fig. 7.1.2.**). The chromanol rings of the four vitamers differ in the number and location of

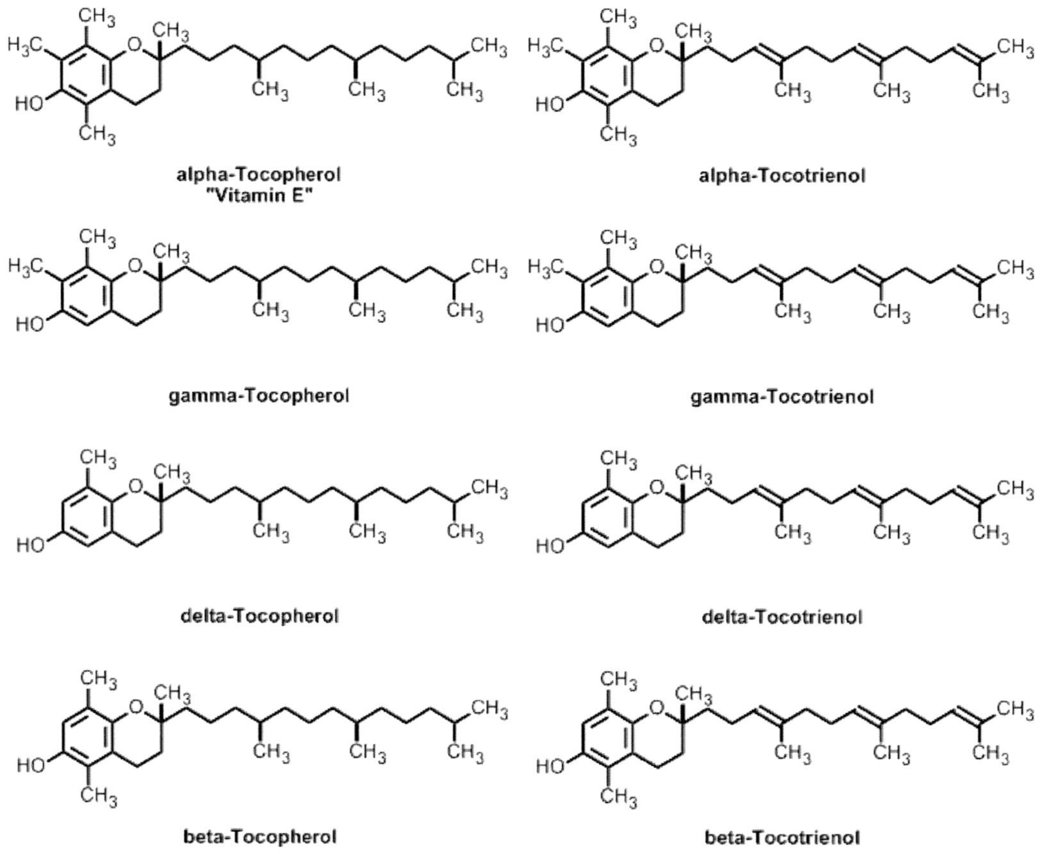

Figure 7.1-2: Structures of the tocopherols and tocotrienols.

methyl groups. Vitamers in both groups are specified as alpha, beta, gamma, and delta. Alpha-tocopherol has the greatest biologic activity for meeting human requirements.

7.1.2.1. Metabolism

The first oxidation product of alpha-tocopherol is a tocopheroxy radical. Metastable tocopheroxide is formed as an intermediary product in this oxidation reaction, and it is speculated that tocopheroxide may actually be the primary tissue oxidation product of vitamin E. The major route of alpha-tocopherol excretion is via feces. Fecal tocopherol arises from incomplete absorption, from secretion from enterocytes back into the intestinal lumen, from desquamation of intestinal epithelial cells, and from the biliary route. The vitamin is excreted in bile conjugated with glucuronic acid. Another possible excretion or secretion route for alpha-tocopherol is the skin [3].

7.1.2.2. Function of Vitamin E

The main function of vitamin E is as an antioxidant. Vitamin E protects the membranes from destruction through its ability to prevent the oxidation of unsaturated fatty acids contained in the phospholipids of the membranes. It maintains intracellular membrane integrity. Vitamin E prevents the peroxidation of unsaturated fatty acids contained in the phospholipids of the cellular membranes. Vitamin E located in membranes can break the chain of radical attack by reacting with peroxide radicals and preventing further abstraction of H from the fatty acids. Together vitamin E and selenoenzyme glutathione peroxidase protect specifically against peroxidation of membrane lipids, thereby reducing the potential for cellular destruction. Tissues with cell membranes vulnerable to hydroperoxidation are the lung, brain, and erythrocytes. An adequate supply of vitamin E is very important in protecting these tissues against oxygen toxicity and in some cases, vitamin E supplementation may be helpful in ameliorating conditions produced by oxygen toxicity [3].

In addition, vitamin E takes part in immune function, regulation of gene expression, and other metabolic processes. Vitamin E may help prevent or delay coronary heart disease (CHD) by reducing oxidation of low-density lipoprotein (LDL) cholesterol. It might also aid in preventing the formation of blood clots that could result in a heart attack or venous thromboembolism. Because vitamin E is an antioxidant, it may protect certain cells from the damaging effects of free radicals that might contribute to cancer development. Moreover, vitamin E might block the formation of carcinogenic nitrosamines formed in the stomach and protect against cancer by enhancing immune functions. However, some studies have found that vitamin E is not effective in most cases. Antioxidant nutrients, possibly including vitamin E, may prevent or delay Age- Related Macular Degeneration (AMD) and cataracts that are common causes of significant vision loss in older people.

7.1.2.3. Vitamin E storage

Absorbed tocopherols mingle into chylomicrons in the enterocyte for transport through the lymph and then into circulation. All of the tocopherol and tocotrienol vitamers are absorbed with similar efficiency. During transport in the chylomicrons, tocopherols transfer to other lipoproteins, including HDLs and LDLs.

However, when VLDLs are released from the liver to transport lipids to peripheral tissues, only α-tocopherol is included, due to specificity of a vitamin E binding protein.. Vitamin E is mostly found in cell membranes. There is no single storage organ for vitamin E. The greatest amount of the vitamin is concentrated in an unesterified form in fat droplets in adipose tissue. The concentration of the vitamin in adipose tissue depends on the dose of vitamin E, but release of vitamin E from adipose tissue is slow. The liver, lungs, heart, muscle, adrenal glands, spleen and brain take up small amounts of vitamin E.

7.1.2.4. Sources of Vitamin E

In its diverse forms, vitamin E is mostly found in plant foods, especially the oil from plants. Examples are wheat germ, sunflower, canola, and safflower oils. Oils that have largest amount of α-tocopherol are, soybean and corn oils. Full fat foods made from vegetable oils, such as salad dressings, mayonnaise, and margarine, nuts and food made from them, like peanut butter, are considered to be good sources of vitamin E. Whole-grain cereals and some fruits and vegetables are other plant sources of vitamin E.

7.1.2.5. RDA and Deficiency of Vitamin E

The RDA for vitamin E (**Table 7.1.3**) for adult men and women, including women during pregnancy, is 15 mg (22.4 IU) of α-tocopherol. For lactating women recommendations are somewhat higher, with an RDA

TABLE 7.1-2: RDAs for vitamin E [6].

The Recommended Dietary Allowance (RDA) for Alpha-Tocopherol			
Life Stage	Age	Males; mg/day (IU/day)	Females; mg/day (IU/day)
Infants (AI)	0-6 months	4 mg (6 IU)	4 mg (6 IU)
Infants (AI)	7-12 months	5 mg (7.5 IU)	5 mg (7.5 IU)
Children	1-3 years	6 mg (9 IU)	6 mg (9 IU)
Children	4-8 years	7 mg (10.5 IU)	7 mg (10.5 IU)
Children	9-13 years	11 mg (16.5 IU)	11 mg (16.5 IU)
Adolescents	14-18 years	15 mg (22.5 IU)	15 mg (22.5 IU)
Adults	19 years and older	15 mg (22.5 IU)	15 mg (22.5 IU)
Pregnancy	all ages	-	15 mg (22.5 IU)
Breast-feeding	all ages	-	19 mg (28.5 IU)

of 19 mg (28.4 IU) of α-tocopherol. Smokers may have higher requirements for vitamin E but there is no specific recommendation yet.

Vitamin E deficiency rarely occurs in humans. A small number of people are at the risk for deficiency, including premature infants, people with fat malabsorption disorders like cystic fibrosis, and people with hepatobiliary system disorders, particularly chronic cholestasis. People with genetic defects in either lipoproteins or the α-tocopherol transfer protein are also at risk. Some signs of vitamin E deficiency are skeletal muscle pain and weakness, ceroid pigment accumulation, hemolytic anemia, and degenerative neurological problems, including peripheral neuroparhy, ataxia, loss of vibratory sense, and loss of coordination of limbs.

7.1.2.6. Toxicity

No studies have found any detrimental impact from consuming excessive vitamin E in food. The Tolerable Upper Intake is 1,000 mg of α-tocopherol or 1100 IU of synthetic all-rac tocopherol a day for adults because there is an increasing tendency for bleeding due either to antiplatelet effects or abnormal blood clotting, and sometimes the two cases at the same time. Moreover, intake of vitamin E at 1,000 mg or larger is connected with gut distress, including nausea, diarrhea, and flatulence, in addition to impaired blood coagulation, possible increased severity of respiratory infections, and occasional reports of muscle weakness, fatigue, and double vision [6].

Higher doses (800 mg to 3.2 g) of vitamin E consumption could cause muscle weakness, fatigue, nausea, and diarrhea. Gastrointestinal disturbance is the most commonly occurring complaint. Studies in animals show that high intakes of vitamin E can interfere with intestinal absorption of vitamins A and K [3].

7.1.2.7. Assessment

Normal levels of tocopherol range from 0.8 to 1.5 mg/dL serum in adults with values less than 0.5 mg/dL considered indicative of deficiency.

A crude estimation of vitamin E status can be obtained from erythrocyte hemolysis tests which compare the amount of hemoglobin released by red cells during dilute hydrogen peroxide versus distilled water incubations. The result is expressed as a percentage; > 20% indicates a deficiency of vitamin E.

7.1.3. Structure, Function, and Storage of Water Soluble Vitamins

Water-soluble vitamins are organic compounds with regulatory functions that are required in the diet if the species (humans) are unable to synthesize them [7]. Vitamins are essential because there is no way for the body to produce them. Vitamins can be classified as either water-soluble or fat-soluble. The body handles removal and storage between these vitamin classes quite differently.

Water-soluble vitamins are absorbed into portal blood and cannot be retained in the body for long periods of time. These vitamins dissolve in water and are excreted from the body in urine when plasma levels exceed renal thresholds [7]. The water-soluble vitamins include the following: thiamin, riboflavin, niacin, pantothenic acid, biotin, vitamin B6, folate, vitamin B12, and ascorbic acid. Since these vitamins are excreted, usually into urine, with a half life that is measured in days, we need a regular supply in our diet. There is a longer biological half life for the water-soluble vitamins that are bound to enzymes or proteins.

Most of the water-soluble vitamins make up the B complex family of vitamins, which are important to many areas and functions of the body. The B complex vitamins function as essential coenzymes that help the body obtain energy from food. The vitamins promote healthy appetite, healthy vision, healthy skin, healthy central nervous system function, and normal red blood cell formation. Many of the B complex vitamins play a physiological role in electron transfer reactions and carboxylation/decarboxylation reactions [7]. Throughout history many instances of water-soluble vitamin deficiencies have resulted in epidemics of harmful disease. There is less risk of toxic effects than for the lipid-soluble vitamins, but deficiency of water-soluble vitamins may occur much faster [8]. Scurvy, beriberi, pellagra, and pernicious anemia are four well-known water-soluble vitamin deficiencies. These deficiencies are not common in the United States due to the enrichment and fortification of foods, however they can have a huge impact on populations with limited nutritional sources. Populations at risk for acquired deficiencies include patients with anorexia nervosa, cystic fibrosis, patients receiving long-term tube-feeding and those with perceived or real food allergy. These conditions can cause various micronutrient, protein, and vitamin deficiencies [4].

7.1.3.1. Ascorbic Acid (Vitamin C)

Scurvy or vitamin C (ascorbic acid) deficiency results in the body's inability to synthesize collagen. Collagen is a vital component of the connective tissue. Collagen synthesis aids in wound healing, the assistance in bone and tooth formation, and strengthens the walls in the blood vessels. Persons suffering from Scurvy may have skin changes and easy bruising, tooth loss and gum decay, lethargy and edema. Over time, if not treated, scurvy can lead to eventual death as seen and experienced by crusaders and sailors. However death from scurvy is very rare today. Citrus fruits are excellent sources of ascorbic acid, along with some green vegetables such as brussell sprouts and green peppers [7]. The Adequate Intake (AI) for ascorbic acid is 75 mg. Ascorbic acid is transported in the blood as a free solute, however small amounts are found in plasma due to its rapid uptake in the cells. Tissue concentrations usually exceed plasma concentrations and are highest within white blood cells, cells of the eyes, brain, liver, spleen, kidneys, heart, lungs and muscle with the greatest concentration in the adrenal and pituitary glands [9].

7.1.3.2. Thiamin (B1)

Beriberi or deficiency of thiamin (B_1) causes nervous system ailments and complications of the muscular and gastrointestinal systems. There are two types of beriberi: wet beriberi and dry beriberi. Dry beriberi can be associated with decreased function of the muscular system and mental confusion, loss of the ability to walk, body aches and pains, as well as gastrointestinal sickness. Dry beriberi can eventually lead to paralysis and permanent disability. Wet beriberi can be associated with cardiovascular problems such as increased heart rate, shortness of breath and poor circulation. Thiamin is typically found in the body in its phosphorylated form, but free thiamin is usually found in the plasma

in its unphosphorylated form, bound to albumin, or as thiamin monophosphate (TMP). Only free thiamin or TMP can cross cell membranes and enter cells where it is then phosphorylated [7]. The body contains approximately 30 mg of Thiamin with most of its concentration in liver, skeletal muscle, heart, kidneys and brain. Skeletal muscle is said to contain about half of the total body's concentration. Thiamin deficiency in the United States is quite low but cases have been seen with alcohol abuse. The RDA or AI for thiamin is 1.1 mg a day and yeast, pork, seeds and legumes are best sources of thiamin [9].

7.1.3.3. Niacin (B3)

Pellagra, or niacin (B3) deficiency, causes mental and physical illness and was seen as one of the most common vitamin deficiencies in the early 1900's. Pellagra is most common in societies that obtain most of their nutritional value from corn. Pellagra symptoms are associated with the four D's: diarrhea, dermatitis, dementia, and death.

Niacin deficiency has often been linked to tryptophan deficiency because the body converts this available tryptophan into niacin. Niacin is found predominantly in the plasma as nicotinamide in the forms of nicotinamide dinucleotide (NAD) or NADP. About 1/3rd of this concentration is found bound to plasma proteins. Nicotinamide serves as a precursor for NAD, which is used in all tissues in the body as a reactant [7]. The RDA or AI of niacin is 14 mg per day, and meats and fish provide great sources of niacin [9]. Tuna supplies 11.3 mg of niacin in one 3-oz. serving, almost reaching the daily allowance in one serving.

7.1.3.4. Cobalamin (B12)

Vitamin B12 absorption follows a complex pathway. First, B12 within the stomach is bound to R proteins found in saliva and gastric juice. The R protein is then digested in the small intestine and releases the bound vitamin B12. Vitamin B12 then binds with intrinsic factor and forms the B12-IF complex which binds to receptors on enterocytes in the ilium and gets internalized by endocytosis [7]. This absorption process is disrupted by the autoimmune condition present with pernicious anemia. The body attacks its own intrinsic factor, therefore inhibiting the binding of vitamin B12 and creating a deficiency in B12 absorption. Unlike other water-soluble vitamins, vitamin B12 can be stored and retained within the body, with high concentrations in the liver [1]. Cobalamin is found only in animal foods and some fermented food products. Liver is a valuable source of vitamin B12 because it is the storage site for most animals. The RDA or AI for cobalamin is 2.4 μg per day [9].

7.1.3.5. Enrichment and Fortification of Foods

Occurance of deficiencies in these important water-soluble vitamins has been reduced and in some cases almost eliminated by the process or fortifying and enriching foods. Enriching a food source means that manufacturers add nutrients into the food source that were lost or depleted during food preparation. Fortifying foods means that nutrients are added into the food source, however these nutrients were not initially present naturally in this food. Enrichment and fortification can be a very helpful tool in improving the nutritional state of people within a population

that lacks variety within their diet. Many popular food choices within the United States are fortified with added nutrients, many of them being fortified with water-soluble vitamins. Prime examples of these food choices are milk products, breads, cereals, and rice.

The fortifying process allows popular foods that may lack nutritional benefit to become sources of essential vitamins and nutrients. Lifestyle choices as well as convenience to the consumer have greatly influenced the way food is purchased and consumed. Zink [10] states, "The trend toward dining outside the home is likely rooted in lifestyle changes such as households with two working parents. The number of home-delivered meals, the ultimate convenience food, has also increased, even though the most popular foods consumed today (pizza and hamburgers) are generally the same as those of 20 years ago. This indicates that the types of foods consumed do not change rapidly, but the way these foods are consumed has changed." The process of fortifying foods and enriching foods will continue to occur as consumers purchase food based more around taste and value of the ingredients as well as price. This brings up a question as to how we can make fortified foods obtainable and valuable.

TABLE 7.1-3: Water Soluble Vitamins and Food Sources.

Vitamins	Foods containing the vitamin
Vitamin B1 - Thiamin	Whole grains cereals, fortified cereals, legumes, yeast, nuts, pork, liver
Vitamin B2 - Riboflavin	Fresh milk and other milk products, eggs, liver, meat, dark-green leafy vegetables, full grain cereals, enriched grains, fortified cereals, nuts, yeast, mushrooms
Vitamin B3 - Niacin	Tryptophan-rich foods: milk, eggs, poultry meat; Foods rich in niacin: whole grain cereals, enriched grains, lean meats, poultry, fish
{Vitamin B4 – Adenine – No longer considered to be a vitamin}	Choline: meat, whole grain cereals, yolk, peas and legumes
Vitamin B5 – Pantothenic acid	In all foods except cultivated and refined: vegetable and animal fibers, liver, kidney, eggs
Vitamin B6 - Pyradoxine	Foods rich in protein, liver, whole grain cereals, fortified cereals, eggs, fish, fruits and vegetables, seeds
Vitamin B7 - Biotin	Yolk, liver, kidney, mushrooms, dark-green leafy vegetables, tomatoes, yeast
Vitamin B9 – Folic acid	Green leafy vegetables, whole grain cereals, oranges, bananas, lentils, seeds, wheat germ, liver
Vitamin B12 - Cobalamin	Foods of animal origin (meat, fish, shellfish, poultry, eggs, milk, cheese) and fortified cereals
Vitamin C – Ascorbic acid	Fresh fruit (citrus and nuts, strawberries, mango) and vegetables (peppers, tomatoes, potatoes, cabbage, kale, green leafy vegetables)

7.1.3.6. Vitamin Supplementation

Another factor influencing prevalence of water-soluble vitamins in the diet is the supplementation of a daily multivitamin. In 1999-2000, the National Health and Nutrition Examination Survey showed that 52% of adults reported taking a dietary supplement while 35% took a multivitamin or multimineral [11]. Multivitamins contain most of the B-complex vitamins, so those taking daily multivitamins can have high intake. However, does taking a daily multivitamin cause one to eat healthier or less healthy? No matter how conscious someone is about their diet it is impossible to achieve 100% of the requirements for each of your essential vitamins and minerals. No one's diet is perfect, therefore a daily supplement may be beneficial. Supplements are likely to increase the concentration of B vitamins in blood and tissue in the short term, even if a large fraction of the additional intake is excreted.

7.1.3.7. Alcoholism and Water-Soluble Vitamins

Alcoholism has shown to greatly inhibit the uptake of water-soluble vitamins. Biotin is a water-soluble vitamin that is required for cellular metabolism, growth and is used in many metabolic processes. Mammals, including humans, have lost the ability for de novo biosynthesis of biotin and therefore must obtain the vitamin from exogenous sources via intestinal absorption. Circulating biotin undergoes filtration in the renal glomeruli and is salvaged via reabsorption by renal proximal tubular epithelial cells. In humans, chronic alcohol use is associated with a marked reduction in plasma biotin levels [12]. Research has shown that excess alcohol consumption in rats led to decreased plasma biotin concentration. Excess alcohol exposure led to an inhibition of intestinal absorption of Biotin. Subramanian et al. [12] found that chronic alcohol feeding of rats inhibited the entry and the exit steps of biotin in the polarized renal reabsorptive epithelia, i.e. reducing transport across the brush border membrane and basolateral membranes, respectively. There was also reduction in expression of sodium-dependent multivitamin transporter protein, mRNA, and heterogeneous nuclear RNA (hnRNA) [12].

7.1.4. Storage of Trace Minerals: Introduction

Trace or microminerals, are identified as minerals that make up less than 0.01% of total body weight or nutrients needed in concentrations of one part per million or less [13]. Indeed, trace minerals are needed in very small amounts but the implications of mineral imbalance can be very serious. So, what happens when our diets don't provide consistent mineral intake? What if supplementation provides an excessive amount of certain trace minerals; how does the body respond?

Dr. Forest Nielson, a leading USDA scientist in the field of nutritionally essential minerals defines four categories by which an element may be defined as nutritionally essential;

- A dietary deprivation in some animal model consistently results in a changed biological function, body structure, or tissue composition that is preventable/reversible by an intake of an apparent physiological amount of the element in question

- Element fills the need at physiological concentrations from a known in vivo biochemical action to proceed in vitro

- Element is a component of known biologically important molecules in some life forms

- Element has an essential function in lower forms of life

Apart from the traditionally accepted essential minerals described below, by this standard; boron, vanadium, chromium, and arsenic may be defined as nutritionally essential [14].

7.1.5. Iron

Dietary iron can be classified as either heme iron or non-heme iron. The majority of iron that is acquired by consuming animal meat comes from either hemoglobin or myoglobin. The iron contained in these proteins is called heme iron. The remaining portion of iron found in meat, along with the iron found in vegetables, grain products, and nutritional supplements is referred to as non-heme iron.

In North America, the majority of iron is acquired through the consumption of meats and seafood. High levels are also found in dark leafy vegetables (such as spinach or mustard) and beans (mainly kidney, garbanzo, and navy). Many processed food products (mainly those made with refined flour) contain high amounts or iron, however, the iron in enriched and plant-based foods is typically less bioavailable than that from meat or seafood.

With regard to iron intake, the RDA for adult women is 18 mg/day. It is recommended that adult men consume 8 mg/day. Once women enter menopause, the loss of iron through menstrual bleeding is no longer an issue and the RDA drops to 8 mg/day. The average American iron intake is about 17 mg/day and 12 mg/day for men and women, respectively [5].

After iron is consumed, it crosses the brush border membrane of the small intestine. Here, within the enterocytes, iron-binding proteins are made. These proteins are important with regard to iron absorption and in the regulation of overall iron status. Of these proteins, one of the most important is ferritin. **Ferritin** binds and stores mucosal iron, thus inhibiting the its entrance into the bloodstream [26]. The enterocytes produce ferritin in response to the amount of body iron storage. For example, a young menstruating women who consumes about 60% of the RDA probably has low iron stores. As a result, less ferritin will be produced and essentially, more iron can then enter the bloodstream. On the other hand, a young man who consumes large amounts of animal flesh and approximately 120% of the RDA probably has high iron stores. In this case, the enterocytes will produce more ferritin so that more iron binding is facilitated. Although some of this ferritin-bound iron will remain in the intestinal iron pool, much of it will be excreted once the intestinal cells are sloughed off, typically after several days. The process by which this protection against toxicity occurs is known as the "mucosal block" because it essentially blocks excess iron from entering the bloodstream and thus, prevents excess accumulation.

After absorption into the enterocytes, a certain amount of iron, based on the body's needs, is released into the intestinal iron pool. From here, iron is transported to the interstitial fluid for release into the blood. This transport is accomplished by a protein called **ferroportin**. In order for absorbed iron to be transported to the body's cells it must be oxidized from the ferrous (Fe^{2+}) to the ferric (Fe^{3+}) form by either hephaestin (an enzyme in the enterocyte) or ceruloplasmin (in the blood) and bound to transferrin [16].

Transferrin receptors, located on the surface of the cell membrane (all cell types) brings in the transferrin-iron complex [17]. The amount of iron brought into the cell is regulated according to the synthesis of the transferrin receptors. The number of receptors is dependent on the needs of the cell. If more iron is required, more receptors will be synthesized and vice versa. Following receptor binding, transferrin is engulfed into the cell by endocytosis [15]. After endocytosis, transferrin is broken apart in the lysosomes. Iron is released and the receptor-protein complex is recycled back up to the cell surface. At this point the iron can be either used immediately for cellular activities or it can be stored in the form of ferritin or hemosiderin. Storage of iron is highly regulated as it is difficult for the body to excrete iron once it has been absorbed and the majority (about 90%) of the iron we use daily is recycled and reused. If iron is not needed right away for cellular activities, it will be transported by transferrin and stored. The liver holds approximately 60% of the body's stored iron. The remainder is stored within the reticuloendothelial (RE) cells in the spleen and bone marrow [7]. Some iron may also be stored between the muscle fibers. The RE cells are a prime storage location for iron because of the phagocytosis of red blood cells and breakdown of hemoglobin that occurs within these cells.

Iron is primarily stored as ferritin within the cells. Within the ferritin molecule is apoferritin; it is here that iron atoms are deposited. The bone marrow, intestine, liver, and spleen are important sites of ferritin synthesis. Ferritin consists of 24 protein subunits that are classified as either H or L, depending on molecular mass. Ferritin found in the liver and spleen is mostly of the L form, which is slow to take up iron, in contrast to the H form. Pores or channels allow iron to enter apoferritin. It is within these pores that oxidation of ferrous iron into ferric oxyhydroxide crystals or ferrihydrite occurs [7].

Because of constant degradation and re-synthesis, ferritin provides an available pool of iron for cellular use. It is likely that the amount of iron within the cell has some influence on ferritin synthesis at the translational level. An iron regulatory/response element binding protein (IRE-BP) responds to the amount of iron within the cell. Essentially, if iron concentrations are high, IRE-BP is found as a 4Fe-4S cluster that exhibits aconitase activity. Aconitase plays a role in the TCA cycle by converting citrate to isocitrate within the mitochondria. Alternatively, if iron concentrations are low, IRE-BP is found as a 3Fe-4S cluster that binds to iron response elements (IREs) in ferritin mRNA. This binding action inhibits the translation of ferritin [7].

Hemosiderin, another iron storage protein, is a degradation product of ferritin.

Typically, more hemosiderin than ferritin is found in tissues with high iron concentrations; the opposite is true when iron concentrations are low. Also, when compared to ferritin, hemosiderin is slower to release iron.

In order for iron to be released from storage, Fe^{3+} must be mobilized and a reducing substance and a chelator must be used to facilitate diffusion through ferritin pores. Fe^{2+} is sent to the surface of the cell where it is re-oxidized for transport out of the cell; ceruloplasmin is required for this re-oxidation [7].

Serum ferritin is commonly used as an indicator of iron body stores because equilibration occurs between tissue ferritin and serum ferritin. This type of measurement can sometimes be misleading following an episode of illness or inflammation because ferritin is a reactant protein. In this situation, serum ferritin may appear to be within normal limits while the body's iron stores may be quite low.

Within developing countries, nearly two-thirds of all children and women of child-bearing age are iron deficient [18]. This is less of a problem in the United States but nevertheless, it is a serious public health concern. Initially, symptoms of iron deficiency may be subtle because the body is capable of utilizing it's stored iron. As time passes, if iron intake doesn't improve, these stores will become low and iron deficiency anemia may result. Symptoms of iron deficiency anemia include impaired energy metabolism and depressed immune function [5]. Premature infants, young children, and women of child-bearing age are at the highest risk of iron deficiency and iron deficiency anemia [7].

Iron toxicity is a threat to human health and for that reason, an Upper Level (UL) of 45 mg/day has been set [5]. Consuming more that 45 mg/day may result in nausea, vomiting, and diarrhea. Intakes greater than the UL may also compromise the body's ability to absorb other trace minerals. For children, iron overload is most commonly the result of accidental overdose from iron containing chewable vitamins.

In fact, accidental iron overdose is the leading cause of poisoning in the United States for children under six years of age [15]. For adults, iron overload is most typically the result of excess supplementation, frequent blood transfusions, or hemochromatosis. Hemochromatosis is a genetic condition that causes the mucosal block to be ineffective [19]. Without proper functioning of the mucosal block, excess amounts of iron are absorbed and transported to the tissues. Because iron is difficult to excrete once absorbed, this defect leads to iron deposits within the body. Without medical intervention, this condition may eventually result in either liver or heart failure.

7.1.6. Zinc

Zinc is essential for normal human growth and development and can be readily obtained through the consumption of meats and seafood. Nuts, beans, and whole grains can also contribute significant amounts of zinc. An important note regarding the zinc contribution of whole grain bread and cereals is that foods that are high in phytic acid, such as unleavened breads, may offer a significant amount of zinc but a great portion of it is not bioavailable. The RDA for adult men is set at 11 mg/day and 8 mg/day for adult women [5]. This amount is based on the estimated losses of zinc via body excretions and on 40% absorption. On average, recommended zinc intakes are met by adult Americans [20].

After consumption, zinc is absorbed in the small intestine by simple diffusion and active transport. Metallothionein is a zinc binding protein that is produced when the enterocytes absorb zinc. Metallothionein plays an important role in absorption because it binds up the zinc and prevents it from leaving the intestinal cells [21]. This results in excretion as the intestinal cells are sloughed off and shed in the feces. Here we have another example of a mucosal block that helps prevent excess absorption. Zinc absorption varies according to individual intake and the body's requirements. For example, if intake is low, animal protein intake is high, or if the body's need is higher than normal, absorption will increase. Alternatively, if intake is in excess of what the body requires, if non-heme iron intake is excessive, or if phytic acid intake is high, absorption will decrease.

Absorbed zinc will bind to proteins such as albumin and then be transported to the liver. Once in the liver, zinc is repackaged and bound to alpha-2-macroglobulin, albumin, and other proteins [15]. Zinc can be found in all organs but is found primarily in the bones, muscle, liver, skin, and kidneys. The zinc from soft tissues will not be released when intakes are low. Additionally, the zinc stored in bone (as part of apatite) is released very slowly and cannot compensate for low dietary intakes. When dietary intake is low, zinc-containing metalloproteins and liver metallothionein are degraded by lysosomal proteases so that zinc may be redistributed according to the body's needs [7].

When thionein binds a mineral such as zinc, it becomes known as metallothionein.

Metallothionein is thought to be both the primary storage form of zinc and a chaperone which facilitates transfer to acceptor proteins. Various forms of metallothionein can be found throughout the body: MT-1, MT-2, MT-3, and MT-4 (MT-1 and MT-2 are the most common) [22]. Zinc stores affect the expression of thionein through their interaction with the metal response elements (MREs) or with a metal transcription factor (MTF) [7].

Glucagon and interleukin 1 also affect thionein expression. Interleukin 1 induces thionein transcription and in turn increases the amount of metallothionein-bound zinc in the liver during infections [23].

When zinc is consumed in inadequate amounts, symptoms of deficiency may be observed. This condition is uncommon in the United States but it has been reported in young children, individuals undergoing dialysis, individuals with Crohn's disease, infants with acrodermatitis enteropathica, and people who consume diets that restrict animal- based foods [24]. Some of the many symptoms of zinc deficiency are as follows [15]:

• -Loss of appetite

• -Delayed growth and sexual maturation

• -Dermatitis

• -Impaired vitamin A function

• -Alopecia

• -Decreased taste sensitivity

• -Poor wound healing

• -Immune dysfunction

• -Severe diarrhea

• -Birth defects

• -Increased infant mortality

The upper limit for zinc is set at 40 mg/day [5]. Intakes above this amount may cause toxicity. In the case of acute toxicity nausea, vomiting, intestinal cramps, and diarrhea may be observed. Excessive intake of zinc over a long period of time may result in mineral-mineral interactions and impaired copper absorption.

7.1.7. Copper

Copper is an important enzyme component and is closely linked to the metabolic functions of iron. Copper also functions as a part of the superoxide dismutase enzymes and is involved in neurotransmitter regulation. Good sources include organ meats, shellfish, nuts, seeds, and legumes. Potatoes, soy products, and dark chocolate are also high in copper. The RDA is currently set at 900 micrograms/day for both male and female adults [5]. The average American's daily intake well exceeds this amount. The RDA is based on the typical amount needed by copper-containing enzymes and proteins.

Copper is typically bound to organic components. Therefore, digestion is needed to free up the copper before absorption can take place. Within the stomach, pepsin and hydrochloric acid help the release of copper. Within the small intestine, additional hydrolysis and copper release is facilitated. Some absorption takes place within the stomach but the majority occurs within the small intestine. It is believed that copper is absorbed by active carrier-mediated transporters and by passive diffusion but its action is not completely understood [7].

Copper is stored within the body as part of metallothionein and can be stored for 2-3 days within the intestinal cells. If it is not released from storage for use, it will be lost with intestinal cell turnover. Copper can be found within many of the body's tissues but the liver, brain, and kidneys contain the most per gram of weight. The liver is the primary site of copper storage; here it can be found bound to metallothionein. Very little copper is actually stored within the body (in comparison to other trace minerals) because the liver and kidneys actively extract copper from the blood. Thionein synthesis within the kidney and liver is positively influenced by copper; however, this is not the case in the intestine. It is believed that the liver is responsible for regulating the amount of copper available to other tissues by excreting copper into bile, synthesizing ceruloplasmin, and incorporating copper into metallothionein [7].

Though copper deficiencies are rare in humans, some have been reported in formula-fed infants, those recovering from malnutrition, patients on total parenteral nutrition, and individuals with Menkes disease [25]. Deficiency symptoms may present as anemia, leukopenia and neutropenia, or osteopenia. Recently, it has been suggested that there is a correlation between copper deficiency and the development of neurological disorders. Long-term marginal intakes have also sparked concern in researchers but the difficulty lies in the reliable detection of changes in copper status. Symptoms commonly seen in those with marginal deficiency include glucose intolerance, elevated serum cholesterol, depressed immune function, and cardiac abnormalities [15].

The UL for copper has been established as 10 mg/day [5]. Copper toxicity is relatively uncommon in humans but it has been reported in children suffering from accidental overdoses. It has also been noted in individuals who have consumed contaminated food or water and those affected by Wilson's disease. The most common symptoms of toxicity include abdominal pain, nausea, vomiting, and diarrhea. In chronic toxicity cases, copper tends to accumulate in the liver and brain; cirrhosis or neurological damage may result.

7.1.8. Manganese

Manganese functions much like zinc and copper, serving as an enzyme co-factor within the body. This mineral can be obtained by consuming whole-grain cereals, nuts, legumes, and tea. Currently, there are inadequate data to reflect the absolute requirement for manganese, so an AI of 2.3 mg/day has been established for adult males and 1.8 mg/day for adult women [5].

After ingestion, manganese is absorbed within the small intestine at an estimated rate of <5% [7].

After absorption, manganese may remain free or bind as Mn^{2+} to alpha-2 macroglobulin before heading to the liver where removal is essentially absolute. Mn^{2+} may remain free or bind to albumin, globulins, or be oxidized to Mn^{3+} and bind with transferrin [26]. Manganese is quickly removed from the blood and accumulates within the mitochondria of tissues [27]. Here manganese is present as hydrate Mn^{2+} or Mn^{3+} and as $Mn^{3+}(PO^4)_2$ [28]. Manganese accumulates in most organs and tissues but is found in high concentrations in the bone (as a component of apatite), liver, pancreas, and kidneys.

The symptoms of manganese deficiency are not clearly defined because only a few cases have been reported. In those cases where deficiency was suspected, individuals demonstrated evidence of poor growth and skeletal abnormalities, impaired glucose metabolism, and impaired reproductive function [29].

Manganese toxicity is not considered to be likely but it has been reported in children that required long-term parenteral nutrition or suffered from inhalation of toxic emissions [29]. Because the incidents involving toxicity have resulted in severe neurological impairment, an UL of 11 mg/day has been set [5].

7.1.9. Iodine

Iodine is present in food as iodide (I^-) and as other non-elemental forms [15]. Iodine has one very important task; thyroid hormone synthesis. Common food sources include saltwater seafood, iodized salt, and molasses. Plant-based foods offer varied amounts of iodine depending on the soil in which they were grown. Furthermore, bioavailability may be an issue with many iodine-containing foods. Compounds known as goitrogens decrease iodine absorption and impair utilization by the thyroid gland. Goitrogens are commonly found in strawberries, soy, peaches, and potatoes; just to name a few. The RDA for iodine is based on the amount needed for use by the thyroid gland and is currently set at 150 micrograms/day [5].

Iodine can be found free, primarily as iodate (IO^{3-}) or iodide (I^-) or bound to amino acids. If iodinated amino acids are not degraded, they can be absorbed but this occurs at a lesser rate than the absorption of the iodide ion [7]. Iodide is efficiently absorbed throughout the stomach and intestine. After absorption, iodide is carried by the blood to the tissues; highest concentration occurs in the thyroid gland with smaller amounts being found in the ovaries, placenta, skin, and the salivary, mammary, and gastric glands. The thyroid gland utilizes a sodium-dependent, active transport system and holds about 70%- 80% of the total iodide within the body. An additional 120 micrograms of iodide is taken up by the thyroid gland each day [7].

Iodine deficiency disorders have been reported throughout the world and are closely associated with goiter, a condition characterized by enlargement of the thyroid gland. When iodide intake is insufficient, thyroid iodine stores diminish; as a result, thyroid hormone (T4 and T3) output declines. Because of the low concentration of T4 in the blood, the pituitary gland is triggered to release thyroid stimulating hormone (TSH) which results in hyperplasia of the thyroid. Iodine deficiency may occur in a fetus if the mother has an iodide deficiency. This may result in one of two conditions; either hypothyroid cretinism or neurological cretinism. Hypothyroid cretinism can sometimes be corrected with iodine treatments but if no action is taken, thyroid failure will result.

Indications of neurological cretinism include mental deficiency with hearing loss or deaf mutism; spasticity or muscular rigidity may also be observed. Both of these conditions are referred to as iodide deficiency disorders (IDD) [7].

Iodine toxicity may result in enlargement of the thyroid gland and decreased synthesis of thyroid hormone. Excess dietary iodine may also increase the risk of developing autoimmune thyroid disease and thyroid cancer. In order to prevent toxicity related health risks, an Upper Level of 1100 micrograms/day has been set [5]. Toxicities have been documented in situations where environmental iodine was a factor and when excessive iodine fortification has occurred.

7.1.10. Selenium

Selenium functions as an important component of various enzymes and proteins within the body. Most importantly, selenium functions as a part of antioxidant molecules that prevent lipid peroxidation and cell membrane damage. Selenium is also required for the conversion of thyroxine to triiodothyronine in some tissues and is therefore important for proper thyroid metabolism [30]. Selenium may be important for immune function but additional studies are needed to clarify it's role in the prevention of disease. The selenium content in food varies greatly according to where it was grown and the relative selenium content of the soil; typically, seafood, meats, nuts, and grain products are good sources [31]. Currently, the RDA for adults is set at 55 μg/day [6]. The RDA was established based on the amount of selenium needed for optimal glutathione peroxidase activity in the blood. In North America, the average adult consumes adequate amounts daily.

Selenium is commonly found in plant foods as selenomethionine and in animal products as selenocysteine. Inorganic forms of selenium such as selenide, selenite, and selenate are found in various vegetables and yeast. With regard to dietary supplements, the most commonly found forms of selenium are selenomethionine, selenate, and selenite. Selenium absorption occurs very efficiently in the small intestine. Afterwards, it is bound to transport proteins and makes its way to the liver and other tissues. It is unclear exactly how selenium is released from transport proteins and taken up by the tissues. It is known however, that many tissues contain high concentrations of selenium; the thyroid gland, liver, kidneys, muscle, heart, and pancreas contain the highest levels. Smaller amounts of selenium can be found in the lungs, brain, bone, and red blood cells. It has been noted that the administration of selenomethionine results in higher selenium tissue concentrations than the administration of selenite [7]. The opposite is true with regard to selenium uptake by glutathione peroxidase; selenite administration yields higher mineral incorporation [31].

Deficiencies specific to inadequate selenium intake have not been reported.

However, it is believed that inadequate intake may negatively affect thyroid metabolism and may lead to the development of Keshan disease, a condition of insufficient cardiac function. Typically, this type of deficiency occurs in situations where individuals consume regionally restricted diets, where the soil provides very little selenium [7].

Selenium toxicity has been reported; for this reason, an UL of 400 µg/day has been set [6]. Intake that exceeds the UL may result in nausea, diarrhea, fatigue, hair loss, and dermatological issues [6]. This type of toxicity can occur in a situation where an individual is consuming excessive selenium through vitamin or mineral supplements, or in areas with high selenium levels in drinking water.

7.1.11. Chromium

The importance of chromium in the diet is not fully understood but it is believed to have an impact on insulin activity and the regulation of blood sugar [5]. Chromium is commonly supplemented by athletes because it is believed to enhance strength and muscle mass, however, at this time, there is not sufficient evidence to support this belief.

Chromium can be obtained from foods such as meat, eggs, liver, mushrooms, and dried beans.

After consumption, it is believed that chromium is absorbed in the small intestine [5]. Absorption is estimated to take place at a rate of 0.4 to 2.5% and occur by either diffusion or by carrier-mediated transport. Within the blood, Cr^{3+} binds with transferrin and is transported with iron; albumin may also work as a transporter. If the concentration of chromium is extremely high, globulins and lipoproteins transport the mineral as well. It is possible that unbound chromium circulates within the bloodstream but the mechanism by which this occurs remains unclear [7]. Estimations of chromium body stores range from 4-6 mg [5]. Chromium is believed to be stored along with ferric iron and is found in high concentrations in the kidneys, liver spleen, heart, pancreas, bone, and muscle tissue. There is evidence that chromium concentrations within the tissues declines over time [5].

Identifying the deficiency symptoms associated with low intake of chromium is a difficult task. However, cases have been reported in individuals receiving chromium-free parenteral solutions. Symptoms observed in these cases included weight loss, nerve damage, and glucose intolerance [15]. The effects of consuming chromium in high amounts is a concern but evidence of overdose or toxicity is limited therefore, an Upper Level has not been set at this time [5].

7.1.12. Molybdenum and Ultratrace Minerals

Though molybdenum is needed in very small amounts, it is essential for the activity of multiple enzymes. This mineral can be obtained from foods such as grains, legumes, and nuts but the actual content is variable and depends on the soil where the food was grown. Because of its important role as an enzyme co-factor, an RDA has been established and is currently set at 45 micrograms/day [5]. Both deficiencies and toxicities related to molybdenum intake are rare, however, an Upper Level has been set at 2000 µg/day because of the undesirable effects noted in research animals. The amount of molybdenum found in human tissues is very low, roughly 0.1-1.0 micrograms/gram of wet weight [7]. Within the tissues, molybdenum is found as molybdate, free molybdopterin, or enzyme-bound molybdopterin; the highest concentrations are in the liver, kidneys, and bone [5].

Much less is known about the ultratrace minerals boron, nickle, silicon, and vanadium. The bodily functions which they support have not been clearly defined as of yet. It is suspected that they participate as co-enzymes but additional research is needed before RDAs or Adequate Intakes can be determined. Due to concerns associated with toxicity, Upper Levels have been established for boron (20 mg/day), nickel (1 mg/day), and vanadium (1.8 mg/day) [5].

7.1.13. Boron

Boron, an element with the atomic number of five is found naturally as boric acid or its salt borax. Borate compounds have a low toxicity in mammals similar to sodium chloride. Due to its antimicrobial properties, it was first used a food preservative in 1870 to extend the shelf-life of meat and dairy products especially during World War I and World War II. Use of boric acid in food, however, fell out of favor as tolerable upper limits (4 g/day) were established due to gastrointestinal distress and was widely disapproved for use in food in the 1950s [32]. Despite bans, borax is still used today to preserve caviar and illegally to enhance the texture of noodles in Asian countries.

Due in part to its restriction as a food additive, boron is has not been considered a nutrient for humans. It is, however, widely accepted as an essential nutrient for the life cycle of plants and is found in all plant cell walls. Its exact biochemical function for plant reproduction, however, has evaded scientists since the 1920s. Boron has also been found to be required for the reproductive cycle of frogs and zebra fish without a clear explanation of its function [32]. Boron-deprived frogs display atrophied sex organs, sperm dysfunction, and 80% of resulting embryos died within four days of development [33]. To date there are no studies directly showing that boron is essential to complete the life cycle in mammals [32]. Low dietary boron intake has been associated with increased incidence of certain types of cancer in the reproductive system of humans, however. In an epidemiological study, individuals with low boron intake had a higher risk of prostate cancer [34]. Similarly in a survey of 1059 women classified into categories of high to low boron intake, fifteen women in the low intake group (<1.26 mg/day) were diagnosed with cervical cancer while no cases were found in the high intake group [35]. This may be evidence that boron plays a role in the reproductive cycle of humans.

Boron has been most strongly researched in relation to bone development and health. Boron supplementation has been shown to prevent the gross bone abnormalities which generally present in vitamin D deficient animal models [32]. Cheng [36] found that supplementation of boron in ostrich chicks, which are used as animal model for osteoporosis, promoted bone mineral density and dramatically increased tibia bone strength. Effects in animal models have not yet been fully translated to human models, however. A nutritional survey of free-living Korean females found a daily average intake of 0.92 mg boron but did not find a statistical correlation between increased boron intake and bone mineral density. Researchers, however, noted that subjects did not display increased risk of osteoporosis despite calcium deficiency. This may indicate need for boron was met at the levels in the Korean diet and no further benefit could be garnered from additional consumption. At present, it would be presumptuous to claim boron as essential for bone health although one study actually linked boron deficiency with the presentation of Kashin-Beck Disease, a malady of bones characterized by death of cartilage cells in the growth plate and joints [37].

There is not yet enough evidence that boron is an essential nutrient for health and development in humans. Current research, however, suggests that there may be health benefits to sufficient boron consumption. Given the present status of current research, it is apparent that boron's effect on health and its biochemical mechanisms of action in mammals are deserving of further research.

7.2. Muscle

Muscle constitutes the greatest fraction of body mass for healthy weight individuals. Muscle (and muscle foods) contains a substantial content of many vitamins and minerals. However, this tissue is mainly associated with protein synthesis, storage, and functions.

In order to store protein and other nutrients in muscle, adequate intake of the correct amount of amino acids from dietary protein is needed. Humans require dietary protein because it contributes to the body's supply of indispensable amino acids and to its supply of nitrogen for synthesis of dispensable amino acids. The **quality of a protein** depends on its digestibility and indispensable amino acid composition. Quality can be measured directly from digestibility studies in animals, along with the amino acid profile. Animal growth is dependent on their muscle and other tissue receiving adequates quanities of essential amino acids in ratios that the tissue needs for protein synthesis, and the blood supply or tissue metabolism must also make non-essential amino acids at a rate sufficient for **translation** of messenger RNA into new proteins. The body cannot make a protein with a missing amino acid! Commonly, the proteins in plant sources of food do not contain amino acids that are essential for humans in the ratio that our tissue need. If a dietary protein is poorly digestible, due to food processing effects or the ability of a plant to protects its tissue from degradation, the lower rate of absorption also will limit the ability of that type of protein to support tissue growth.

Therefore, foods that label their protein content as a percentage of the Daily Value for protein adjust the crude protein content by a factor calculated from the protein digestibility corrected amino acid score (PDCAAS). This measurement combines an animal-based digestibility study with the amino acid chemical score, defined as the ratio of the most limiting essential amino acid in the food to the requirement for that amino acid in the diet of growing children.

7.2.1. Introduction to Contractile protein functions

Protein is a key component in a human body that is involved in several different pathways and systems in order for the body to maintain good health. Proteins function as enzymes, messengers, hormones, immunoprotectors, transporters, buffers, fluid balancers and structural elements [7]. Proteins play an important role in organ development and structure. The physical structure of proteins includes gross classifications as contractile proteins, fibrous proteins and globular proteins [7]. Each different type of protein has a unique role in how it aids the body and in maintaining healthy organs.

In muscle fibers, actin and myosin interact within sarcomeres, which are contractile units of muscle cells [7] in all muscle types: skeletal, smooth, and cardiac. Although there are several other contractile proteins such as tropomyosin, troponin, and actinin, actin and myosin are the biggest contributors to muscle [38]. Actin is copious in the human muscle, but it can also be found in many other cells [38]. Actin functions properly when it has been polymerized to form a longer and stronger filament, capable of involvement in muscle contraction via interaction with myosin [38]. While actin serves as a "cable to lengthen sarcomere" [29], myosin aids in the opposite action in the sarcomere, shortening the muscle fiber unit during contraction. Myosin does this via converting "chemical energy in ATP into force that shortens the sarcomere." [38]. These two contractile proteins are found in other body cells besides muscle, but the concentration of the two tend to vary according to species and muscle cell and body type. Myosin and actin activity for contraction of cells is very dependent on ionic activity of calcium [7].

Phosphorus is a component of ATP, which is the major form of energy that is stored and transferred within the body. As the phosphate bond of the ATP molecule is broken, energy is then released. It is also a source of energy in the form of creatine phosphate, which can donate the phosphate group to adenosine diphosphate (ADP) to create ATP. The muscles utilize

this energy during strenuous activities and exercise [7]. Many biochemical reactions that require hydrolysis of the high-energy bonds of ATP result in ADP plus free inorganic phosphate ions. However, in muscle contraction, ATP donates its terminal phosphate to a binding site on myosin, which permits a change in the protein structure to shorten the length or the actin-myosin complex.

Another contractile protein with a role in muscle and cell activity is tropomyosin. Although the name suggests this protein is related to myosin, in actuality tropomyosin is associated with actin. Tropomyosin binds to actin when the muscle cell is at rest to block the actin-myosin interactions that result in contraction [38]. The structure of tropomyosin found in muscle differs from the tropomyosin found in other cells [38].

Troponin is another protein involved in muscle contraction. The subunit troponin I has binding capability with tropomyosin and the subunit troponin C binds to calcium when an action potential signals Ca^{++} release from the sarcoplasmic reticulum. Ca^{++} binding to troponin C weakens the troponin I binding to tropomyosin, which allows the tropomyosin to uncover the actiin-myosin interaction sites and muscle contraction can occur until the sarcoplasmic reticulum actively reabsorbs the Ca^{++} ions. The sequential binding allows for the relaxation of muscle and hence troponin-tropomyosin complexes are known as "relaxing proteins" [38].

7.2.1.1. Protein Turnover in Humans

Proteins are constantly being synthesized, degraded, recycled and oxidized in the human body. The combination of these events is referred to as Whole Body Protein Turnover (WBPT). Inputs to the amino acid pool come from dietary intake, the degradation and recycling of endogenous proteins, and de novo synthesis of non-essential amino acids. The liver is the main site of amino acid metabolism and is involved in maintaining the amino acid pool, which is small in terms of total body protein, and is not intended as a long-term storage of proteins, but as a means to support the ongoing flux described above between the fed and fasted states. An in vitro study of various cell types reported that the free amino acid pools had a similar composition of amino acids across a variety of cell lines, suggesting this is a well-regulated process [39].

The concept of protein balance refers to the net effect of protein synthesis less protein degradation. A healthy adult is said to be in protein balance when these two events are equal. Positive protein balance reflects greater synthesis than degradation, which is associated with periods of growth, while negative protein balance reflects greater degradation than synthesis, which is associated with disease, aging, and endurance athletics. These will be discussed in greater detail in the next section. There are several techniques for measuring protein balance, which are well described by Lui et al [40]. Briefly, Nitrogen Balance studies compute nitrogen intake via dietary records and nitrogen excretion via urinary and fecal loss. This is a simple measurement that does not give tissue-specific information, but it is non-invasive and relatively easy to compute, so it is a useful measure. Tracer Methods use isotopes of essential amino acids (e.g. leucine or phenylalanine) to monitor protein synthesis and degradation. 3-Methylhistidine is a method for measuring skeletal muscle protein degradation by quantifying urinary excretion of 3-methylhistidine, and Non-Tracer Methods study protein synthesis pathways via mRNA using tools such as Northern Blot Analysis (for detecting mRNA) and Polymerase Chain Reaction (for amplifying mRNA).

Studies of various protein intake levels can provide insights into protein storage and the regulation of whole body protein turnover (WBPT). A study in healthy adult males using a tracer method found that those who were fed a high protein diet (2.5g/kg/day) had higher leucine oxidation and higher urea production, than those fed 1.0g/kg/day, while both diets had similar nitrogen balance (nitrogen intake less nitrogen excretion) [41]. This study also showed that while both the high and low protein diets resulted in similar declines in protein degradation by exogenously replenishing the amino acid pool, the high protein diet stimulated a greater level of protein synthesis, suggesting that protein gains from high protein diets are the result of both increased synthesis and reduced degradation, while the protein gains on a low protein diet were caused primarily by a reduction in degradation. A similar study of low (0.8 g/kg), moderate (1.8 g/kg), and high (3.6 g/kg) protein diets using a leucine tracer in male runners showed that protein oxidation increased with high protein diets, and that runners on the low-protein diet were in negative nitrogen balance, suggesting that the current RDA might not meet their protein needs [42]. Finally, a cross-over study using a glycine tracer and nitrogen balance analysis in non-elderly adult men and women reported that nitrogen excretion was significantly higher when protein was 21% versus 12% of an isocaloric diet [43]. Protein synthesis and breakdown were both higher in the 21% protein diets than in the 12% protein diet. These three studies supports the theory that excess protein is not stored for long-term use.

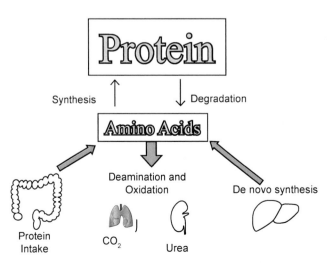

Figure 7.2-1: Overview of amino acid metabolism.

7.2.1.2. Events Associated with Protein Storage and Protein Degradation

Growth and development periods (childhood, pregnancy, and lactation) are times of positive protein balance which would dictate higher dietary protein requirements to meet these needs as recommended in the DRIs. Events associated with a loss of body protein stores include aging, illness and trauma, and endurance exercise, which also might indicate the need for more protein in the diet to offset increased protein degradation.

Increased protein synthesis in growth and development must be supported by adequate protein intake, so protein RDAs for children are greater than for adults. Bangladeshi children between age 3 and 11 who consumed an energy-adjusted diet of higher protein had a significantly higher weight gain, but not height gain [44] than those on a lower protein diet. Among malnourished children recovering from shigellosis, a bacterial infection of the intestine, those who received a high protein diet (15% of total energy) had a significantly higher rate of linear growth and a small decline in diarrheal morbidity compared to those on a standard protein diet (7.5% of total energy) [45]. Leucine tracer protein kinetics in asymptomatic infants with HIV showed a higher percentage of leucine oxidized compared to a healthy control group. The reduced access to leucine for protein synthesis may help explain the weight loss that is often observed in HIV infants [46].

There has been significant research into whether athletics has an impact on whole body protein turnover, and as a result, on dietary protein requirements. A cross-over nitrogen balance study in 14-year old male soccer players fed varying protein levels (1.0 g/kg, 1.2 g/kg, and 1.4 g/kg) reported a negative nitrogen balance at 1.0 g/kg, suggesting that the RDA of .85g/kg for athletes in this age group may be too low [47]. Adult athletes do not have the added protein demands associated with increased growth seen in these pubescent athletes and therefore different protein kinetics would be anticipated in the adult athlete. Tarnopolsky reviewed the research on protein requirements in adult endurance athletes and found that moderately to well-trained endurance athletes show negative nitrogen balance at ranges above the current RDA of 0.8 g/kg, with men showing a greater negative balance than women [48]. Protein intake greater than the RDA may be needed to fully meet the protein requirements in athletes.

Lower protein synthesis rates in elderly than in younger people [43] may be explained by several regulatory variable changes, including lower growth hormones and lower total energy and protein intakes due to reduced appetites. Ryazanov et al. [49] hypothesized that a decline in protein synthesis and an increase in protein damage creates a positive feedback loop that contributes to the process of aging. Dorrens et al [50] report the occurrence of sarcopenia in up to 60% of people over 80 years old and provides a succinct review of the effects of aging on whole body and muscle protein turnover. A randomized, double-blinded placebo-controlled study in healthy men and women ages 65-88 showed that administration of Growth Hormone (GH) increased protein synthesis in both men and women [51].

7.2.2. Role of Vitamin D in muscle

Recent research also suggests that the benefits of vitamin D may extend to the musculoskeletal system as well. This finding may not be too surprising, given in vitro data showing that muscle, white adipose tissue, and bone cells can derive from the same type of stem cells when exposed to different cytokines. Many children may have insufficient serum concentrations of vitamin D, which could prevent optimal muscle development and function. Vitamin D deficiency in animal models results in negative effects on muscle fiber structure and calcium/phosphorus handling, suggesting an integral role of vitamin D in skeletal muscle function. While there is a dearth of data in humans, the available evidence demonstrates a positive association between vitamin D status and muscle function. The association between vitamin D and muscle is strengthened by these observations and the fact that $1,25(OH)_2D$ exerts its action by binding to VDRs. Flux of Ca^{2+} in skeletal muscle is differentially affected by $25(OH)D$ and $1,25(OH)_2D$. But future research is necessary to elucidate whether $1,25(OH)_2D$-stimulated synthesis of these Ca^{2+}-binding proteins in muscle is dependent on activation of the VDRE gene [7].

7.3. References

1. Young JF, Luecke RH, Pearce BA, Lee T, Ahn H, Moon H, Dye DW, Davis TM, & Taylor SJ. (2009) Human organ/tissue growth algorithms that include obese individuals and black/ white population organ weight similarities from autopsy data. Journal of Toxicology and Environmental Health, Part A, 72:8, 527-540, DOI: 10.1080/15287390802647203

2. Kohlmeier, M. Fat-soluble vitamins and non-nutrients. In: Nutrient Metabolism. 1st ed. San Diego, CA. Academic Press: 2003: 464-501

3. Hunt, S.M. & Groff, J. L. The Vitamins Part 2: The Fat-soluble vitamins. In: Advanced Nutrition and Human Metabolism. 8th ed. St. Paul, MN. West Publishing Company: 1990: 226-252

4. Heath, ML, and Sidbury R. (2006) Cutaneous manifestation of nutritional deficiency. Current Opinion in Pediatrics. 18.4: 417-22.

5. National Research Council. Dietary Reference Intakes for Vitamin A, Vitamin K, Arsenic, Boron, Chromium, Copper, Iodine, Iron, Manganese, Molybdenum, Nickel, Silicon, Vanadium, and Zinc. Washington, DC: The National Academies Press, 2001

6. Institute of Medicine . (2000). Dietary Reference Intakes for Vitamin C, Vitamin E, Selenium, and Carotenoids. Washington, DC: National Academies Press. Retrieved from http://www.nap.edu/catalog/11767.html

7. Gropper SS, Smith JL. Advanced nutrition and human metabolism. 6th Ed. Belmont (CA) Cengage Learning;2013

8. Bojanić V Radović J, Bojanić Z, Lazović M. (2011) Hydrosouble vitamins and sport. Acta medica medianae, 50(2): 68 - 75

9. Otten JJ, Hellwig JP, Meyers LD, (Editors) Dietary Reference Intakes: The Essential Guide to Nutritrient Requirements. 2006. Washington DC: National Academies Press. Retrieved from http://www.nap.edu/catalog.php?record_id=11537

10. Zink,D L. (1997) The impact of consumers demands and traends on food processing. Emerging Infectious Diseases. 3(4): 467-69.

11. Radimer, K., Bindewald, B., Hughes, J., Ervin, B., et al. (2004). Dietary supplement use by US adults: data from the National Health and Nutrition Examination Survey, 1999-2000. Am J Epidemiol, 160(4), 339- 349.

12. Subramanian VS, Subramanya SB, and Said HM. (2011) Chronic alcohol exposure negatively impacts the physiological and molecular parameters of the renal biotin rabsorption process. American Journal of Physiology, Renal Physiology. 300(3): F611- F617.

13. Taylor A. (1996) Detection and monitoring of disorders of essential trace elements. Ann Clin Biochem. 33:486-510.

14. Nielson, F.H. (2000) Importance of making dietary recommendations for elements designates as nutritionally beneficial, pharmacologically beneficial, or conditionally essential. J. Trace Elem. Exp. Med. 13: 113-129.

15. Byrd-Bredbenner C, Moe G, Beshgetoor D, Berning J. Trace Minerals. In: Wardlaw's perspectives in nutrition. 8th ed. New York, NY: Mc-Graw-Hill: 2009: 534-571.

16. Donovan A, Roy C, Andrews N. (2005) The ins and outs of iron homeostasis. Physiology. 21:115.

17. Souminen P, Mottonen T, Rajamaki A, Irjala K. (2000) Single values of serum transferrin receptor and transferrin receptor ferritin index can be used to detect true and functional iron deficiency in rheumatoid arthritis patients with anemia. Arthritis Rheum. 43:1016.

18. Muller O, Krawinkel M. (2005) Malnutrition and health in developing countries. Can Med Assoc J. 173:279.

19. Franchini M, Veneri D. (2005) Hereditary hemochromatosis. Hematology. 10:145.

20. Food Surveys Research Group. What we eat in America, NHANES 2001-2002. 2005 [cited 2012 Dec]. Available from: http://www.ars.usda.gov/SP2UserFiles/Place/ 12355000/pdf/0102/usualintaketables2001-02.pdf.

21. Kang YJ. (2006) Metallothionein redox cycle and function. Exp Biol Med. 231:1459.

22. Cousins RJ, Liuzzi JP, Lichten LA. (2006) Mammalian zinc transport, trafficking, and signals. J Biol Chem.281:24085-89.

23. McMahon R, Cousins R. (1998) Mammalian zinc transporters. J Nutr.128:667-70.

24. King JC, Cousins RJ. Zinc. In: Shils ME, Shike M, Ross A, Caballero B, eds. Modern nutrition in health and disease. 10th ed. Philadelphia: Lippincott Williams & Wilkins; 2006.

25. Beshgetoor D, Hambidge KM. (1998) Clinical conditions altering copper metabolism in humans. Am J Clin Nutr. 67:1007S.

26. Critchfield J, Keen C. (1992) Manganese+2 exhibits dynamic binding to multiple ligands in human plasma. Metabolism. 41:1087-92.

27. Jeng A, Shamoo A. (1980) Isolation of a Ca^{2+} carrier from calf heart inner mitochondrial membrane. J Biol Chem. 255:6897-903.

28. Korc M. Manganese as a modulator of signal transduction pathways. In: Prasad AS, ed. Essential and Toxic Trace Elements in Human Health and Disease: An Update. New York: Wiley-Liss, 1993, 235- 55.

29. Grider A. Zinc, copper, and manganese. In: Stipanuk MH, ed. Biochemical, physiological, molecular aspects of human nutrition. 2nd ed. St. Louis, MO: Sanders; 2006.

30. Papp LV, Lu J, Holmgren A, Khanna KK. (2007) From selenium to selenoproteins: Synthesis, identity and their role in human health. Antioxid Redox Signal. 9:775.

31. Whanger P, Butler J. (1998) Effects of various dietary levels of selenium as selenite or selenomethionine on tissue selenium levels and glutathione peroxidase activity in rats. J Nutr . 118:846-52.

32. Nielson, F.H. (2008) Is boron nutritionally relevant? Nutr. Rev. 66(4), 183-191.

33. Fort, D.J.; Stover, E.L.; Strong, P.L.; Murray, F.J.; Keen, C.L. (1999) Chronic feeding of a low boron diet adversely affects reproduction and development in xenopus laevis. J. Nutr. 129, 2055-2060.

34. Cul, Y.; Winton, M.I.; Zhang, Z.F.; Ralney, C.; Marshall, J.; De Kernion, J.B.; Eckhert, C.D. (2004) Bietary boron intake and prostate cancer risk. Oncol. Rep. 11, 887-892.

35. Korkmanz, M.; Uzgoren, E.; Bakirdere, S.; Aydin, F.; Ataman, O.Y. (2007) Effect of dietary boron on cervical cytopathology and on micronucleus frequency in exfoliate buccal cells. Environ. Toxicol. 22: 17-25.

36. Cheng, J.; Peng, K.; Jin, E.; Zhang, Y.; Liu, Y.; Zhang, N.; Song, H.; Liu, H.; Tang, Z. (2011) Effect of additional boron on tibias of African ostrich chicks. Biol. Trace Elem Res. 144: 538-549.

37. Peng, X.; Lingxia, Z.; Schrauzer, G.N.; Xiong, G. (2000) Selenium, boron, and germanium deficiency in the etiology of kashin-beck disease. Biol. Trace Elem. Res. 77: 193-197.

38. Stossel, T. P. [1978]. "Contractile Proteins in Cell Structure and Function." Annual Review of Medicine, 29:427-457

39. Young VR, Marchini JS. (1990) Mechanisms and nutritional significance of metabolic response to altered intakes of protein and amino acids, with reference to nutritional adaption in humans. Am J Clin Nutr [internet]. 51:270-289.

40. Lui Z, Barrett EJ. (2002) Human protein metabolism: its measurement and regulation. Am J Physiol Endocrinol Metab [internet]. 283:E1105-E1112.

41. Forslund AH, Hambraeus L, Olsson RM, El-Khoury AE, Yu YM, Young VR. (1998) The 24-h whole body leucine and urea kinetics at normal and high protein intakes with exercise in healthy adults. Am J Physiol Enocrinol Metab [internet]. 275:E310-320.

42. Gaine PC, Pikosky MA, Martin WF, Bolster DR, Maresh CM, Rodriguez NR. (2006) Level of dietary protein impacts whole body protein turnover in trained males at rest. Metabolism [internet]. 55:501-507.

43. Pannermans DLE, Halliday D, Westerterp KR, Kester ADM. (1995) Effect of variable protein intake on whole-body protein turnover in young men and women. Am J Clin Nutr [internet]. 61:69-74.

44. Torres A, Orav J, Willett W, Chen L. (1994) Association between protein intake and 1y weight and height gains in Bangladeshi children aged 3-11y. Am J Clin Nutr [internet]. 60:448-454.

45. Kabir I, Rahman MM, Haider R, Mazumder RN, Khaled MA, Mahalanabis D. Increased height gain of children fed a high-protein diet during convalescence from Shigellosis: a six-month follow-up study. J Nutr [internet]. 1998;128(10):1688-1691.

46. Jahoor F, Abramson S, Heird WC. (2003) The protein metabolic response to HIV infection in young children. Am J Clin Nutr [internet]. 78:182-189.

47. Boisseau N, Vermorel M, Rance M, Duche P, Patureau-Mirand P. (2007) Protein requirements in male adolescent soccer players. Eur J Appl Physiol [internet]. 100:27-33.

48. Tarnopolsky M. (2004) Protein requirements for endurance athletes. Nutrition [internet]. 20:662-668.

49. Ryazanov AG, Nefsky BS. (2002) Protein turnover plays a key role in aging. Mechanisms of Ageing and Development [internet].123:207-213.

50. Dorrens J, Ronnie MJ. (2003) Effects of aging and human whole body and muscle protein turnover. Scand J Med & Sci Sports. 13(1): 26-33.

51. Huang X, Blackman MR, Herreman K, Pabst KM, Harman SM, Caballero B. Effects of growth hormone and/or sex steroid administration on whole-body protein turnover in healthy aged women and men. Metabolism [internet]. 2005;54:1162-1167.

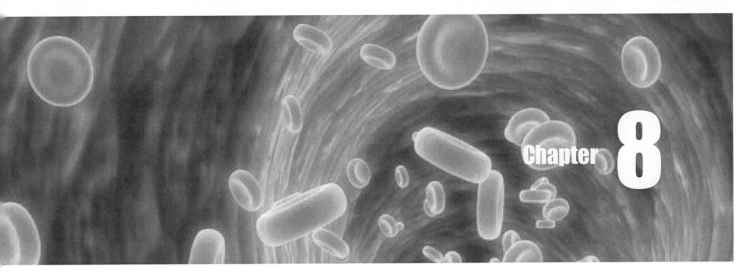

Chapter 8

Nutrients that Build and Comprise Blood

Learning Objectives

After reading this chapter, you will be able to:

1. Identify proteins that are important components of blood serum and describe their functions.

2. Describe the role of blood iron, zinc, and copper in development of blood oxygen carrying capacity.

3. Outline the functions of folate and cobalamin in blood cell development and prevention of anemia.

4. Describe how vitamin K promotes blood clotting and how this activity determines vitamin K requirements.

5. Explain the importance of electrolyte ions in blood and how their concentration is maintained.

6. Explain the functions of water in the body

7. Describe how water is absorbed and transported in the body

8. Evaluate how the body regulates water balance

9. Identify factors that affect the body's maintenance of proper hydration

10. Explain how the different organ systems work together to maintain water homeostasis

8.1. Introduction

Protein, as described in the previous section, is also an important constituent of blood, where it has enzymatic, osmotic, and transport functions. The soluble proteins in the plasma fraction are synthesized by the liver and other organs, whereas the cell fractions develop in the bone marrow.

Albumin constitutes 60% of the protein in serum. Its primary functions are maintaining osmotic pressure in the vascular compartment, and binding small molecules for transport to target tissues throughout the body [1]. Alpha-1-antitrypsin is a serum protease inhibitor. **Ceruloplasmin** aids in copper transport, and **transferrin** is the major transport protein for iron. **C-reactive protein** (CRP) is an indication of

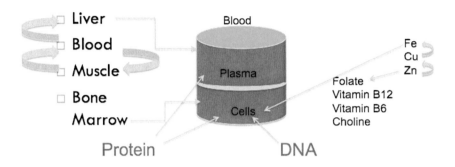

Figure 8.1-1: Diagram of nutrient constituents in the component parts of a centrifuged blood sample.

the level of systemic inflammation. Serum **ferritin** is an indicator of the iron status of an individual, and **prealbumin** can be an indicator of general protein and energy nutritional status. **Haptoglobin** is a blood protein that helps retain hemoglobin that is present in serum when red cells lyse. **Immunoglobulins** (IgA, IgD, IgE, IgG, and IgM) are antibodies produced by white blood cells that aid in immunity. As a whole, they make up a major fraction of the globular proteins in blood. Each of these antibodies has a somewhat different function, but all have the capacity to bind to specific antigenic sites on proteins. **Lipoproteins** have the capacity to coalesce lipids, such as cholesterol and triglycerides, into transportable particles and deliver the lipid by lipoprotein binding to specific receptors at targets throughout out the body. Other proteins that can be measured in blood or serum as indicators of health or disease states are orosomucoid (a drug binding protein), alpha-2-macroglobulin, beta-2-microglobulin, complement, cystatin-C, prealbumin, and rheumatoid factor [1].

Proper red blood cell maturation depends on the B vitamins listed in **Figure 8.1.1,** folate, cobalamin, and pyridoxine, (along with others) as well as iron. Synthesizing the oxygen carrying capacity of red

blood cells with their iron-containing hemoglobin also depends on adequate copper and zinc nutrition.

8.2. Iron

Every cell within the human body contains iron as it is an essential part of many enzymes. Red blood cells require iron, bound to hemoglobin, in order to transport oxygen throughout the body. Muscle cells require iron in myglobin for a similar function, storing oxygen for delivery to the muscle cell for metabolism that must suddenly start or stop. Mitochondrial cytochromes also require iron molecules to shuttle electrons during oxidative metabolism. Given the importance of oxygen as a terminal electron acceptor in aerobic metabolism, and the function of iron in transporting oxygen, it is clear that iron has acritical role in the aerobic metabolism of nutrients.

Iron is an essential component of the oxygen carrier present in blood. **Hemoglobin** transports oxygen from the lungs to all tissues and assists in transport of some carbon dioxide back to the lungs for expiration. **Erythropoietin** is a hormone that targets the bone marrow to produce more red blood cells. When the oxygen carrying capacity of blood begins to decline the kidneys will produce the erythropoietin hormone. Red blood cell formation begins with a hemocystoblast (stem cell) in the bone marrow and proceeds through six steps until a mature blood cell is formed and released into circulation. The average life span of a red blood cell in the circulation is 120 days. If a person's diet or body storage of iron needs are not met, red blood cell synthesis will be reduced and erythrocytes that are produced in the low iron environment will have less than the normal amount of functional hemoglobin. The amount of red blood cells and hemoglobin will fall so low that the amount of oxygen carried in the blood will decrease, a condition referred to as **anemia**. Iron deficiency is the major type of anemia found world-wide.

Over the past twenty years, a growing body of evidence has linked iron metabolism with insulin resistance. Even though an iron deficiency can result in anemia, high levels of iron promote the formation of reactive oxygen species (ROS). Pancreatic β cells are thought to be particularly vulnerable to ROS generation. An examination of multiple studies revealed that increased iron, either heme-iron intake or circulating levels of ferritin, is a risk factor for type II diabetes [2]. It has been shown that in healthy individuals, independent of known risks for diabetes, higher iron stores are associated with an increased chance in acquiring type II diabetes [3].

The hypothesis underlying the mechanism for the role of iron in type II diabetes initiates from its ability to cause adipose cells to release free fatty acids (FFA). The FFA, according to the hypothesis, are then utilized by the muscle, leaving excess glucose in the blood. This stresses the β cells, leading to insulin resistance. When adipocytes are treated with ferritin or iron *in vitro*, their ability to take up glucose is decreased [4]. It unclear if the iron is causing ROS damage, if the cells themselves cause the damage, or if it is a combination of both. Irrespective of the mechanism, there is clearly a strong relationship between iron and glucose metabolism [5]. Insulin has been shown to increase the uptake of transferrin in several cell types [6], and iron can influence glucose metabolism. In lab tests involving rats that were fed different protein diets consisting of 19.5 to 67.5% casein, researchers observed decreased insulin sensitivity in the high protein fed rats [7]. In another study, when patients with transfusional iron overload were given a glucose tolerance test, they had two-hour blood glucose levels above the fasting level. This indicated a disruption in their glucose metabolism [8]. Animal studies using ob/ob mice (leptin knockout mice) fed a low iron diet demonstrated many beneficial effects, including the ability of the diet to reverse insulin insensitivity. The authors were also able to demonstrate an effect with iron chelation [9].

Given that iron is a risk factor for type II diabetes, one may wonder about the metabolic and endocrine effects of removing iron from the blood, similar to the studies with the ob/ob mice. Leeches and bleeding were once common practices within the medical profession, and there is some evidence that phlebotomy may be a successful therapy for patients with various metabolic diseases. Patients with non-alcoholic fatty liver diseases, which confer a higher risk of type II diabetes, had lower serum glucose and insulin levels after iron depletion [10]. Men who donate blood frequently had increased insulin sensitivity and decreased iron stores [11]. Patients with type II diabetes, as well as those with high serum ferritin, displayed metabolic benefits from blood clotting [12].

The effects of iron are not limited to hepatocytes and β cells. New evidence is beginning to relate iron, in the form of serum ferritin, with altered adipocyte signaling. Adiponectin is an adipokine that improves insulin sensitivity. A recent paper linked iron to metabolic effects via changes in adiponectin. They demonstrated higher levels of serum ferritin in metabolic syndrome patients and type II diabetics, lower adiponectin, and an inverse correlation between serum adiponectin and serum ferritin. The researchers confirmed their findings in humans using mice that were fed low iron diets. The mice with low iron diets had higher adiponectin. Further, they confirmed previous reports showing a benefit for blood clotting. Men treated with phlebotomy had improved glucose tolerance after treatment [13].

8.3. Zinc and Copper

Zinc and copper minerals can influence the absorption of one another, and of iron. Zinc in high concentration inhibits Cu absorption by activating transcription of the metallothonein gene, producing enough metallothionein to complex copper entering enterocytes. In blood, Cu carried by the ceruloplasmin enzyme reduces Fe^{3+} to the Fe^{2+} form that can bind to transferrin. Transferrin is needed to move iron to reticulocytes for their maturation into erythrocytes. Therefore, as excess Zn reduces Cu absorption, the low ceruloplasmin level can decrease red blood cell synthesis.

More common, however, is the chronic Zn deficiency that affects 1/3 of the world's population. This zinc insufficiency is estimated to reduce immunity and may be associated with numerous disease impacts, such as 16% of lower respiratory tract infections,18% of malaria cases, and 10% of diarrheal disease [14].

8.4. Folate and cobalamin

Folate and vitamin B_{12} deficiencies produce a number of similar signs and symptoms. The two vitamins share a close relation due to their biochemical reactions. Both are responsible for DNA synthesis. In the target cells, such as erythroblast precursors, all forms of folate are converted to their coenzyme form tetrahydrofolic acid (THFA). Folate coenzymes act as acceptors and donors of one-carbon units in a variety of reactions used in the synthesis of DNA, metabolism of nucleic acids, and red blood cell formation. THFA transfers a one-carbon methlyne group (-CH_2) to uridylate to form the nucleotide thymidylate, which is an essential component of DNA and cellular replication. Myleloid stem cell conversion to erythroblasts and erythrocytes requires rapid cell division, but insufficient thymidine synthesis from uridine blocks the cell division process and leads to large nucleated erythroblast release, or erythrocytes that have had a longer period of cytoplasm development and cell size increase before cell division and denucleation of the erythrocytes (megaloblasts) takes place. The result of the folate or vitamin B_{12} deficiencies is **megaloblastic anemia**.

Pernicious anemia or cobalamin (B_{12}) deficiency is caused when the body's intestines cannot absorb vitamin B_{12}. Vitamin B_{12} is an important factor in the body's synthesis of red blood cells. Pernicious anemia is associated with a weakened stomach lining as well as an autoimmune condition that causes the body's immune system to attack the cells that produce the intrinsic

factor protein that is needed to bind with vitamin B_{12} in order for it to be absorbed.

8.5. Vitamin K

Vitamin K, the antihemorrhagic vitamin is also known as the clotting vitamin because without it blood may not clot. Compounds with vitamin K activity have a 2-methyl 1, 4- naphthoquinone ring with a substitution at position 3 (See **Figure 6.8.1**.) Phylloquinone (Vitamin K1) and menaquinone (vitamin K2) are the naturally occurring forms of vitamin K.

8.5.1. Metabolism

Dietary vitamin K is provided as phylloquinone in plant foods and as a mixture of menaquinones in animal products, but mostly by plant foods and therefore most of the vitamin consumed is phylloquinone. Phylloquinone is absorbed from small intestine (jejunum) by an energy dependent process. The menaquinones appear to be absorbed from the distal ileum and colon by diffusion. Menaquinone is synthesized by bacteria in the lower digestive tract and can be absorbed from the colon to some extent by humans [15].

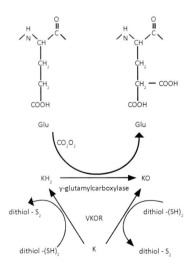

Figure 8.5-1: Vitamin K - protein interactions. "Carboxylation reaction vitamin K cycle" by Lomeloth - Wikimedia Commons - http://commons.wikimedia.o rg/wiki/File:Carboxylation_ reaction_vitamin_K_ cycle.p ng#mediaviewer/File:Carboxylation_ reaction_vitamin_K_cyle.png

TABLE 8.5-1: RDAs for vitamin K. From Reference [15]. Adequate Intake (AI) for Vitamin K			
Life Stage	Age	Males (µg/day)	Females (µg/day)
Infants	0-6 months	2.0	2.0
Infants	7-12 months	2.5	2.5
Children	1-3 years	30	30
Children	4-8 years	55	55
Children	9-13 years	60	60
Adolescents	14-18 years	75	75
Adults	19 years and older	120	90
Pregnancy	18 years and younger	-	75
Pregnancy	19 years and older	-	90
Breast-feeding	18 years and younger	-	75
Breast-feeding	19 years and older	-	90

Absorbed vitamin K becomes part of the chylomicrons and is carried by the chyclomicron remnants to the liver. In the liver the vitamin is incorporated into very low- density lipoproteins (VLDLs) and is carried to extrahepatic tissues via low density lipoproteins (LDLs). Selected tissues, such as the bone and kidney, are also sites for the synthesis of vitamin K-dependent proteins (Gla-proteins).

Metabolites of menaquinones are conjugated either with glucuronate or sulfate and are excreted in the urine or in the feces via the bile. Metabolites of phylloquinone are excreted primarily as glucuronides in the urine and in the feces via the bile.

8.5.2. Functions of Vitamin K

Vitamin K is a catalyst for the specific carboxylation reaction that converts selective glutamate side chains to gamma-carboxyglutamate (Gla) residues [16, 17]. The reaction is catalysed by a microsomal enzyme, γ-glutamyl, or vitamin K-dependent carboxylase, which in turn is linked to a cyclic salvage pathway known as the vitamin K epoxide cycle (**Figure 8.5.1.**).

The basic function of vitamin K involves post-translational processing of coagulation proteins called clotting factors (factors II (prothrombin), VII, IX and X), anticoagulation proteins (proteins C, S, Z, and M), and bone proteins osteocalcin and matrix-Gla protein, and certain ribosomal proteins.

The essential roles of gamma-carboxyglutamic acid residues are to allow protein to connect with membrane surfaces that result in blood clotting proteins attached to membranes of platelets and endothelial cells. The anticoagulant Warfarin blocks the conversion of vitamin K oxide (KO) to vitamin K. The second important role of the gamma carboxyglutamate group is to share in shaping proteins during intrachain calcium linkage, mediating interactions that connect two gamma- carboxyglutamic acids to a calcium ion. Hence, adequate plasma $[Ca^{2+}]$ is required for blood clotting.

8.5.3. Vitamin K Storage

The liver stores about 90% of menaquinones and 10% of phylloquinone. However, liver concentrations are reduced to about 25% of initial levels after 3 days without intake. Vitamin K is also stored in cell membranes in many tissues, including the lungs, kidneys, bone marrow, lymph nodes, and adrenal glands.

8.5.4. Sources of Vitamin K

Vitamin K is provided mostly as phylloquinone from plant foods. Vegetables that are the main dietary sources of vitamin K include leafy green vegetables, especially collards, spinach, turnip greens, some salad greens, and broccoli. Oils and margarine from plants are considered to be the second best sources of the vitamin. Cereals, fruits, dairy products, and meats contain a small amount of phylloquinone. Foods produced by fermentation using certain bacterial species are good sources of menaquinone.

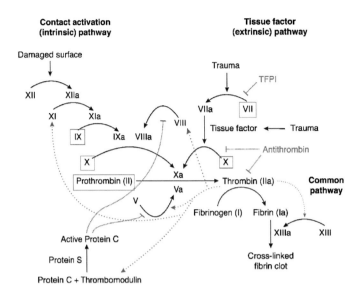

Figure 8.5-2: An overview of the enzyme cascade necessary for blood clotting. Factors in boxes are vitamin-K dependent. Modified From http://upload.wikimedia.org/wikipedia/commons/b/b6/Coagulation_full.svg

8.5.5. RDA and Deficiency of Vitamin K

Vitamin K deficiency is unlikely in adults. Newborn infants, people being treated chronically with antibiotics, people with severe gastrointestinal malabsorptive disorders, and the elderly, are the people most likely to be at risk. A newborn's diet of breast-milk is low in vitamin K. The RDA for vitamin K (**Table 8.5.1.**) for infants, is 2 µg of vitamin K. In addition, their stores of the vitamin are low because insufficient amounts cross the placenta and their intestinal tract is not yet populated by vitamin K-synthesizing bacteria. Thus, intramuscular injection of 0.5 to 1 mg of phylloquinone is recommended for all infants after birth [18].

Acute vitamin K deficiency is connected with bleeding episodes (hemorrhage). The undercarboxylated blood clotting factors cannot bind with calcium and interact with cell membrane phospholipids exposed on tissue injury, this interaction is important for thrombin generation and clot formation. Furthermore, cardiovascular disease or arterial calcification, and inflammation are connected with vitamin K deficiency.

8.5.6. Toxicity

The natural forms of vitamin K, even when supplemented in large amounts have caused no symptoms of toxicity and no Tolerable Upper Intake Level for the vitamin has been determined. Toxic effects reported in infants supplemented with menadione (synthetic product) include hemolytic anemia, hyperbilirubinemia, and kernicterus [15].

8.5.7. Vitamin K in Blood Clotting

Vitamin K plays a role in carboxylation of glutamic acid to form γ-carboxyglutamate in proteins involved in both blood clotting and the inhibition of clotting. A series of reactions, or enzyme cascade, is required to clot blood. There are two pathways that result in clotting, intrinsic and extrinsic; these pathways lead to a final common pathway in which thrombin activates fibrin, the protein required to form a clot. The intrinsic pathway begins with the activation of Factor XI or XII. Factor XIa (activated) then activates factor IX. Thrombin activates factor VIII, which associates with factor IXa and factor Xa (which was activated by factor IXa). FactorXa associates with prothrombin (factor II) and factor Va, which was activated by thrombin. Factor Xa then activates prothrombin to thrombin. Thrombin and factor XIIIa form fibrin that produces a clot. In the extrinsic pathway, factor VII is activated by thrombin, and factors Xa and XIIa, Factor VIIa activates factors IX and X. Here begins the common

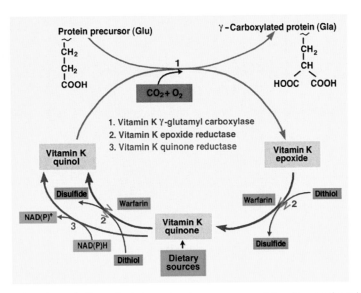

Figure 8.5-3: Catalysis of carboxylation of glutamate. (source www.bloodjournal.org)

pathway where factor Xa activates thrombin, leading to the formation of insoluble fibrin as discussed above in the intrinsic pathway (**Figure 8.5.2.**) [16].

Factors II (thrombin), VII, IX, and X are dependent on vitamin K for carboxylation. Carboxylation of proteins involved in blood clotting is performed in the liver, and vitamin K is required in its reduced form to begin the reaction. Oxidized vitamin K quinone is reduced by reductases to vitamin KH2, which can carboxylate glutamic acid with the addition of carbon dioxide and oxygen. This reaction also produces a vitamin K epoxide, which is then reduced back to a quinone, and the cycle can start again (**Figure 8.5.3**) [16].

8.6. Assessment

The major criterion for assessing vitamin K status is the direct measure of plasma prothrombin concentrations. Normal range is 80 to 120 µg/mL [15].8.6. Electrolytes are a major constituent of blood.

8.6.1. Sodium

Sodium helps regulate body pH and is essential for nerve transmission and muscle contraction. This macromineral is important in determining the membrane potential of cells. When sodium channels within a neuronal cell open, the cell is depolarized. This

depolarization creates an action potential, which signals to neuron to respond in a particular way [19]. Active transport from the sodium/potassium ATPase pump regulates the extracellular concentration of sodium and intracellular concentration of potassium.

8.6.2. Potassium

Potassium is the major intracellular cation. Ninety five percent of potassium is found within the cell [16]. The intracellular stores of potassium are analogous to the extracellular storage of sodium [20]. Potassium is obtained from fruits, especially bananas, cantaloupe, honeydew, mango, etc. This macro mineral helps keep blood pressure low and influences the contractility of smooth, skeletal, and cardiac muscle. High intracellular concentration of potassium is maintained by active transport, via the sodium/potassium pump [20]. The opening of potassium channels in the cell allows potassium to flow outward, down its concentration gradient and causes the cell to polarize. The re-polarization of a cell after it has been depolarized by sodium marks the end of an action potential. Because of this mechanism, potassium is extremely important for the excitability of nerve tissue [19]. Appropriate concentrations sodium, chloride, and potassium in blood allow for the electrochemical gradiaents in excitable cells.

8.6.3. Chloride

Chloride is the most abundant anion in extracellular fluid. Chloride balances the positive charge of sodium in the extracellular fluid. Approximately eighty eight percent of chloride is found in the extracellular fluid and the other twelve percent is found in the intracellular fluid. Chloride is normally the anion that accompanies sodium in foods.

Because table salt is sodium chloride, most foods that deliver sodium will also deliver chloride. Common foods that are high in chloride are salts, eggs, and meats [16].

Chloride is important for maintaining electrolyte balance and producing hydrochloric acid in the stomach to kill foreign organisms passing through the gastrointestinal tract. Gastric hydrochloric acid is secreted from the parietal cells in the stomach and denatures unwanted bacteria, virus, and proteins ingested with food.

Chloride is also released by white blood cells during phagocytosis to degrade unwanted, foreign material. Lastly, chloride is an exchange molecule for $HCO3^-$ in red blood cells. This is process is denoted the chloride shift. The chloride shift allows the transport of carbon dioxide from tissues to the lungs to be expelled. The transporter protein chloride bicarbonate exchanger takes the $HCO3^-$ out of the cell and into the plasma and chloride is transported into the red cell at the same time [21]. The presence of chloride is important because without it bicarbonate transport comes to a halt [16].

8.7. Water: Our Most Abundant Nutrient

Water is the most important nutrient required for sustaining life. Essential for every stage of life, water plays key roles in digestion, absorption, transport, metabolism, and excretion of substances. Because the body cannot synthesize or store adequate amounts of water, sufficient amounts must be consumed regularly to replace daily losses [22]. The following chapter discusses digestion, absorption, and excretion of water, the role of water in body composition, the methods by which the body regulates and maintains water balance, the systems of the body dependent on water to function properly, the nutritional role in general metabolic pathways, and the adverse affects of water deficiency.

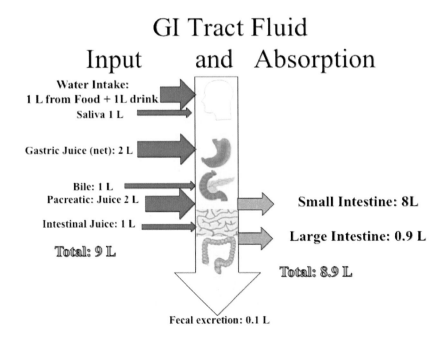

Figure 8.6-1: Description of fluids ingested, secreted, absorbed, and excreted along the gastrointestinal tract.

8.7.1. Digestion and Absorption of Water

In normal conditions, about sixty-percent of the human body weight is made up of water, which makes it the most abundant nutrient within our body [16]. Water is introduced to the body by the consumption of beverages and foods. The greatest amount of ingested water comes from beverages and liquid foods; however, many fruits and vegetables contain as much as 75- 95% water by weight [23]. Water within the human body serves several important functions including regulation of body temperature, joint lubrication, moistening of tissues, organ and tissue protection, prevention of constipation, movement of waste products, solvent for metabolic processes, maintenance of blood volume and transport of nutrients and oxygen to cells in the body [16].

8.7.1.1. Absorption along the Gastrointestinal Tract

Ingested nutrients are absorbed along the gastrointestinal tract (GI tract) which consists of the oral cavity, esophagus, stomach, small intestine, and large intestine. **Figure 8.7-1** describes fluids ingested, secreted, absorbed, and excreted along the gastrointestinal tract.

In the oral cavity, the salivary glands secrete about one liter of saliva per day [16]. At 99.5% water, saliva aids in the breakdown and lubrication of foods before they are transported down the esophagus to the stomach [16].

Within the stomach, water becomes an important solvent for foods and the enzymes that assist in digestion. Along with the pancreas, the stomach secretes the largest amount of liquids relative to other organs of the GI tract. The innermost tissue layers, the mucosa and submucosa, are made up of epithelial cells that contain millions of gastric glands that secrete gastric juice. Gastric juice consists of water, electrolytes, hydrochloric acid, enzymes, mucus and intrinsic factor. When gastric juice is mixed with food, a semi-liquid mass of partially digested food, refered to as chyme, is produced. Very little absorption of water occurs in the stomach [16].

The small intestine has the highest rate of digestion and absorption along the GI tract [16]. About ten liters of water enter the GI tract daily [23]. The small intestine is responsible for absorbing about 90% of the water, while the remaining water is absorbed in the large intestine. Chyme from the stomach enters the duodenum after passing through the pyloric sphincter. Anatomical advantages found along the epithelial lining allow for high nutrient and water absorption. The mucosa of the small intestine has a surface area of about 300 m^2. Folds within the small intestinal surface, called folds of Kerckring, villi, and microvilli, contribute to the large surface area which favors absorption. Between the villi are the crypts of Lieberkuhn, which extend down to the submucosa and contain multi-potential cells that can be modified into absorptive cells. Water is directly linked to ion absorption [21].

While water permeability of the colon is low, it is a significant site of water absorption.

Although 90% of total water gets absorbed within the small intestine, the colon is responsible for absorbing 90% of the remaining 1.5-2 L of ileal effluent that passes through the ileocecal valve [16]. Water absorbed in the colon is dependent on the rate of sodium absorption. The absorption rate of sodium and water is much greater within the proximal segments.

Love, et al., [25] measured oral intake and various solute levels by examining stool samples. Patients fasted for 12 hours, and then continuously drank an electrolyte fluid. Stool samples were analyzed for water and sodium content. When patients drank more water per hour, the kinetics of sodium and water were increased as a result of the continuous ingestion of fluids, increased surface area due to the increased volume in the small intestine, and hydrostatic pressure increase in the lumen [25].

Aldosterone also plays an important part in regulation of water and electrolyte absorption within the colon. Aldosterone is typically produced by the adrenal glands and causes the kidneys to retain sodium and consequently, water [23]. However when rats were given a prolonged intravenous infusion of aldosterone, a decrease in fecal sodium excretion indicated an increase in intestinal sodium absorption [26]. Once the infusion was removed, sodium excretion rate increased. Aldosterone effectively increases the number of sodium channels and Na+/K+ ATPases to promote absorption [26].

8.7.1.2. Transportation and Exchange

Most cell membranes are semi-permeable and solute specific. Depending on the membrane's permeability to a particular solute, water is transported between the compartments of intracellular and extracellular fluids. Permeability depends on the size of pores within cell membranes and can be altered in response to pressure and hormones. Transport through the semi-permeable membrane is possible because the higher concentration of solutes on one side of the membrane creates osmotic pressure and water flows into the side of higher osmolarity or higher concentration of solutes.

Absorption is fostered by a concentration gradient established by electrolytes, monosaccharides, and amino acids [16]. Macromolecules, such as proteins, have a higher concentration in plasma than in the interstitial fluid. Due to their large particle size, macromolecules cannot permeate through the capillary endothelium. Mammals typically have a protein concentration that is high in the blood and low in the tissue. This difference in protein concentration creates higher osmotic pressure in the blood. As a result, water flows from tissues into the capillaries. This osmotic pressure, also known as the colloid osmotic pressure, separates plasma and interstitial fluid [16]. In 2002, Wright, et al., challenged this concept of passive water transport [27]. Their experimental data showed that water could be coupled to solute transport in the same direction

through solute-water cotransport [7], although others have disputed this concept [28].

Interstitial fluid (ICF) hydrates extravascular cells and creates a pathway for cell to cell transport of nutrients and metabolic products. Interstitial fluid (ICF) is rich in potassium, magnesium, and proteins while the extra-cellular fluid (ECF) contains sodium, chloride, and bicarbonate ions. Sodium is transported to the extracellular space by basolateral Na^+/K^+ ATPases via a paracellular pathway that functions to create osmotic pressure. NaCl is followed by water down an osmotic gradient that creates a hypertonic fluid at the luminal end of the ICF space. The high concentration of Na^+ pumped out of cells near the tight junctions creates an osmotic gradient that allows water, along with sodium, to diffuse into the capillary [29].

8.7.1.3. Filtration Forces for Exchange in Tissues

Across the capillary endothelial surface, water transport is regulated by the forces of filtration and re-absorption (**Figure 8.7-2**). Filtration is the net movement of water out of the capillaries and absorption is the net movement of water into capillaries. Four forces control fluid movement from plasma to the endothelial surface. First, hydrostatic pressure (Ppl) generated by the pumping of the heart creates a filtration force in the capillaries with an average value of 25 mm Hg.

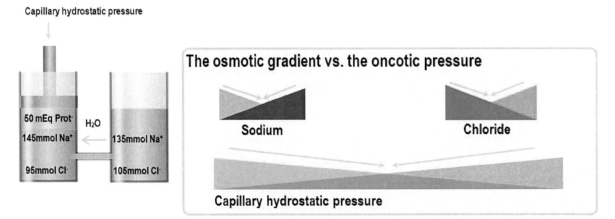

Figure 8.7-1: Hydrostic and oncotic pressure change through the length of a capillary, causing fluid to move out, then in.
From: http://www.derangedphysiology.com/php/Physiology-of-fluids-and- electrolytes/The-Gibbs-Donnan-effect.php

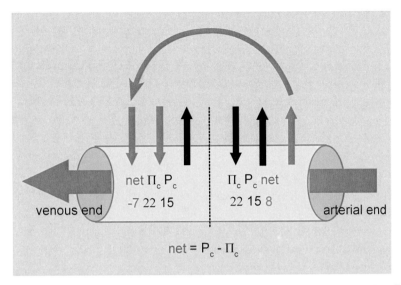

Figure 8.7-2: These four forces are used to express the net filtration in Starling's equation:Filtration pressure = (hydrostatic pressure + ISF colloid osmotic pressure) − (plasma osmotic pressure + ISF hydrostatic pressure) Using the average value of the four forces, you get a positive filtration pressure of 8 mm Hg. This states that the net filtration of water from plasma to the ISF takes place at the arteriolar end of the capillaries. The opposite occurs on the venule end.

Hydrostatic pressure is dependent on arterial and venous blood pressures. Second, there is very little protein concentration in the ISF, therefore the ISF colloid osmotic pressure (IIisf) is a negligible weak filtration force of about 5 mm Hg. Third, capillary osmotic pressure (IIpl) provides the major reabsorption force that opposes the plasma hydrostatic pressure. IIpl has a value of 28 mm Hg. Finally, ISF hydrostatic pressure (Pisf) is a weak filtration force with an average force of -6 mm Hg (**Figure 8.7-3**) [16].

The above-mentioned filtration forces express the net filtration in Starling's equation: Filtration pressure = (hydrostatic pressure + ISF colloid osmotic pressure) − (plasma osmotic pressure + ISF hydrostatic pressure) [16]. The average value of the four forces, yields a positive filtration pressure of 8 mm Hg. Therefore the net filtration of water from plasma to the ISF takes place at the arteriolar end of the capillaries. The opposite occurs on the venule end. The filtration pressure is negative, indicating that there is re-absorption of water from the ISF to the plasma [16].

Most of the fluid that is filtered is reabsorbed. A small amount of fluid enters the lymph vessels and flows through tissue spaces assisting in the removal of proteins, which is essential for healthy human function. The lymphatic system can only carry away a small amount of fluid. If capillary pressure rises too high, the net filtration pressure increases, forcing more fluid into the lymphatic system. The result is edema, an abnormal level of fluid and swelling in tissues. On the other hand, if capillary pressure decreases significantly, net reabsorption of fluid into the blood would occur at the expense of tissue fluid volume [16].

8.7.1.4. Water Absorption in the Kidney

Each kidney contains about 1 to 1.5 million functional units called nephrons. Capillaries enter the nephron in the glomerular network that is contained within the Bowman's capsule. After filtration, the filtered substances continue through the renal tubule, passing through the proximal convoluted tubule, loop of Henle, distal convoluted tubule, and collecting duct. Many of the unwanted substances in the body are water-soluble and therefore are excreted in the urine. The liver also has the ability to convert some fat-soluble compounds into water soluble compounds in order to facilitate their removal via urine [16]. Urea, the nitrogen- containing by-product of protein metabolism, is a major body waste product excreted in urine. Urine output increases with increasing protein consumption, as urea must be excreted. Similarly, urine sodium content increases with increased sodium intake. As a result, blood volume and blood pressure are controlled [23].

Much of the water in the blood that enters the kidney capillaries is filtered out through the capillary lining, or endothelium. This water either becomes the solvent for urine, or is reabsorbed into the bloodstream. The kidney's purpose is to excrete unneeded solutes while trying to conserve nutrients such as glucose, sodium, water, and other filtered substances. Antidiuretic hormone (ADH), produced by the hypothalamus and stored and secreted by the posterior pituitary gland, increases water permeability of the distal tubule and collecting duct of the nephron allowing for the re-absorption of water into the peritubular capillaries. ADH is released when there is high extracellular osmolarity or low intravascular plasma volume in order to increase body water volume. Aquaporins are water transport proteins present in collecting duct cells and utilize second messenger cAMP to make the distal nephron more permeable to water re-absorption into the capillaries. ADH secretion decreases with increasing fluid intake because blood becomes diluted and osmotic pressure is decreased [16].

8.7.1.5. GI Diseases that Affect Water Absorption

Diarrhea, a common GI tract problem, is a loose, watery stool occurring greater than three times per day [22]. Diarrhea can be the result of bacterial or viral infection, food intolerances, or a defect of absorption, secretion, or motility processes, so that rather than absorbing fluid, the GI tract secretes fluid. Treatment of diarrhea is aimed at preventing dehydration by encouraging fluid and electrolyte consumption [22].

In 1932, Dr. Burrill B. Crohn and his colleagues published a paper describing the aspects Crohn's disease (CD) [31]. CD is a serious, chronic inflammatory bowel disease that can cause inflammation anywhere along the digestive tract, however the terminal ileum and/or colon are most commonly affected [22, 31]. Patches of inflammation extend deeply into the intestinal walls decreasing the intestine's ability to absorb water and nutrients. Symptoms of this disease include fever, diarrhea, abdominal pain, rectal bleeding, weight loss, and other symptoms. **Table 8.7.1.** from Head and Jurenka's review of CD [31], provides nutrient deficiencies associated with Crohn's disease and

TABLE 8.7-1: Specific nutrients deficient in patients with Crohn's disease and the daily recommended intake for altered absorption status.

Nutrient	Status	Daily Recommendation (adult)
Vitamin A	Deficient	5,000-25,000 IU; not to exceed 7500 IU in pregnancy
Beta-carotene	Deficient	25,000-100,000 natural mixed cis/trans beta-carotene
Vitamin D	Deficient	400-800 IU
Vitamin E	Deficient	400-800 IU
Vitamin K	Deficient	500 mcg-1 mg
Vitamin C	Deficient	500-1,000 mg
Vitamin B1 (thiamine)	Deficient	100 mg
Vitamin B2 (riboflavin)	Deficient	100 mg
Vitamin B3 (niacin)	Deficient	100 mg
Vitamin B12	Deficient	1 mg
Folic Acid	Deficient	400-800 mcg
Biotin	Deficient	300 mcg-1 mg
Calcium	Deficient	1,000 mg
Magnesium	Deficient	500 mg
Iron	Deficient in serum; elevated in gut mucosa	Supplement with 50-75 mg daily well-absorbed form only if anemic; otherwise avoid supplementation
Zinc	Deficient	15-30 mg
Copper	Elevated	Avoid unless supplementing with > 15 mg zinc for long period of time; then supplement with 1-2 mg
Selenium	Deficient	200-400 mcg

recommended supplementation to restore adequate nutrition.

Short-bowel syndrome (SBS) is caused by the surgical removal of two thirds or more of the small intestine in response to the damage caused by Crohn's disease, tumors, injury, etc. [32]. As a result of surgery, the small intestine is reduced to a length of 100 cm or less. In severe cases, parts of the colon may also be removed [32]. Due to the less available surface area for absorption, SBS patients experience malabsorption of water and other nutrients [33]. Therefore, SBS patients must be provided with parenteral nutrition (PN) in order to survive [33].

A study of 124 adults with nonmalignant SBS, a determined bowel length of <100 cm, and PN dependency were followed in order to determine permanent intestinal failure [33]. Once patients were on PN for at least 2 years, the probability of permanent intestinal failure was 94%. With a continuity of the terminal ileum and/or colon, probability of survival and weaning off PN was higher. It was suggested that selection of treatments other than PN be considered, such as intestinal transplantation [33].

8.7.2. Excretion of Water

Excretion is the process of discarding waste matter from the blood, tissues, or organs. The body does not store water in large amounts, therefore daily water intake must equal or exceed daily loss in order to maintain a healthy water balance. The majority of water in the body is consumed by mouth through fluids and food and excreted through skin, lungs, urine, and stool [22]. The renal, endocrine, gastro-intestinal, central nervous and cardiovascular systems work together to maintain homeostasis of the body's water balance [34].

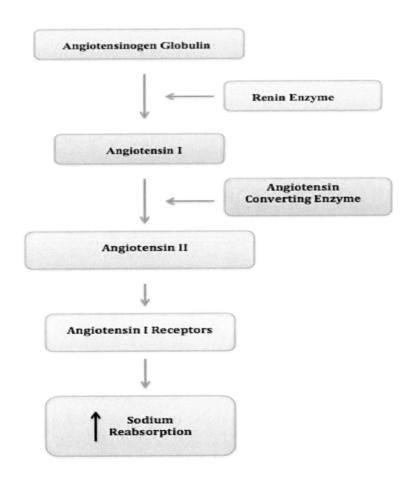

Figure 8.7-3: The Renal Renin-Angiotensin-Aldosterone System.

Insensible water loss occurs through the skin by diffusion and sweat. The average adult loses approximately 450 mL of water per day through insensible diffusion. Daily sweat loss varies widely among individuals. Sweat loss is influenced by metabolism and many environmental factors [21]. Water is lost from the lungs through evaporation during the process of respiration. Daily losses average around 200-350 mL per day for sedentary people and can rise as high as 500-600 mL per day for active people [21].

Urinary water loss can vary depending on macronutrient, salt and water intake. Average urine output for healthy adults is 1-2 liters per day [23]. Body hydration status is inversely proportional to urine output. Exercise and high environmental temperatures reduce urine output while cold temperatures increase output [21]. About 100-200 mL of water is lost in the feces per day [21].

8.7.2.1. Excretion and Blood Pressure

Through a series of sensitive hormone responses, the kidney plays a key role in controlling blood pressure by either excreting or retaining sodium [16]. Remember, where sodium goes, water usually follows. The kidney receives signals to activate either pathway via the renin-angiotensin-aldosterone system, depicted in **Figure 8.7-4**.

The juxtaglomerular apparatus of the kidney is responsible for sensing blood pressure [16] Renin is synthesized in the juxtaglomular cells of the afferent arteriole and released into intravascular space when stimulated by decreases in sodium and ECF volume, or low blood pressure [35]. Renin acts as an enzyme to cleave angiotensinogen, a globulin formed in the liver, into angiotensin I, which is then converted to angiotensin II by angiotensin-converting enzymes located in the lung. Angiotensin II stimulates the adrenal cortex to release aldosterone and stimulates the hypothalums to release antidiuretic hormone (ADH) also known as vasopresin. Aldosterone acts on the kidney causing sodium retention and potassium excretion, while ADH acts on the kidney to retain water, effectively raising blood pressure [16]. In this system, the generation of angiotensin II stimulates sodium transport in multiple nephron segments by binding

to plasma membrane angiotensin I receptors in the proximal tubule and the cortical collecting duct [36]. Angiotensin I receptors stimulate sodium transport and angiotensin II receptors stimulate renal reabsorption of sodium [36]. Therefore, angiotensin receptors are often targeted by prescription drugs in an attempt to control blood pressure, as the blocking of angiotensin receptors affects the sodium balance and controls water excretion and reabsorption [36].

When blood pressure is high, the heart releases atrial natiuretic peptide (ANP) and brain natiuretic peptide (BPN). ANP and BNP block aldosterone by inhibiting the renin- angiotensin aldosterone system, hence promoting sodium excretion, thus water excretion, from the kidney. Additionally, ANP and BNP, increase glomerular pressure and filtration rate, which in turn contributes to a greater volume of sodium and water excretion [16].

In patients with high blood pressure, diuretics may be prescribed [36]. A coordination of actions involving the nephron's glomerulus, proximal tubule, diluting segment, distal tubule and collecting duct induces water excretion. During this process, the glomerulus and proximal tubule work together to provide iso-osmotic ultrafiltrate to the diluting regions of the kidney for processing. Once ultrafiltrate passes through the proximal tubule, the distal diluting segments extract sodium and chloride. At this point, antidiuretic hormone (ADH) is suppressed; therefore water generated at the distal diluting areas is excreted, rather than being re- absorbed from the collecting ducts and returned to the blood stream [36].

8.7.3. Storage of water and role in body structures

8.7.3.1. Total Body Water

Total body water (TBW) is the sum of water in the body at any given time. TBW can be divided into two compartments: extracellular fluid (ECF) and intracellular fluid (IFC). TBW varies depending on life stage, body composition, and gender. **Table 8.7-2** depicts changes in the percentage of TBW during different life stages. As shown in Table 1, TBW tends to decrease with age. Infants between the ages of 0-6 months have a high TBW average of 74%, compared to adults, who have a TBW average of around 60% [21].

TABLE 8.7-2: Percentages of total body water at different life stages. Adapted from Dietary Reference Intakes for Water, Potassium, Sodium, Chloride, and Sulfate [21]

Life stage	Total Body Water (TBW) as a % of Body Weight
0-6 months	74
6 months- 1 year	60
1-12 year	60
Males, 12-18 years	59
Females 12-18 years	56
Males 19-50 years	59

Many factors must be taken into consideration when determining TBW. Fat mass and fat-free mass vary significantly in water content. For example, fat free mass in adults is composed of roughly 70-75% water, while adipose tissue is composed of only 10-40% water [21]. There is great body composition variation among individuals, therefore the percentage of TBW can range from 45-75% within a population [21]. On average, men's body weight is made up of a greater percentage of water than is women's because women tend to have a higher percentage of adipose tissue [22]. Additional differences in TBW can be found in athletes, who commonly have higher TBW percentages due their low percentage of adipose tissue [21].

8.7.3.2. Distribution of Water

Water in the body is distributed between the two compartments of ECF and ICF. ICF constitutes about 65% of TBW, and ECF constitutes about 35%. In the average adult male, ECF is comprised of about 11 L of interstitial fluid and 3 L of plasma fluid while the ICF contains approximately 28 L, and the two compartments total a volume of roughly 42 L. The ECF and ICF volumes and the amount of water exchanged between the ECF and ICF are ever changing due to variances in daily water loss and intake caused by changes in environmental conditions, physical activity level, illness, and trauma [21].

8.7.3.3. Exchange of Water between ECF and ICF

Water passes through water permeable cell membranes separating the ICF and ECF compartments. Water travels from an area of low solute concentration to an area of high solute concentration in the process of osmosis. The content of sodium cations and chloride and bicarbonate anions determine the volume of the ECF. The concentration of potassium and magnesium cations and protein anions in the ICF determine its water volume. The different contents of sodium and potassium in the ECF and ICF are maintained by ion pumps within the cell membranes [21]. (Refer to section 8.7.1. for a more detailed discussion on filtration and exchange.)

8.7.3.4. Metabolic Water

The average person must consume about 2900 mL of water per day to maintain an adequate fluid balance [21]. The body produces a small amount of water, about 250 mL, each day through metabolism. This water is referred to as metabolic water. Metabolic water production is proportional to energy expenditure, as it is a byproduct of the oxidation of energy- yielding substances contained in food [21]. The body is not capable of synthesizing adequate amounts of water to meet its requirements through this process. Therefore, water is classified as an essential nutrient that must be consumed daily in amounts adequate to maintain proper body function [22].

TABLE 8.7-3: metabolic water content of some nutrient sources [28]

Nutrient (100 grams) (grams)	Water content
Water	100
Fat	107
Protein	41
Starch	55

Metabolic water is a product of oxidative metabolism. The Kreb's cycle utilizes glucose to generate adenosine triphosphate, an energy source, and water, a by-product. The formation of metabolic water is essential in bird species during extended flying times and in desert mammals that may not have regular access to water. In humans, eight to ten percent of the daily water requirement can be met through the energy metabolism. The metabolism of carbohydrates, proteins, and fats produces water in direct proportion to the energy generated (**Table 8.7-3**) [37].

For each nutrient metabolized, enough metabolic water is produced to remove the waste products or by-products of the metabolic reaction [37]. Urea, for example, is a by-product of protein metabolism [16]. In humans, most of the metabolic water generated during protein metabolism is utilized in the excretion of urea through the urine. However bird species do not produce urine, therefore birds can utilize the metabolic water generated from protein metabolism for functions other than excretion [37].

In cases of dehydration, metabolism of fat can generate enough water to maintain the body's metabolic needs. Stahl, et al., related hydration status in children and their dietary profile [38]. Direct correlation existed between food intake and hydration status of a group of people with limited water access. The water content of food as well as metabolic water, allowed individuals consuming enough food to remain healthy, with no water-related health issues, when water was restricted [38]. It should be noted that this study dealt with water restrictions, not water exclusion, daily water was available. The human body cannot produce enough metabolic water to sustain itself. A relatively large amount of water must be consumed every day.

8.7.3.5. Water Requirements

The body's methods of maintaining water balance are very complex. Consequently, an Estimated Average Requirement for hydration has not been determined [21]. However, an adequate intake (AI) has been established for total water intake that is considered to prevent dehydration and its negative effects on the body [21]. The AI for total water was determined based on survey data collected in the U.S. The median total water AI for young men is 3.7 L per day, and the AI for young women is 2.7 L per day. A Tolerable Upper Intake Level (UL) for water has not been determined since healthy individuals have the ability to excrete excess amounts

of water quickly, effectively maintaining a healthy water balance. Water toxicity can occur, however, in cases of rapid and excessive consumption of fluids at a rate exceeding the kidney's maximum excretion rate [21].

8.7.3.6. Estimating Hydration Status

Determining the body's hydration status can aid in diagnosing and treating harmful symptoms of dehydration. Commonly used methods for determining an individual's hydration status include body weight changes, plasma osmolality, plasma sodium, plasma volume, urine specific gravity, urine osmolality, and saliva specific gravity [39].

Body weight changes: The amount of water consumed each day normally equals the amount of water excreted; therefore hydration status can be calculated by tracking changes in body weight. This method is done by first establishing an individual's baseline body weight and subsequently attributing weight loss (that is not apparent tissue loss) to fluid loss and evaluating hydration status based on those values [22].

Plasma and serum osmolality, plasma sodium concentration, and plasma volume changes: The body regulates plasma osmolality, plasma sodium concentration, and plasma volume to control water balance; therefore hydration levels can be evaluated based on those values. Plasma osmolality is controlled by antidiuretic hormone / arginine vasopressin (ADH), which alters the volume of urine output. A negative relationship exists between total body water and plasma osmolality. This relationship can be seen when plasma osmolality in the ECF increases in the face of water deficiency, causing water to move from the ICF into the ECF. The movement of water into the ECF signals the release of ADH, resulting in reabsorption of water into the renal tubules of the kidney. The release of ADH is proportionate to the increase in plasma osmolality and the decrease in plasma volume. Therefore plasma osmolality is an indicator for dehydration. The loss of water in the body increases the amount of sodium cations in the ECF. Therefore, plasma sodium concentration can also be used as a hydration marker. Additionally, dehydration causes a decrease in plasma volume, another indicator for hydration status. However, plasma volume is not a very accurate measurement of hydration as body composition can vary widely among individuals [21].

Urine Indicators: Urine volume and color, urine specific gravity, and urine osmolality can be evaluated as indicator of hydration status. Well-hydrated individuals commonly have a urine output between 1-2 L per day that is light in color. In a case of dehydration, urine becomes more concentrated and darker in color. Urine indicators are not the best methods to determine hydration status because factors such as diet, vitamin intake and medications can affect urine output and color [21].

Saliva Specific Gravity: A less reliable marker of hydration status is saliva specific gravity. Although salivary flow rates tend to decrease during levels of dehydration exceeding 2%, there is not a direct statistical correlation between hydration status and salivary output. The saliva of research subjects who were hydrated at different levels did not accurately correlate to the participants' hydration status [40].

Thirst: The body attempts to control hydration status by the sensation of thirst.

Unfortunately, thirst does not occur before the fluid is lost, and this often results in dehydration. By the time a person is thirsty, they may have already lost up to 2% of their body weight in fluid loss [22]. The thirst sensation is activated by an increase in plasma osmolality and a decrease in plasma volume. Normally, thirst stimulates an adequate intake of water to compensate for daily losses, however in cases of high stress, illness, hot temperatures, intake of diuretics, and/or high physical activity individuals often struggle to maintain appropriate levels of water intake [41]. These conditions predispose individuals to dehydration.

8.7.3.7. Dehydration

Dehydration is defined as a 1% or greater loss of body weight due to fluid loss [22]. The effects of dehydration

TABLE 8.7-4: Cognitive and Motor Control Functions Affected by Dehydration [17]

Function	Conditions	Results
Perception of fatigue	2.8% dehydration by exercise or climatic heat	Increased rating of fatigue
Rating of mood	2.8% dehydration by exercise or climatic heat	No effect on mood
Target shooting	2.5% dehydration by climatic heat	Reduced speed and accuracy and increase in physiologic strain
Perceived discrimination	2.8% dehydration by exercise or climatic heat	Discrimination impaired
Choice reaction time	6-h exercise in the heat, causing 2.5% or 5% dehydration visual	Faster response time to peripheral stimuli, no effect on response time to central visual stimuli
	2.8% dehydration by exercise or climatic heat	No effect on response time
Visual-motor tracking	1, 2, 3, or 4% dehydration, induced by exercise in the heat	Tracking impaired at 2% or more dehydration
Short-term memory	2.8% dehydration by exercise or climatic heat	Short-term memory impaired
	1, 2, 3, or 4% dehydration, induced by exercise in the heat	Short-term memory impaired at 2% or more dehydration
Long-term memory	2.8% dehydration by exercise or climatic heat	Impaired recall, especially following exercise
Attention	1, 2, 3, or 4% dehydration, induced by exercise in the heat	Attention impaired at 2% or more dehydration
Arithmetic efficiency	1, 2, 3, or 4% dehydration, induced by exercise in the heat	Arithmetic ability impaired at 2% or more dehydration

occur when the body's fluid is significantly reduced by as much as 2%-3% of body weight [41]. Fluid loss beyond 2% affects short-term memory, attention, coordination, reaction time, and visual functions. Further dehydration leads to compromised physiological and performance responses as well as negative cardiovascular affects and thermoregulatory responses [41]. Further symptoms of dehydration include loss of appetite headache, tiredness, dizziness, dry mouth and eyes, dark urine, muscle cramps, and heat sensitivity and intolerance [22].

8.7.3.8. Physical Effects of Dehydration

Exercise can cause the body's fluid loss to be greater than its fluid intake. Fluid is lost during physical activity through sweat and urine. Dehydration occurs more frequently in individuals engaging in moderate to rigorous physical activity, however dehydration can occur in individuals during normal day-to-day activities, depending on climate conditions and water intake [34].

Depending on an individual's body composition and acclimation to varying climates, dehydration decreases physical capacity. A fluid loss of 1-2% of body weight decreases endurance, reaction time, and overall physical performance. Dehydration also causes anorexia [42]. Food consumption is regulated by neural circuits that either inhibit or stimulate hunger. Dehydration activates both circuits simultaneously, resulting in suppression of hunger until rehydration occurs. Rehydration has a rapid effect on the body's central processes, inducing arousal and heightened consciousness while up-regulating ingestive behavior in an attempt to correct any deficits brought on by dehydration. Individuals may become enthusiastically hungry after physical activity and rehydration [42].

8.7.3.9. Cognitive Effects of Dehydration

Dehydration has negative effects on cognitive functions such as vision, short-term memory, alertness, and reasoning abilities [41]. **Table 8.3-4** summarizes a study observing the effects of dehydration and cognitive function at different levels of dehydration in otherwise healthy individuals [41]. The study confirmed that healthy individuals with water deficits of as little as 1% exhibited impaired cognitive functions.

A similar study found that respondents who had lost 1-2% of body weight due to fluid loss were less capable of recalling short stories or redrawing simple patterns than respondents who were well-hydrated. The two studies linked decreasing hydration status to decreasing performance in basic processing skills, vision, and memory, demonstrating that the maintenance of a healthy water balance is essential to maintaining optimal cognitive functions [41].

8.7.3.10. Other harmful effects of Dehydration

Dehydration has many additional adverse effects on the body including increased risks of urinary tract infection, kidney stones, gallstones, bladder cancer, colon cancer, and blood clots. Dehydration has also been shown to cause negative effects on bone health. Water deficiency has a negative effect on the cardiovascular system by causing ventricular contraction during exercise, putting the body at risk of cardiorespiratory arrest [21].

8.7.4. Hyponatremia

Hyponatremia, low serum sodium, is a disorder which has many different causes [16].

Inappropriate secretion of the antidiuretic hormone vasopressin (ADH) is one example of a cause of hyponatremia [43]. In some cases, antidepressant agents, non-steroidal anti-inflammatory drugs, and neuroleptic agents may cause hyponatremia [43]. Normally, when body fluid increases and causes a rise in total blood volume and ECF volume, the kidney increases excretion of water and sodium in the urine. In hyponatremia caused by inappropriate secretion of ADH, the posterior pituitary and hypothalamus secrete ADH in response to stimulus other than osmotic [43]. The release of ADH inhibits excretion of water and sodium resulting in excessive retention of water [44].

Hyponatremia can be treated by fluid restriction. Treatment is aimed at decreasing daily water intake to levels below daily water loss in an attempt to create a negative fluid balance in the body, which in turn increases serum sodium concentration and therefore corrects hyponatremia [44]. In addition to decreasing fluid intake, patients may also be prescribed vaptans or agents that bind to ADH receptors in the kidney, blocking the binding of ADH [43].

8.7.5. Hyperhydration

Hyperhydrating can prevent dehydration. Water is lost during physical activity through perspiration and respiration. A body that is sufficiently hydrated can perform physically and avoid dehydration for longer periods of time. Intriguingly, studies have shown that ingestion of glycerol can induce hyperhydration and decrease dehydration. Glycerol-induced hyperhydration (GIH) can expand the body's total water volume. Such hyperhydration may have potential benefits for athletes, active people, and other professionals such as astronauts who may encounter difficulties in consuming sufficient amounts of fluid [34].

8.7.6. Environmental Factors

Increased physical activity, high temperatures and stress are factors that impact the body's water balance. Evaporation is the body's primary cooling method accomplished through perspiration and increased respiratory rate [41]. Performing moderately hard exercise will raise fluid loss to 1-2 L per hour and can increase to 4-6 L per hour in high temperatures [22]. While fluid loss is most often associated with increased physical activity and high temperatures, individuals exposed to cold temperatures or high altitude levels will also experience an increase in respiratory water loss [21].

8.7.7. Diet

Consumption of common diuretics such as caffeine and alcohol can have a profound affect on the regulation of body water. Diuretics depress the production of ADH. Typically kidney responds to ADH by reabsorbing water; however when diuretics are present, the release of ADH is depressed and urinary water loss increases [22].

Dietary fiber intake can also have an impact on hydration. Foods high in fiber have the ability to bind water [16]. Fonnesbeck investigated the consumption and excretion of water by horses receiving all hay and

hay-grain diets [45]. Six different diets were fed to the horses and water was provided free choice. Results indicated that water intake was greater for horses consuming all hay diets (very high fiber diets) with a daily water intake of 31.4 kg; while horses consuming the hay-grain diet (lower fiber diet) only consumed 17.5 kg of water per day [45]. High dietary fiber intake increases the water carrying capacity of the gut and serves as a water reservoir for the body [16].

8.7.8. Pregnancy

Body weight increases during the average pregnancy by about 12 kilograms. The majority of weight gained during pregnancy can be attributed to water. Pregnant women need to retain higher amounts of fluid to account for the additional ECF space, the needs of the fetus, and amniotic fluid. Pregnancy requires at least 30 mL per day of additional water [22].

8.7.9. Water: Metabolic Functions

Water is needed in many different functions within the body and each function would fail if it did not have the required amount. Within our bodies, water provides the environment where every metabolic reaction takes place. Water allows our organs to operate in a semi-suspended state that protects them from damage.

Water moves from one body compartment to another through the process of osmosis In many cases, solutes will follow the water through these cell or epithelia membranes. Water, as a key component in blood, transports nutrients and the products of metabolisim throughout the body, while simultaneously removing waste products for excretion after metabolic reactions are completed. Body temperature regulation depends on the high specific heat of water and its ability to absorb the heat generated from metabolic processes, in turn releasing that heat outside of the body through perspiration. During illness, water functions as a dilution factor in the lymphatic system, transporting substances to fight infections. The lungs require oxygen in order to move oxygen in and carbon dioxide out of our bodies. Water is an essential component of joint fluid. **Table 8.7-4** provides an overview of how water functions within organ systems.

TABLE 8.7-5: How water functions within organ systems. Reference [16]

Major Organ Systems	Functions	Water Use
Circulatory System	Pumping and circulating blood flow	Plasma is over 90% water and enables blood to travel through the veins and arteries
Digestive System	Digestion and processing of food	Mucus lining and gastric bile are mainly comprised of water and are need to protect and digest food particles
Endocannabinoid System	Neuromodulation of lipids in the communication of the body	Lipids are insoluble in water and so this system is not directly affected by water availability
Endocrine System	Hormone communication within the body	Through hormone communication the kidneys are signaled to release or reabsorb water in the urinary tract based on water saturation of the cells
Integementary System	Outer protective barrier	Aids in body temperature regulation as water is released to expel internal heat
Immune System	Internal disease protection	Dilutes problematic bacteria and disease until the foreign bodies can be destroyed
Lymphatic System	Circulate lymph cells throughout the body	Acts as the transportation of the immune system
Musculoskeletal System	Structure and movement	Insulation of the joints and a major component of muscle and skeletal tissue
Nervous System	Collecting and processing information	Channels proteins in the peripheral nervous system and is a major component of spinal fluid
Reproductive System	Sex organs	Provides the environment for sperm transportation, egg fertilization, and fetus growth
Respiratory System	Inhalation and expiration	Gas exchanges are dissolved in water to form aqueous solutions for transportation throughout the body
Urinary System	Maintain fluid balance	Directly affected by water as it filters urine and contributes to water re- absorption
Vestibular System	Contributes to the sense of balance or orientation	The inner ear is fluid filled and is key for internal balance

8.7.10. Metabolic Pathways - Summary

The need for water consumption increases when the body is exercised [21]. Water is utilized to maintain body temperature through the release of water and heat as sweat [21].

Additionally, exercise increases respiration rates, which increases water loss through the lungs [21]. There is an increased need for water in metabolic processes in exercising individuals.

Working muscles require more energy, therefore metabolic rate is increased to meet the energy demand. In exercising individuals, it may be beneficial to consume specialized sports drinks to combat mild dehydration by increasing the rate of water absorption [46]. Specialized sports drinks aid in rehydration by providing sufficient sodium, an electrolyte that promotes intestinal water absorption [46]. When consumed during exercise, specialized sports drinks also provide a quick glucose supply that readily feeds into the Kreb's cycle within the muscles [46].

While water is essential in all organ systems, water plays a very specific and unique role in each organ. In the digestive system, the lubrication and dissolving power of water from saliva, gastric juice, pancreatic juice and bile assists in digestion. Water liquefies and lubricates food as it passes through the GI tract, and aids in absorption of water-soluble nutrients, including the water soluble vitamins [16].

Bile begins in the liver as a largely water based mixture, then travels into the gallbladder where over ninety percent of the water is reabsorbed. Reabsorbing the water concentrates the components in the bile. The pancreas secretes bicarbonate, electrolytes, and enzymes, into the small intestine, effectively regulating pH. In the large intestine, water is secreted in the form of mucus by goblet cells. Mucus lubricates the fecal material [16].

As discussed in Chapter 5, the excretory systems's role within the body is for the purpose of filtering water as it is excreted. The kidney is the main regulatory organ that maintains water homeostasis through a series of hormone-sensitive responses [16]. The kidneys also regulate sodium, potassium, chloride and bicarbonate re-absorption in order to maintain steady pH levels in the blood plasma. The respiratory system regulates carbonic acid production through respiration rates and breathing patterns [16]. The respiratory system also requires water as a transporter of oxygen and carbon dioxide. Water loss due to respiration is affected by physical activity, ambient temperatures, relative humidity, and barometric pressure [21].

In an experiment utilizing dairy cattle, the difference in dietary cation-anion balance was altered to determine if urine excretion or blood volume was similarly altered [47]. While the kidneys have the ability to reabsorb cations and anions, the absorption rates equal animal needs, creating an internal balance with a steady pH range [47]. Decreased water availability, decreased consumption, or excessive excretion of water can disturb this balance leading to such problems as kidney stones. Kidney stones result when minerals are not diluted enough to pass safely through the urinary tract and can precipitate, forming stones [47].

A study on water consumption and blood glucose and insulin in diabetic individuals showed that a six hundred percent increase in water intake during a meal did not have an impact on blood volume or insulin and glucose concentrations. However, the high water intake contributed to increased gastric emptying rates and a dilution of nutrient concentration in the stomach and intestines. The kidney and circulatory system effectively communicated to maintain water homeostasis within the body [48].

8.8. Literature Cited

1. Janetscheck RJ. (2016). Special protein testing in the clinical laboratory: Overview of available assays. American Laboratory, 48(6): 14-17.

2. Zhao Z, Li S, Liu G et al. (2012) Body iron stores and heme-iron intake in relation to risk of type 2 diabetes: a systematic review and meta-analysis. PLoS One 7, e41641.

3. Jiang R, Manson JE, Meigs JB et al. (2004) Body iron stores in relation to risk of type 2 diabetes in apparently healthy women. JAMA 291, 711-717.

4. Green A, Basile R & Rumberger JM (2006) Transferrin and iron induce insulin resistance of glucose transport in adipocytes. Metabolism 55, 1042-1045.

5. Fernandez-Real JM, Lopez-Bermejo A & Ricart W (2002) Cross-talk between iron metabolism and diabetes. Diabetes 51, 2348-2354.

6. Davis RJ, Corvera S & Czech MP (1986) Insulin stimulates cellular iron uptake and causes the redistribution of intracellular transferrin receptors to the plasma membrane. J Biol Chem 261, 8708-8711.

7. Rossetti L, Rothman DL, DeFronzo RA et al. (1989) Effect of dietary protein on in vivo insulin action and liver glycogen repletion. Am J Physiol 257, E212-219.

8. Dandona P, Hussain MA, Varghese Z et al. (1983) Insulin resistance and iron overload. Ann Clin Biochem 20 Pt 2, 77-79.

9. Cooksey RC, Jones D, Gabrielsen S et al. (2010) Dietary iron restriction or iron chelation protects from diabetes and loss of beta-cell function in the obese (ob/ob lep-/-) mouse. Am J Physiol Endocrinol Metab 298, E1236-1243.

10. Valenti L, Fracanzani AL, Dongiovanni P et al. (2007) Iron depletion by phlebotomy improves insulin resistance in patients with nonalcoholic fatty liver disease and hyperferritinemia: evidence from a case-control study. Am J Gastroenterol 102, 1251-1258.

11. Fernandez-Real JM, Lopez-Bermejo A & Ricart W (2005) Iron stores, blood donation, and insulin sensitivity and secretion. Clin Chem 51, 1201-1205.

12. Fernandez-Real JM, Penarroja G, Castro A et al. (2002) Blood letting in high-ferritin type 2 diabetes: effects on insulin sensitivity and beta-cell function. Diabetes 51, 1000-1004.

13. Gabrielsen JS, Gao Y, Simcox JA et al. (2012) Adipocyte iron regulates adiponectin and insulin sensitivity. J Clin Invest 122, 3529-3540.

14. Williams JH, Phillips TD, Jolly PE, Stiles JK, Jolly CM, Aggarwal D. (2004) Human aflatoxicosis in developing countries: a review of toxicology, exposure, potential health consequences, and interventions. Am J Clin Nutr 2004 80: 1106-1122

15. National Research Council. *Dietary Reference Intakes for Vitamin A, Vitamin K, Arsenic, Boron, Chromium, Copper, Iodine, Iron, Manganese, Molybdenum, Nickel, Silicon, Vanadium, and Zinc.* Washington, DC: The National Academies Press, 2001

16. Gropper SS, Smith JL. *Advanced nutrition and human metabolism. 6th Ed.* Belmont (CA) Cengage Learning;2013

17. Kiran, M. B. (n.d.). Vitamins, Fat-Soluble. Retrieved 2013, from http://www.faqs.org/nutrition/Smi-Z/Vitamins-Fat-Soluble.html

18. Czajka-Narins DM, Matarese L. (1996) Chapter 5 Vitamins. IN: Mahan KL, Escott-Stump S (eds) *Krause's Food, Nutrition, & Diet Therapy (9th Ed).* Philadelphia: W.B. Saunders. pp. 77-120.

19. Boron, WF., and Boulpaep EL. *Medical Physiology.* Philadelphia, PA: Saunders, 2012. Print.

20. Patrick, J. (2012)Assessment of Body Potassium Stores." Kidney International 11(1977): 476-490. Web. 05 Dec.. <http://www.nature.com/ki/journal/v11/n6/pdf/ki197765a.pdf>.

21. Panel on Dietary Reference Intakes for Electrolytes and Water, Standing Committee on the Scientific Evalutation of Dietary Reference Intakes. *Dietary Reference Intakes for Water, Potassium, Sodium, Chloride, and Sulfate.* Washington, DC; The National Academies Press, 2005.

22. Kleiner SM: Water: An essential but overlooked nutrient. J Am Diet Assoc 1999, 99:200- 206.

23. Byrd-Bredbenner, C., Moe, G., Beshgetoor, D., and Berning, J. Wardlaw's Perspectives in Nutrition. 9th ed. Boston: McGraw-Hill Publishers. 2012. 485-496.

24. Tortora, Gerard J., Derrickson, Bryan. "Absorption of Electrolytes." Principles of Anatomy and Physiology.12th ed. Hoboken, NJ: John Wiley, 2009. 958. Web. 24 Nov. 2012.

25. Love, A.H.G., Mitchell, T.G., Phillips, R.A. (1968): Water and sodium absorption in the human intestine. Journal of Physiology. 195. 133-140. Web. 24 Nov.2012.

26. Thompson, B. D., and C. J. Edmonds. (1971) Comparison of effects of prolonged aldosterone administration on rat colon and renal electrolyte excretion. Journal of Endocrinology ,50(1): 163-69. Web. 24 Nov. 2012.

27. Loo, D.D.F., Wright, E.M. & Zeuthen, T.(2002). Water pumps. Journal of Physiology 542: 53– 60.

28. Lapointe, J.Y., Gagnon, M., Poirier, S.& Bissonnette, P. (2002). The presence of local osmotic gradients can account for the water flux driven by the Na$^+$– glucose cotransporter. Journal of Physiology 542: 61–62.

29. Sandle GI. (1989) Segmental heterogeneity of basal and aldosterone-induced electrogenic Na transport in human colon. Pflügers Arch 414:706–12.

30. Smif, P. Starling Forces across the capillary. Digital image. Pete Smif. N.p., 31 Aug. 2010. Web. 26 Nov.2012. http://pcwww.liv.ac.uk/~petesmif/petesmif/body%20fluid%20 compartments/simple%20starling.gif

31. Head K, and Jurenka, J. (2004): Inflammatory Bowel Disease Part II: Crohn's Disease. Alternative Medicine Review 9(4): 360-401. Web. 28 Nov. 2012.

32. "Short Bowel Syndrome Overview." Cleveland Clinic. Cleveland Clinic, n.d. Web. 28 Nov. 2012. <http://my.clevelandclinic.org/disorders/short_bowel/dd_overview.aspx>.

33. Messing, B., P. Crenn, P. Beau, M. Boutronruault, J. Rambaud, and C. Matuchansky. Long term survival and parenteral nutrition dependence in adult patients with the short bowel syndrome. Gastroenterology 117.5 (1999): 1043-050. 3 Aug. 1999. Web. 28 Nov. 2012.

34. Koenigsberg PS, Martin KK, Hlava HR, Riedesel ML (1995): Sustained hyperhydration with glycerol ingestion. Life Sci, 57:645-653.

35. Harrison-Bernard L (2009): The renal renin-angiotensin system. Adv Physiol Educ, 33:270-274.

36. Sica DA (2006): Sodium and water retention in heart failure and diuretic therapy: Basic mechanisms. Clev Clin J Med, 73(Suppl 2):2-7.

37. Kreutler PA, Czajka-Narins DM. *Nutrition in Perspective* Englewood Cliffs, N.J. : Prentice-Hall, c1987. pp. 309-312

38. Stahl, A, A Kroke, K Bolzenius, and F Manz. (2007) Relation between hydration status in children and their dietary profile - results from the DONALD Study. European Journal of Clinical Nutrition 61: 1386-1392.

39. Armstrong LE, Johnson EC, Munoz CX, Swolka B, Le Bellego L, Jimenez L, Casa DJ, Maresh CM (2012): Hydration Biomarkers and Dietary Fluid Consumption of Women. J Acad Nutr Diet, 112:1056-1061.

40. Ship JA, Fischer DJ (1999): Metabolic indicators of hydration status in the prediction of parotid salivary-gland function. Arch Oral Biol, 44:343-350.

41. Suhr JA, Hall J, Patterson SM, Niinisto RT (2004): The relation of hydration status to cognitive performance in healthy older adults. Int J Psychophysiol, 53:121-125.

42. Watts AG (1999): Dehydration-associated anorexia: Development and rapid reversal. Physiol Behav, 65:871-878.

43. Gross P (2012): Clinical management of SIADH. Ther Adv Endocrinal Metab, 3:61- 73.

44. Schrier RW (2006): Water and sodium retention in edematous disorders: Role of vasopressin and aldosterone. Am J Med, 119(Suppl 7):47-53.

45. Fonnesbeck PV (1968): Consumption and excretion of water by horses receiving all hay and hay-grain diets. Journal of Animal Science, 27:1350-1356.

46. Shirreffs, S M. (2009)Hydration in sport and exercise: water, sports drinks and other drinks. British Nutrition Foundation 34: 374-379. Web

47. Delaquis AM and Block E. (1995): Acid-base status, renal function, water, and macromineral metabolism of dry cows fed diets differing in cation-anion difference. Journal of Dairy Science 78(3): 604-619.

48. Gregersen S, Rasmussen O, Winther E, and Hermansen K. (1990) Water volume and consumption time: influence on the glycemic and insulinemic responses in non- insulin-dependent diabetic subjects. American Journal of Clinical Nutrition 52: 515-518.

Study Questions:

1. What molecules make up macrominerals?

2. Where are macrominerals stored within the body?

3. What are the functions of the macrominerals?

    a. How is storage regulated?

    b. What food provides these major minerals?

4. On average, how much of the human body weight can be attributed to water?

5. Where is the majority of water consumed, absorbed?

6. List 2 chronic diseases that negatively affect water absorption:

7. Describe the process of osmosis:

8. Water homeostasis will be maintained if the amount of water_____equals the amount of water_____.

9. How is total body water divided in the body? What are the functions of each of these compartments?

10. Discuss the role of antidiuretic hormone (ADH) in maintaining water homeostasis in the body:

11. Where is AHD produced?

12. What type of urine will be released when ADH levels are high?

    a. Low osmolarity, low volume

    b. High osmolarity, high volume

    c. Low osmolarity, high volume

    d. High osmolarity, low volume

13. Explain the complex system that regulates blood pressure:

14. List 4 ways in which water is lost from the body:

15. Explain how water is derived from cell metabolism:

16. What is insensible water loss?

17. Is water toxicity a common problem? Explain:

18. Define dehydration:

    a. List 2 causes of dehydration:

    b. List 4 negative effects of dehydration:

19. List 4 substance that when consumed, affect water requirements:

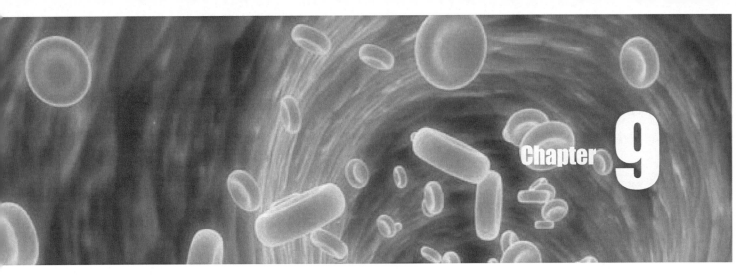

Storage, Body Structure and Metabolism: Carbohydrate.

Learning Objectives

After completing this chapter, you should be able to:

1. Outline the catabolic and anabolic pathways involved in glucose, fat, and protein metabolism and be able to identify what processes happen in each pathway

2. Explain causes for important diseases that are associated with glycogen storage

3. Outline carbohydrate structure and role in metabolism

4. Examine glycogenesis and its hormonal regulation

5. Understand glycolysis and its hormonal regulation

6. Explain how the DRIs for carbohydrates were established

7. Understand and explain the catabolic pathways of glucose metabolism

8. Describe and explain the pathway of glycolysis metabolic pathway

9. Explain the pathways of oxidation of pyruvate and TCA cycle

10. Explain the function of electron transport chain and oxidative phosphorylation in glucose metabolism

11. Understand the metabolic function of fructose

9.1. Storage of Carbohydrates in the Body

Living organisms require energy for their daily activities and metabolic processes. Energy in human beings is obtained from the digestion and utilization of food nutrients such as carbohydrates, proteins and lipids. Carbohydrates are the most readily utilized macronutrient in the body to provide energy after ingestion. Therefore most of the carbohydrates that are consumed are conveyed to metabolic pathways for energy production within a short time.

9.1.1. What are carbohydrates?

Carbohydrates are the major source of energy and fuel in the average human diet, and an indispensable structural unit within the genetic material of all organisms. Energy obtained from carbohydrates plays an important role in the myriad of homeostatic processes of the human body. Carbohydrates are polyhydroxy aldehydes, ketones, or substances that produce these compounds when they are hydrolyzed [1]. Carbohydrate food nutrients are largely obtained from starchy and fibrous foods such as bread, corn, rice and foods that contain a high proportion of sugar. Carbohydrates can be classified as either simple or complex based on the number of sugar units present. Simple carbohydrates include mono and disaccharides. Monosaccharides are the major energy providing nutrients for cell metabolism. These are aptly named because they consist of single sugar units (monomers) and they include molecules such as glucose and fructose (**figure 9.1**-1). The monosaccharaide carbohydrate molecule bears three to seven carbon atoms.

Disaccharides consist simply of two monosaccharides joined to one another by glycosidic bonds, in the a 1-4, 2 1-4, or a 1-6 configuration. Examples of such molecules include maltose and lactose (**figure 9.1-2**).Disaccharides are carbohydrate sugars that contain two types of carbohydrate molecules, which are attached to each other through acetal bonds. Polysaccharides are long chain carbohydrate polymers that are joined to each other through glycosidic bonding.

Complex carbohydrates (polymers) or starches include the oligosaccharides and polysaccharides. Oligosaccharides contain between three and ten sugar

units, and polysaccharides are chains of more than ten sugar units. These molecules are prevalent in animal and plant products and are an important part of the diet [1, 2,].

Polysaccharides have much higher molecular weights than other carbohydrates [1]. The term "oligosaccharide" is also used for chains of 2 to 10 monosaccharide units. In the diet, carbohydrates are mainly present in the form of disaccharides and polysaccharides. The process of catabolism (the break down of complex molecules into simple molecules) enables the body to utilize and absorb carbohydrates. The enzymes that hydrolyze carbohydrate compounds are referred to as glycosidase. Examples of these types of enzymes include amylase, maltase and isomaltase.

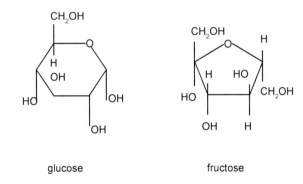

Figure 9.1-1: The structures of glucose and fructose, two of the most common sugars in the human diet

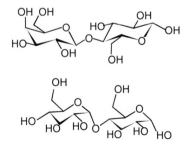

Figure 9.1-2: Structure of Lactose and Maltose.

The vast majority of cellular processes and metabolic pathways in the human body utilize carbohydrate based intermediates. Oxidation and breakdown of these compounds mediates the release of energy. The six most important metabolic pathways incorporating carbohydrates are: glycogenesis,

TABLE 9.1-1: Definitions of metabolic pathways for carbohydrates

Metabolic pathways of carbohydrates	Products of each metabolic pathways
Glycogenesis	Making of glycogen
Glycogenolysis	Breakdown of glycogen
Glycolysis	Oxidation of glucose
Gluconeogenesis	Production of glucose from noncarbohydrate intermediates
Hexose monophosphate shunt	Production of 5-carbon monosaccharides and NADPH
Tricarboxylic acid cycle (TCA)	Oxidation of pyruvate and acetyl CoA

glycogenolysis, glycolysis, the citric acid cycle (also the TCA cycle or the Krebs cycle), gluconeogenesis, and the hexosemonophosphate shunt (**Table 9.1.1**). Glycolysis and the citric acid cycle are the two primary pathways involved with carbohydrate metabolism and energy generation, while the glycogenesis and glycogenolysis pathways have a fundamental role in carbohydrate induced maintenance of euglycemia [1,2,3].

9.1.1.1. Carbohydrate Digestion and Absorption

Although covered in an earlier chapter, carbohydrate digestion and absorption will be briefly reviewed here. Absorption by the intestinal epithelium has some similarities with uptake of glucose in other cells. The small intestine is capable of directly absorbing glucose. Because this is the primary form utilized throughout the body, physical and chemical digestion provides a method for obtaining glucose from complex carbohydrates. Digestion begins in the mouth, via the action of the salivary enzyme a -amylase. This enzyme hydrolyzes a -1-4-linkages. While food spends a limited amount of time in the mouth, the enzyme continues acting on the bolus as it proceeds down the esophagus and into the stomach. The presence of hydrochloric acid in the stomach leads to a decreased pH that ultimately inactivates this enzyme. Upon entering the duodenum, digestion of these partially broken down carbohydrates continues through the actions of pancreatic a-amylase. The final step in the digestion of the resulting small oligosaccharides or

disaccharides occurs via brush border enzymes. These enzymes include lactase, sucrose, and maltase. The end result of this process is that the majority of complex carbohydrates are ultimately hydrolyzed and reduced into their component monomer subunits. These monosaccharides are then absorbed by the intestinal mucosal cells [1,2,3,4].

Absorption of monosaccharides (most notably glucose) into the mucosal cells of the small intestine occurs via active transport. The carrier that facilitates glucose absorption is the sodium-glucose transporter 1 (SGLT 1). This transporter utilizes the sodium gradient created by the sodium-potassium ATPase (adenosince triphosphatase) to assist the movement of two sodium ions and one glucose molecule into the cell. After entering the mucosal cell, the majority of this monosaccharide is then transported into circulation via the glucose transporter 2 (GLUT2) carrier protein. Fructose is transported from the gut into the enterocyte by a protein transporter referred to as GLUT5. All of these monosaccharides are transported out of the enterocyte into the blood stream through a GLUT2 transporter protein. In the blood system, these monosaccharides are transported to body organs like the liver, where glucose is largely metabolized.

As glucose is absorbed from the intestinal tract into the blood stream, two hormones play a critical role in the maintenance of blood glucose levels. These are the peptide hormones insulin and glucagon. Insulin is secreted post-prandially, in response to elevated blood glucose levels. This hormone functions to lower blood glucose in two ways. First, it increases the rate of glucose transport into the liver, kidney, muscle and adipose tissue via the glucose transporter 4 (GLUT 4), and it stimulates glycogenesis in the liver. Glucagon is secreted in response to low blood glucose concentrations. It restores blood glucose concentration to the normal range by stimulating glycogenolysis and gluconeogenesis within the liver [1,2,3,4].

9.1.2. Storage of Carbohydrates

Though carbohydrates are readily degraded to produce energy, when consumed in excess, the body stores the extra carbohydrate. The body requires energy for its bodily processes (basal metabolic rate) and physical activities, i.e. exercise. When all the energy requirements have been met, this excess carbohydrate in the form of glucose is converted to glycogen and stored in the cytosol of the cells. Major sites of glycogen synthesis and storage include the liver and muscle.

Carbohydrates should comprise about 45-65% of the kilocalories taken per day [5]. The recommended dietary allowance (RDA) for carbohydrates is 130 g/day. In pregnant women and lactating women, it is increased to 175 g/day and 210 g/day respectively. The estimated average requirement (EAR) is 100 g/day and increased to 135 g/day and 160 g/day in pregnant and lactating women respectively [5].

As you may recall from section 3.2.3., completely digested carbohydrates are in their simplest forms, called monosaccharides, mainly glucose, galactose and fructose. Monosaccharides are absorbed in the small intestine through the enterocytes of the small intestine. The absorption of monosaccharides in the small intestine is aided by active and facilitated transport mechanisms. Sodium glucose transporter 1 (SGLT1), a protein transporter aids the transport of glucose and galactose into the enterocyte by coupling the monosaccharide uptake to sodium, which enters down its concentration gradient. One ATP is utilized when transported out of the enterocyte to the blood stream through the sodium-potassium pump. The transport of glucose through facilitated transport is aided by the protein transporter GLUT2.

9.1.2.1. Glycogen

Glucose is stored in the liver and muscle cells mainly as glycogen in the cytosol. Glycogen is a multi-branched polysaccharide, which serves as a long-term energy storage of the body. The glycogen structure stored in the liver and muscle cells is in a form that is easy and readily degradable by the body when there is less glucose for energy production in blood or active cells. Glycogen is similar in structure to amylopectin, but glycogen has different bonding patterns in terms of structure. The glycogen structure is made up of glucose molecules that are linked together by α 1-4 glycosidic bond. At every 4th bond of the carbon chain, there is a branching side chain, which is linked by a α 1-6 bond (**Figure 9.1-3**). Energy stores from glycogen are 4.2 Kj/g. Glycogen is in high concentration in the liver. Glycogen in the liver makes up approximately 4% in the fasted state and 8% just after a meal [6]. In the muscle, glycogen makes up less than 1% of the weight of the tissue [1]. Glycogen storage requires water. For every gram of glycogen stored, two to four grams of water are required to be stored as well [7]. Research has indicated that during weight loss programs (exercise and eating low energy diets), the first significant loss of weight is due to loss of glycogen and water in body tissue [8]. Therefore a loss of glycogen in the body contributes to a substantial loss of weight when the body is in a fasted state or consuming a low energy diet, or when doing physical exercise. Since the liver fails to phosphorylate glucose efficiently, glucose is believed to be channeled first to the brain (a more efficient pathway). Where it is efficiently converted to glucose-6-phosphate and then changed to glycogen through the glycogenesis pathway [1].

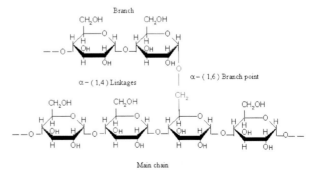

Figure 9.1-3: Branching and linkage. Picture credit: http://webpages.dcu.ie/~faganc/be201/amylopec.gif

The storage of glucose is controlled by hormonal action. The main hormone that is responsible for initiation of glucose storage is insulin, which is secreted when there are high levels of glucose detected in the blood stream.

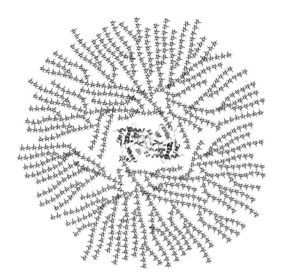

Figure 9.1-4: Structure of Glycogen. Credit: Häggström, Mikael. "Medical gallery of Mikael Häggström 2014". Wikiversity Journal of Medicine 1 (2). DOI:10.15347/wjm/2014.008. ISSN 20018762

9.1.2.2. Glycogenesis

Glycogenesis is the process whereby glucose is converted to glycogen for storage in cell cytosol. The main sites for glycogenesis are in the liver and muscles. Glycogenesis pathway enables the addition of glucose to a glucose-tyrosine primer to make up a complex long chain glycogen molecule (**Figure 9.1.4**). There are two phases in glycogen synthesis. The first phase is initiated by effects of insulin secretion when there is a high concentration of blood glucose. This initiation enables glucose to be transferred to liver or muscle cells. When glucose is within the liver or muscle cells, it is converted to glucose-6- phosphate. The catabolism of glucose to glucose-6-phosphate involves the transfer of a phosphate from Adenosine Triphosphate (ATP) by the aid of an enzyme called hexokinase. The production of hexokinase is responsive to blood insulin levels. As blood insulin goes high, hexokinase activity is elevated hence the conversion of glucose to glucose-6-phosphate is initiated. Phosphorylation of glucose to glucose -6-phosphate in liver and muscle

cells differ in the enzyme that catalyzes the reaction. In the liver, it is aided by a hexokinase, also referred to as glucokinase (hexokinase 4). In the muscle it is aided by a hexokinase type 1 and 2 [1]. The liver glucokinase form is able to phosphorylate glucose at a higher rate than muscle hexokinase because it is not negatively affected by the accumulation of glucose-6-phosphate. Muscle hexokinase is an allosteric enzyme that is negatively affected by glucose-6-phosphate; hence it acts at a slower rate as glucose-6-phosphate accumulates in the cells.

Glucose enters the hepatocyte and is phosphorylated into glucose 6- phosphate by the enzyme glucokinase. This phosphorylation serves two roles. First, glucose 6-phosphate initiates the dephosporylation of the enzyme glycogen synthase, [9,10] which is important for the incorporation of glucose into the glycogen molecule. Second, converting glucose into a phosphorylated intermediate keeps the concentration of glucose within the hepatocyte lower than that within the blood. This concentration gradient of glucose must be maintained for glucose diffusion into the cell to occur [1,4]. While the liver is not dependent on insulin for glucose transport into the cell, the activity and speed (K_m) of glucokinase is increased by this hormone [3] As a result, the speed at which glucose can be converted to the glucose 6-phosphate storage molecule within the hepatocyte is the rate limiting step of this process [9, 10].

The next reaction in the glycogenesis pathway involves the transfer of the phosphate group from the 6 carbon to the 1 carbon and it is catalyzed by phosphoglucomutase. Hydrolysis of uridine triphosphate (UTP) to uridine monophosphate (UMP) provides the energy needed to couple UMP to the glucose 1- phosphate molecule producing uridine diphosphate glucose and pyrophosphate. This molecule is the form in which glucose is incorporated into an existing glycogen molecule [1,2,10,11].

For the last step, the existing glycogen chain is pre-formed by the combination of a glucose residue with a tyrosine protein residue. UDP-glucose is transferred to the glycogen chain and is aided by an enzyme called glycogen synthase. Glucose residues are added to the glycogen chain through a α 1- 4 linkage. When 6-7 glucose units have been added, a branching enzyme transfers these glucose short chains to a six carbon position on the main chain with an α 1-6 linkage. This is referred to as branching action, which is catalyzed by a branching enzyme called amylo (1-4 to 1-6)-transglycosylase. The action of glycogen synthase is stimulated by insulin. When insulin levels are high, glycogen synthase activity is elevated.

Glycogen synthesis is also facilitated by amino acids [12]. Glycogen synthase was measured in human myoblast cells that were starved of amino acids for 5 hours then incubated in media containing 2X the concentration of amino acid. The glycogen synthase increased by 2.5% and 2.0 % after one hour and two hours respectively.

Glycogen is converted back to monosacharides for energy metabolism when the body has insufficient glucose. The process whereby glycogen is broken down for energy metabolism is referred to as glycogenolysis. In this process, glycogen is degraded to glucose-1-phosphate by the action of glycogen phosphorylase enzyme. Later glucose-1- phosphate is converted to glucose-6-phosphate by the action of phosphoglucomutase.

In liver, glucose-6- phosphate is utilized by the glycolysis cycle so as to be converted to pyruvate and enter the citric acid cycle for energy production. Glucose-6-phosphatase enzyme can also dephosphorylate glucose-6-phosphate through the gluconeogenesis pathway to form glucose. In the muscle cells (myocytes), stored glycogen can only be utilized by the surrounding cells or within the muscle tissue itself. Myocytes lack the enzyme glucose-6- phosphatase. Without this enzyme to catalyze the conversion of glucose-6-phosphate into free glucose, the glucose-6-phosphate cannot be moved out of the cell and channeled to other body organs.

9.1.2.3. Hormonal regulation of glycogenesis

As mentioned above, glycogenesis is the process in which glucose is converted into glycogen. The liver is the major site of glycogen production in the human body, and liver cells or hepatocytes are where this metabolic process takes place. The primary regulator of glycogenesis is insulin [9]. Insulin is produced by the β cells within the pancreas and released into circulation as a result of post-prandially induced elevated blood glucose levels. After being secreted into

the blood, insulin travels to the liver where it binds with its receptor (tyrosine kinase receptor) found on the plasma membrane of hepatocytes. Upon binding, insulin receptors phosphorylate themselves, and other intracellular substrates at specific tyrosine residues (hence their name). These insulin receptor substrates activate the enzyme, phosphatidylinositol-3 kinase (PI3K), which ultimately results in phosphorylation of GSK-3. Once phosphorylated, GSK-3 is inactive, meaning it is unable to activate the inactivating kinase protein phosphatase-1. Thus, this net decrease in inhibition results in removal of a phosphate group from and activation of glycogen synthase [9, 10]. During activation of the glycogen synthase enzyme, the activity of the enzyme glycogen phosphorylase, (which is responsible for the breakdown of glycogen) is simultaneously decreased. Thus, the overall result of insulin is the stimulation of the glycogen formation. This occurs by up-regulating the rate of glucose conversion, via the glucokinase enzyme and decreased inhibition of the glycogen synthase enzyme [9,10,11,13].

9.1.2.4. Exercise

Glycogen in the liver is an important source of glucose during prolonged exercise and fasting as the glucose from glycogen can be released into the blood stream and channeled to other organs. Reduced glucose levels caused by exercise and fasting states will trigger release of the hormone glucagon, which initiates glycogen catabolism in the muscle or liver. Therefore the level of glycogen in body reserves is dependent on basal metabolic rate, exercise and eating habits.

There is high usage of glycogen reserves during exercise, which leads to depletion of muscle and liver glycogen stores. When one has depleted his or her glycogen reserves by prolonged exercise, the rate of generation of ATP for muscle contraction drops markedly. This scenario, known as 'hitting the wall', is prevalent in exercise that takes a long time without resting, such as running marathons. Sustained exercise without hitting the wall is more likely in people who have higher amounts of lean muscle tissue and are able to store more glycogen [14]. Odds of hitting the wall can be lowered through carbohydrate loading, a term that refers to the consumption of a lot of low glycemic index carbohydrate foods prior to exercise to maximize glycogen storage. Consumption of carbohydrate fluids during exercise also has been proven to prolong the availablility of glucose during exercise, as glycogen stores are supplemented by glucose absorbed from the gut.

It is important that glycogen reserves be restored after exercise and severe fasted states. Carbohydrate intake during exercise and fasting recovery is the most efficient way to replenish glycogen stores after an exhaustive exercise or fasting period. Intake of protein or amino acids along with carbohydrate can aid in the rate of glycogen resynthesis. Bowtell et al., [8] found that there was a significant 25% increase in glycogen synthesis and storage when 8 grams of glutamine in a 330-mL glucose polymer solution drink was consumed after a glycogen depleting exercise.

Individuals who are subjected to more physical training are able to store glycogen more efficiently than individuals who do not exercise [8]. In one study, 6 endurance-trained and 6 untrained individuals engaged in cycling for two hours, then consumed the same amount of carbohydrate after exercise. Post exercise muscle glycogen accumulation was higher in endurance-trained individuals than untrained individuals after 48 and 72 hours.

The type of carbohydrate consumed after extreme exercise also plays a role in the rate of glycogen restoration. Fructose and galactose containing carbohydrates are likely to be efficient sources of carbohydrates, to enhance glycogen restoration in liver and muscle stores after exercise [5]. When 10 trained individuals exercised and consumed fructose, galactose and glucose-containing maltodextrin separately, the maltodextrin drinks with added fructose and galactose were twice as efficient in glycogen synthesis as maltodextrin drinks with glucose added. Note that maltodextrin is a glucose polymer, sothe non-glucose monosaccharides potentially use a separate pathway for carbohydrate to convert to glycogen in the liver.

Interestingly, there is still ongoing research on glycogenin and proglycogen.

Glycogenin, as discussed earlier, is a protein residue that serves as a primer for glycogen synthesis. Proglycogen is a lower molecular weight intermediate form of glycogen and composes about 15% of total glycogen stores [12]. It is still not clear if proglycogen can be recognized as an independent compound that

is distinct from fully synthesized glycogen, termed macro glycogen. Shearer [15] linked an increase in glycogenin and glycogenin mRNA to glycogen sythesis. She showed glycogen resynthesis results either from an increase in size of the existing glycogen primers or from formation of new glycogen primer from glycogenin residues. In the later scenario, an increase in glycogenin mRNA activity leads to glycogenin and glycogen is formed from proglycogen. She concluded that glycogenin mRNA and glycogenin may facilitate the rapid glycogen synthesis in the form of proglycogen. However, proglycogen synthesis is catalyzed by an enzyme that is similar to glycogen synthase, termed proglycogen synthase [14].

9.1.2.5. Disorders associated with glycogen storage

Glycogen storage can be associated with certain diseases and disorders in the body. The most common disease, which is highly linked to glycogen disorder is called Glycogen storage disease (GSD).

GSD is caused by a malfunction in glycogen synthesis or degradation, which results in excessive storage or depletion of glycogen reserves. GSD can either be genetic or be acquired due to ingestion of intoxicating compounds. The synthesis or degradation of glycogen during GSD is distorted by the lack of enzymes that facilitates these processes. There are many types of glycogen storage diseases depending upon the type of enzyme inhibited, but the four most prevalent ones include [16]:

- Pompe disease (GSD type II, acid maltase deficiency). This type of GSD affects muscle and nerve cells. The deficiency of lysosomal acid alpha-glucosidase enzyme leads to over accumulation of glycogen in the lysosome. The accumulation of glycogen in the lysosome causes muscle weakness.

- Cori disease (GSD type III, debranching enzyme deficiency). This GSD type is hereditary and it is caused by the deficiency of a debranching enzyme. This enzyme is responsible for cleaving the α 1-6 bond of the branching sites of the glycogen structure. The lack of this debranching enzymes therefore leads to an over accumulation of glycogen in body tissue which leads to reduced skeletal and cardiac muscle strength. Reduced cardiac muscle strength may lead to heart failure.

- McArdle disease (GSD type V, myophosphorylase deficiency). This disease is caused by the deficiency of myophosphorylase enzyme in glycogen break down. Symptoms of this disease include fatigue, muscle weakness, cramps and the presence of myoglobin in urine (myoglobinuria). Long-term effects include progressive muscle weakening and wasting.

- Tarui disease (GSD type VII, phosphofructokinase deficiency). This disease is caused by the lack of phosphofructokinase enzyme, which is responsible of phosphorylating fructose-6-phosphate to fructose-1,6- bisphosphate in the glycolysis pathway. This leads to the failure of cells to utilize carbohydrate for energy production. The disease is characterized by high uric acid in urine (hyperuricemia), muscle crumps and weakness usually after exercise and myoglobinuria.

9.2. Glycogenolysis in the Liver

9.2.1. A glucose deficit

A decrease in dietary carbohydrate intake results in decreased blood glucose concentrations. To replenish this concentration, glucose is produced by degrading stored glycogen in the liver. To liberate individual glucose monomers from glycogen, glycogen phosphorylase adds a phosphate group to the end unit of a glycogen molecule. This cleaves the glycosidic bond between glucose 1-phosphate and the remaining glycogen chain. The freed glucose 1-phosphate molecule is then converted back to glucose 6-phosphate via the enzyme phosphoglucomutase. This molecule is then converted to free glucose via glucose 6-phosphatase (G6Pase). The glucose is then shuttled out of the hepatocyte by the GLUT2 transporter and into the blood. [1,2,3,4,17,18]

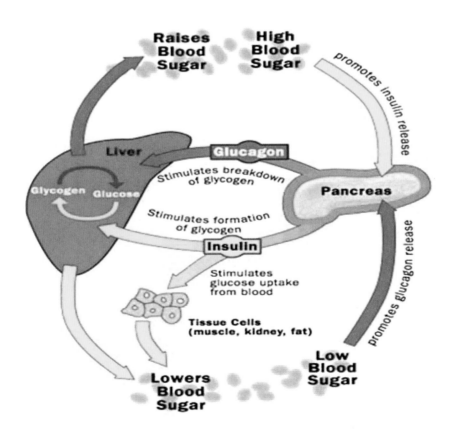

Figure 9.2.1-: Actions of Insulin and Glucagon on Blood Glucose Maintenance.
From: http://destination- yisrael.biblesearchers.com/.a/6a0120a610bec4970c0153932d48cf970b-pi

9.2.2. *Hormonal regulation of Glycogenolysis*

Low blood glucose levels are detected by the pancreas and glucagon is released from its α cells. Glucagon is a catabolic hormone that binds to G-protein coupled receptors (GPCR's) on hepatocytes in the liver. Binding of this ligand to the GPCR causes a conformational change in the receptor, allowing it to interact with G-proteins within the cell, stimulating cyclic adenosine monophosphate (cAMP) production, which activates protein kinase A (PKA). PKA functions to phosphorylate various proteins, particularly phosphorylase kinase, which then activates glycogen phosphorylase [11]. Activated glycogen phosphorylase binds to and inhibits the activity of protein phosphatase-1. Because protein phosphatase-1 is required for activation of glycogen synthase [9,13] inhibition of this enzyme prevents glycogen synthesis and initiates hepatic glycogenolysis [1,2,3,4,17].

9.2.3. *Intake of carbohydrates*

Research has indicated diets containing minimal amounts of carbohydrates have no effect on health or longevity [18]. However, while intake is not necessarily required, it does not mean carbohydrates (particularly monosaccharides like glucose) are not necessary for survival. Indeed, as noted previously glucose is vital for continued functioning of the central nervous system. The metabolic adjustment in the body due to total lack of carbohydrates (such as utilization of gluconeogenesis) has not been studied in a given population for an extended period of time. Nonetheless, given the nature of the hormonal regulation of glucose it is clear that inadequate carbohydrate consumption would prevent the body from maintaining adequate stores of glycogen [19].

With this in mind, the body's endogenous production rate of glucose is an important factor to consider when estimating the average requirement (EAR) for carbohydrate consumption. The brain's requirement for glucose is one of the safest estimates for determining an adequate intake (AI), and estimated average requirement (EAR) for a given population. This is because brain size correlates very well with the endogenous glucose production rate in the postabsorptive state [1,20,21]. While not all glucose

produced is utilized by the brain, such a measure is a safe way to assure adequate amounts of this monosaccharide is present for proper functioning of the central nervous system and maintenance of adequate stores of glycogen for maintenance of euglycemia.

The carbohydrate AI varies between age groups. This is intuitive because infant's brain size relative to their body size is greater than that of adults. Thus the production of glucose is substantially higher in this age group. The AI for infants is shown in **Table 9.2-1** [1].

TABLE 9.2-1: Estimated Adequate Intake of Carbohydrates for Infants, Ages 0 through 12 Months

AI for Infants	Amount of Carbohydrate (grams/ day)
0-6 months	60 g/ day of carbohydrate
7-12 months	95 g/ day of carbohydrate

The brain nearly triples in weight from birth to age 1 year increasing from an estimated 380 g to approximately 1000g in males, and 980g in females [21].

Between 1 and 5 years of age, brain size increases again, to approximately 1,300 g in males and 1,150 g in females. After this time, increase in brain size is minimal.

Given this information and the understanding that the brain consumption of glucose is a function of its size, the EAR for carbohydrate is set based on the information available for adults. It is the same for both genders because brain size and glucose utilization difference for both of these parameters is small. Thus the EAR for children and adults is shown below in **Table 9.2-2** [2].

TABLE 9.2-2: EAR for Male and Female Children and Adults

EAR for:	Amount of Carbohydrate (grams/ day)
Children 1-18 years	100g/ d
Men and Women 19 – 70	100g/ d
Men and Women > 70 years	100g/ d

As a result, the EAR for total carbohydrate consumption for individuals above 12 months of age is established as 100 g/d [2]. This amount is believed to be sufficient for effective functioning of the central nervous system without having to utilize ketones or any protein-derived glucogenic sources. Lastly, the recommended daily allowance (RDA) for carbohydrate is established by utilizing a coefficient of variance of 15 percent, which is based upon the variation that exists in brain glucose use. The values for this recommendation in adults are shown below in **Table 9.2-3** [2].

TABLE 9.2-3: RDA for Carbohydrate for Men and Women ages 19 -70, and > 70 years of age

RDA for Carbohydrate	Amount of Carbohydrate (grams/ day)
Men and Women 19 – 70 years	130 g/ d
Men and Women > 70 years	130 g/ d

In summary, the use of carbohydrates is widespread in the human body, with a central role in providing fuel for the functioning of the central nervous system. To do this, carbohydrate levels are maintained within a narrow range in the blood by the hormonally regulated processes glycogenesis and glycogenolysis. The liver serves a crucial role in the maintenance of glucose concentrations for utilization by the brain both post-prandially, and in the post-absorptive state. An understanding of these metabolic processes, coupled with an estimate of how much glucose the brain uses on a daily basis provides the tools necessary to establish a dietary reference intake for this nutrient.

9.3. Metabolic utilization of carbohydrates: Energy generation from catabolic pathways of glucose metabolism

Glucose metabolism serves an important role as the most common energy source for the energy needs of most people. Carbohydrate metabolism focuses on the synthesis and usage of glucose, a major fuel for most organisms (e.g., brain, red blood cells, and exercising skeletal muscle cells). When cellular energy levels are low, glucose is degraded by the glycolytic pathway, while at high energy levels glucose molecules are not required for immediate energy production and so they are stored as glycogen in

liver and muscle. As mentioned above, the metabolic pathways of carbohydrate consist of glycogenesis (the making of glycogen), glycogenolysis (the breakdown of glycogen), glycolysis (the oxidation of glucose), the hexosemonophosphate shunt (the production of 5-carbon monosaccharides and NADPH), the tricarboxylic acid cycle (TCA cycle) or the citric acid cycle (oxidation of pyruvate and acetyl CoA), and gluconeogenesis (the making of glucose from noncarbohydrate precursors) (**Table 9.1-1**) [22]. The major regulatory mechanisms of these metabolic pathways are hormonal (insulin, glucagon, epinephrine, and the corticosteroid hormones) and allosteric enzyme activation or suppression. Several sugars are important in vertebrates. Besides glucose, other sugars, such fructose, galactose, and mannose, play an important role in human diet [23,24].

9.3.1. Catabolic pathways of glucose metabolism

Metabolism can be divided into two main parts; catabolism, the degradation of molecules, and the production of energy or small molecules useful for cell function, and anabolism, the synthesis of larger biomolecules from small precursors. Catabolic reactions involve the breakdown of carbohydrates, lipids, proteins, and nucleic acids to produce smaller molecules and biological energy in the form of heat or ATP. Glucose polymers can be partially or fully oxidized to release CO_2, and energy, which is used to produce molecules like ATP and heat. Breakdown of glucose, in addition to contributing to ATP synthesis, generates compounds that can be used for biosynthetic purposes. Glucose can be used as the primary oxidized substrate for cells that can grow and divide fast, such as white blood cells, stem cells, and some epithelial cells [25]. Oxidative pathways of glucose include glycolysis, the tricarboxylic acid cycle (or Kreb's cycle) and mitochondrial oxidative phosphorylation/electron transport [1,23,26].

9.3.2. Glycolysis

Glycolysis (**Figure 9.3-1**), also referred to as the Embden-Meyerhof-Parnas pathway (Mckee and Mckee, 2011), is a very important metabolic pathway found in all organisms (for example glucose supplies most of the fuel for the brain). Glycolysis is the process by which each glucose molecule, $(C_6H_{12}O_6)$, a 6C molecule, is converted via fructose-1,6-bisphosphate to two three-carbon units, pyruvate $(CH_3COCO_2^-)$, with the generation of 2 ATP mol and 2 NADH mol (the reduced form of the coenzyme NAD^+) per mol of glucose. In the glucolysis pathway, a total of 10 enzymatic reactions are involved. These enzymes are located in the cytosol, where they are only freely associated with cell structures such as membranes. Under anaerobic conditions, pyruvate is converted to lactate. Under these anaerobic conditions, glycolysis releases a small amount of energy, which is the source of energy for organs that do not contain mitochondria (like red blood cell), by the mechanism of substrate-level phosphorylation of ADP. Under aerobic conditions, complete oxidation of pyruvate generally occurs, with only a small amount of lactate being formed. Pyruvate can be transported in the mitochondria and participate in the TCA cycle, in which it becomes completely oxidized to CO_2 and H_2O. Complete oxidation releases a relatively large amount of energy, as ATP, by the mechanism of oxidative phosphorylation [1,24].

9.3.2.1. Pathways of Glycolysis

The first stage (**Figure 9.1**, glycolysis reactions 1-5), is a preparatory stage in which the hexose glucose is phosphorylated and cleaved to yield 2 molecules of triose glyceraldehyde-3- phosphate using two ATP molecules as energy. The second step (**Figure 9.3-1**, glycolysis, reactions 6- 10), the molecules of glyceraldehyde-3-phosphate are converted to pyruvate, with concomitant generation of four ATPs per glucose (**Figure 9.3-1**). The pyruvate that is produced can be transported to mitochondria for subsequent oxidation (TCA cycle and mitochondrial oxidative phosphorylation/electron transport) or it is converted to lactate under anaerobic conditions. The glycolytic pathway can be summed up in the following equation (1) [1,24,27]:

D-Glucose $+2$ ADP $+2$ Pi $+$ 2 $NAD^+ \rightarrow$ 2 pyruvate$+2$ ATP$+2$ NADH$+2H^+$ $+2H_2O$ (1)

where Pi represents inorganic phospate.

9.3.2.2. Summary of the Reactions of Glycolysis [1,24,27]:

1. **Synthesis of glucose-6-phosphate (Reaction catalyzed by hexokinase):**

Several enzymes, called hexokinases, catalyze the phosphorylation of hexoses with utilization of ATP. This involves the transfer of a phosphoryl group from ATP to glucose to form glucose-6- phosphate. Phosphorylation prevents transport of glucose out of

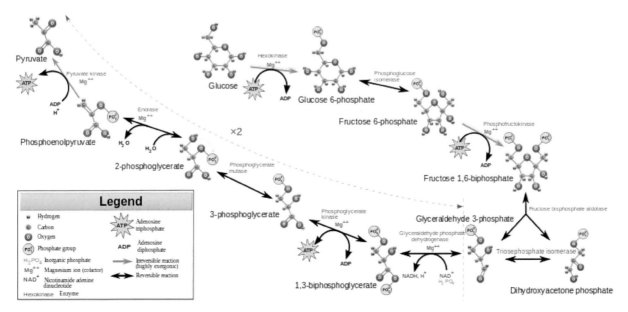

Figure 9.3-1: Glycolysis pathways (http://commons.wikimedia.org/wiki/File:Glycolysis.svg).

the cell and increases the reactivity of the oxygen in the resulting phosphate ester.

2. **Conversion of glucose-6-phosphate to fructose-6-phosphate (Catalyzed by phosphoglucose isomerase):**

Phosphoglucose isomerase catalyzes the reaction of the open chain form of the aldose glucose-6- phosphate into the open chain form of the ketose fructose-6-phosphate.

3. **The phosphorylation of fructose-6-phosphate (Catalyzed by phosphofructokinase):**

Phosphofructokinase-1 (PFK-1) (irreversibly under cellular conditions) catalyzes the phosphorylation of fructose-6-phosphate to form fructose-1,6-bisphosphate, utilizing the second mole of ATP.

4. **Cleavage of fructose-1,6-bisphosphate (Catalyzed by Aldolase):**

Cleavage of fructose-1,6-bisphosphate is catalyzed by Aldolase. Stage 1 of glycolysis ends with the cleavage of fructose-1,6-bisphosphate into two three carbon (trioses) molecules: glyceraldehyde-3- phosphate (G-3-P) and dihydroxyacetone phosphate (DHAP). This reaction is an **aldol cleavage,** with products to be aldehyde and ketone.

5. **The interconversion of glyceraldehyde-3-phosphate and dihydroxyacetone phosphate (Catalyzed by Triose phosphate isomerase):**

In this step, interconversion of glyceraldehyde-3-phosphate (GAP) and dihydroxyacetone phosphate (DHAP) (isomerization of DHAP) catalyzed by Triose Phosphate Isomerase takes place. Of the two products of the aldolase reaction, only GAP serves as a substrate for the next reaction in glycolysis. Triose phosphate isomerase catalyzes the reversible conversion of DHAP to GAP. In this reaction, the glucose has been converted to two molecules of GAP.

6. **Oxidation of glyceraldehyde-3-phosphate (Catalyzed by Glyceraldehyde-3-Phosphate Dehydrogenase):**

Oxidation and phosphorylation of GAP by NAD^+ and Pi, catalyzed by Glyceraldehyde-3-Phosphate Dehydrogenase. GAP, contains a high-energy phosphoanhydride bond, which may be used in the next reaction to generate ATP.

7. **Phosphoryl group transfer (Catalyzed by Phosphoglycerate Kinase):**

This reaction results in the first formation of ATP together with 3-phosphoglycerate from 1,3-bisphosphyglycerate. In this reaction, catalyzed by phosphoglycerate kinase, ATP is synthesized from the transfer of the high-energy phosphoryl group of glycerate-1,3-bisphosphate to ADP.

8. **The interconversion of 3-phosphoglycerate and 2-phosphoglycerate (Catalyzed by Phosphoglycerate Mutase):**

Phosphoglycerate Mutase catalyzes the conversion of glycerate-3-phosphate (energy-poor phosphate ester) to phosphoenolpyruvate (high phosphoryl group), by a two-step addition/elimination cycle.

9. **Dehydration of 2-phosphoglycerate (Catalyzed by Enolase):**

Enolase catalyzes the dehydration of glycerate-2-phosphate to form phosphoenolpyruvate, which introduces a double bond that imparts high energy to the phosphate bond.

10. **Synthesis of pyruvate (Catalyzed by Pyruvate Kinase):**

Pyruvate kinase catalyzes the free energy of phosphoenolpyruvate hydrolysis to the synthesis of ATP to form pyruvate. Two molecules of ATP are formed for each molecule of glucose.

9.3.2.3. Regulation of Glycolysis

The rate at which the glycolytic pathway operates in a cell is controlled by the kinetic properties of hexokinases and the allosteric regulation of the enzymes hexokinase, phosphofructokinase-1 (rate limiting enzyme of glycolysis; inhibited by ATP, citrate; activated by AMP), and pyruvate kinase (activated at high AMP concentration; inhibited by a high ATP concentration). Glycolysis is also regulated by the peptide hormones glucagon (low blood glucose, reducing the level of fructose-2,6-bisphosphate) and insulin (high blood glucose, increasing the level of fructose-2,6-bisphosphate) [28].

9.3.3. Oxidation of Pyruvate and the TCA cycle

9.3.3.1. Pyruvate Dehydrogenase Complex

The pyruvate dehydrogenase complex links glycolysis to the TCA cycle. The pyruvate dehydrogenase complex oxidizes pyruvate to generate acetyl-coA, in the mitochondria of the cell. It is a large multi-enzyme complex composed of three enzymes, Pyruvate dehydrogenase (E1), Dihydrolipoyl transacetylase (E2) and Dihydrolipoyl dehydrogenase (E3) involving five cofactors Thiamine Pyrophosphate (TPP), Lipoic Acid-Lipoamide, Flavin adenine dinucleotide (FAD), Nicotinamide adenine dinucleotide (NAD^+) and coenzyme A (CoASH or CoA) [1,24]. In particular:

- **Pyruvate dehydrogenase (E1)** uses TPP as its prosthetic group.

- **Dihydrolipoyl transacetylase (E2)** uses lipoamide and CoASH as its prosthetic groups.

- **Dihydrolipoyl dehydrogenase (E3)** uses FAD and nicotinamide NAD^+ as its cofactors.

9.3.3.2. Pyruvate Dehydrogenase process

The reaction of converting pyruvate into acetyl CoA and CO_2 is:

2 pyruvate $+ 2 NAD^+ + 2 CoA \rightarrow 2$ acetyl CoA $+ 2$ NADH $+ 2 CO_2$ (2)

This is a five-step reaction (**Figure 9.3-2**) [1,29]:

1. Pyruvate is decarboxylated by E1 with the help of TPP.

2. The reactive carbon (between the N and the S of the five-member ring) of the TPP is oxidized and transferred as the acetyl group to lipoamide (which is the prosthetic group of the dihydrolipoyl transacetylase). This forms hydroxyethyl-TPP. An H^+ ion is required for the intermediate to give off CO_2.

3. E2 oxidizes hydroxyethyl- to acetyl-. The acetyl group is linked to CoASH, forming acetyl-CoA.

4. The E2 is still attached to the acetyl CoA molecule. So, E3 oxidizes the thiol groups of the dihydrolipoamide back to lipoamide.

5. As a side reaction, FADH2 is oxidized by NAD^+, forming FAD, NADH and H^+.

9.3.3.3. Pyruvate dehydrogenase regulation

Pyruvate dehydrogenase is a major regulatory point for entry of materials into the citric acid cycle. The enzyme is regulated allosterically and by covalent modification.

Allosterically Regulation

E2 is inhibited by acetyl-CoA and activated by CoASH, while E3 is inhibited by NADH and activated by NAD^+ [1,29,30].

Covalent Regulation

Pyruvate dehydrogenase kinase, phosphorylates three specific E1 serine residues, resulting in loss of activity of pyruvate dehydrogenase. NADH and acetyl-CoA both activate kinase. The serines are dephosphorylated by a specific enzyme called pyruvate dehydrogenase phosphatase which is activated by Ca^{2+} and Mg^{2+}. Pyruvate dehydrogenase responds to ATP levels by being turned off when ATP is abundant and further energy production is unneeded [1,29,30].

9.3.4. TCA Cycle

The tricarboxylic acid cycle (TCA cycle), also called the Krebs cycle or the citric acid cycle, is at the head of energy metabolism in the body. Over 90% of the energy released from food is estimated to occur as a result of TCA cycle oxidation. The TCA cycle is located within the matrix of the mitochondria. The high-energy output of the TCA cycle is attributed to mitochondrial electron transport, with oxidative phosphorylation being the source of ATP formation. TCA cycle can be considered as the common and final catabolic pathway, because products of carbohydrate, fat, and amino acids that enter the cycle can be completely oxidized (not all the substances are completely oxidized)

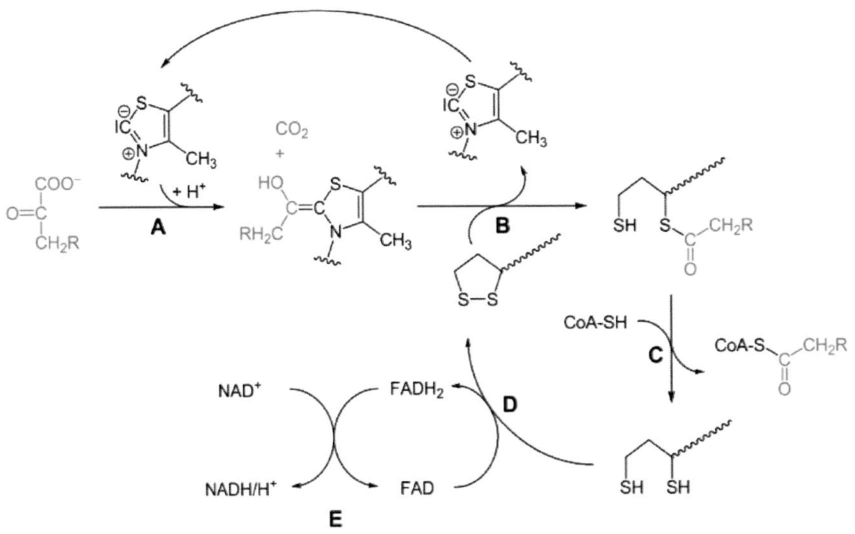

Figure 9.3-2: Pyruvate dehydrogenase process
From: http://commons.wikimedia.org/wiki/File:PDH_schema.png

to CO_2 and H_2O, with the accompanying release of energy. A few TCA cycle intermediates are used in the formation of glucose by the process of gluconeogenesis, and some can be converted to certain amino acids by transamination. Examples of TCA cycle intermediates usage are citrate to fatty acid synthesis, succinyl-CoA to heme synthesis, ketone body activation and malate in gluconeogenesis [24].

From glucose metabolism, the two pyruvates from one glucose molecule during glycolysis, are transported into the mitochondria, where decarboxylation leads to the formation of two acetyl CoA units and two molecules of CO_2. During the TCA cycle, the acetyl group is completely oxidized. The remaining hydrogens and their electrons are removed. Most of the electrons are picked up by NAD to form NADH, and during one point in the process FAD picks up electrons to form $FADH_2$, and the remaining carbon and oxygen atoms are combined to form CO_2. At the end of the TCA cycle, the acetyl group has been completely oxidized to CO_2. From each of the of the pyruvate molecules that enters the TCA cycle, 1 ATP is generated. The three carbons of the pyruvate are released as carbon dioxide (CO_2). The five pairs of hydrogens become attached to hydrogen carriers to become 4 NADHs and 1 $FADH_2$. Both NADH and $FADH_2$ are reoxidized by O_2 through the electron transport chain, in the mitochondrial inner membrane [1,24].

9.3.4.1. TCA Pathways

TCA cycle (Figure 9.3), starts with the entrance of the acetyl CoA (produced from pyruvate dehydrogenase reaction), to begin the TCA reactions pathway [1,27,31]:

1. **Formation of citrate (Catalyzed by citrate synthase)**

Citrate synthase catalyzes the formation of citrate from oxaloacetate and acetyl CoA; the reaction is regulated negatively by ATP. The citric acid cycle begins when Coenzyme A transfers its 2-carbon acetyl group to the 4-carbon compound oxaloacetate to form the 6-carbon molecule citrate.

2. **Isomerization of citrate to isocitrate (Catalyzed by aconitase)**

Aconitase catalyzes the isomerization of citrate to isocitrate, which involves cis aconitate as an intermediate.

3. **Dehydrogenation of isocitrate (Catalyzed by isocitrate dehydrogenase)**

Dehydrogenation of isocitrate, catalyzed by the enzyme isocitrate dehydrogenase, to produce α- ketoglutarate, with the energy to be supplied from reoxidation of the NADH, from Electron Transport Chain. The 6-carbon isocitrate is oxidized and a molecule of carbon dioxide is removed producing the 5-carbon molecule alpha-

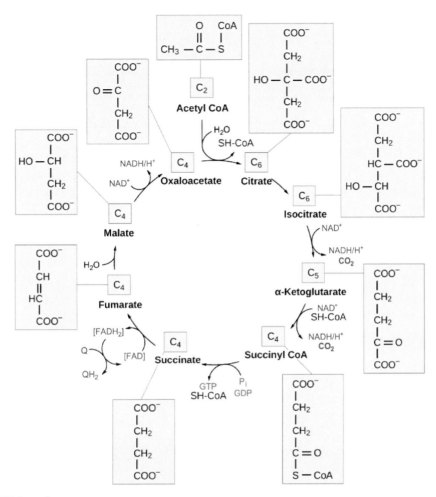

Figure 9.3-3: TCA cycle.
From: http://figures.boundless-cdn.com/18837/full/figure-07-03-02.jpeg.

ketoglutarate. During this oxidation, NAD$^+$ is reduced to NADH$^+$ and H$^+$. During this reaction the first loss of CO2 in the cycle (decarboxylation of an intermediate compound, oxalosuccinate) occurs.

4. **Decarboxylation and dehydrogenation of α-ketoglutarate (Catalyzed by pyruvate dehydrogenase complex)**

In the decarboxylation and dehydrogenation of α-ketoglutarate, NAD$^+$ serves as hydrogen acceptor and forms NADH. Coenzyme A oxidizes the alpha-ketoglutarate, and the instability that is created causes a carbonyl group to be released as CO2. Coenzyme A is added to form the 4-carbon compound succinyl-CoA.

5. **Hydrolysis of thioester bond of succinyl CoA (Catalyzed by succinyl thiokinase)**

The hydrolysis of thioester bond of succinyl CoA bond by succinyl thiokinase releases sufficient energy to drive the phosphorylation of guanosine diphosphate (GDP) by inorganic phosphate, producing an energy molecule of guanosine triphosphate (GTP) (a high-energy phosphate anhydride compound) and leaves behind a molecule of **succinate**. GTP can then be used to make ATP.

6. **Stereospecific dehydrogenation of succinate to fumarate (Catalyzed by succinate dehydrogenase)**

Succinate is oxidized by a molecule of FAD, which removes two hydrogen atoms from the succinate and forces a double bond to form between the two carbon atoms, thus creating **fumarate.** During this oxidation, FAD is reduced to FADH2.

7. **Fumarate hydration to form malate (Catalyzed by fumarase)**

Fumarase adds water to the fumarate molecule to form malate. Malate is created by adding one hydrogen atom to a carbon atom and then adding a hydroxyl group to a carbon next to a terminal carbonyl group.

8. **Dehydrogenation reaction of malate to oxaloacetate (Catalyzed by malate dehydrogenase)**

The conversion of malate to oxaloacetate completes the cycle. Malate dehydrogenase catalyzes oxidation of (S)-malate's hydroxyl group to a ketone in an NAD^+ dependent reaction. During this oxidation, NAD^+ is reduced to NADH and H^+. The end product is oxaloacetate, which can then combine with acetyl-CoA and begin the TCA cycle all over again.

9.3.4.2. Regulation of the TCA Cycle

Regulation of the TCA cycle, like that of glycolysis, occurs at both the level of entry of substrates into the cycle as well as at the key reactions of the cycle. The TCA is regulated by substrate availability (citrate synthase reaction as a result of reduced availability of oxaloacetate), product inhibition (citrate inhibits citrate synthase; alpha-ketoglutarate dehydrogenase is inhibited by NADH and succinyl-CoA), and inhibition by other cycle intermediates. The flux of carbon through the TCA cycle depends on the cellular ratio of $NAD^+/NADH$. TCA rate controlling enzymes are citrate synthase, isocitrate dehydrogenase, and alpha-ketoglutarate dehydrogenase, with the key enzymes to be regulated allosterically by Ca^{2+}, ATP (inhibit isocitrate dehydrogenase) and ADP (activates isocitrate dehydrogenase) [1,32,33].

9.3.5. Electron Transport/Oxidative Phosphorylation

Glycolysis releases only a small amount of the energy stored in a glucose molecule. The pyruvate molecules created in glycolysis retains about 80% of the stored chemical energy. In the presence of oxygen, pyruvate molecules are actively transported into the mitochondria and undergo an intermediate step, which links glycolysis with the TCA cycle. Once the energy intermediates,

NADH and FADH2 are reoxidized by O2 through the electron transport chain/oxidative phosphorylation, this process involves the formation of both water and ATP molecules, in the mitochondrial innermembrane. During oxidative phosphorylation, electrons can be donated from electron donors, NADH and FADH2, to a specialized set of proteins that act as an electron conduit to electron acceptors such as oxygen, in a series of redox reactions, the electron transport chain. As the electrons are passed down the chain, they lose much of their free energy. Some of this energy can be captured and stored in the form of a proton gradient (actively transport H+ into the intermembrane space). The proton gradient is used by the ATP synthase to produce the ATP from ADP [1,34,35]

The events of the electron transport chain involve NADH and FADH2, which act as electron transporters as flowing through the innermembrane. The electron transport chain is made of 4 distinct complexes, which can be isolated and purified (**Figure 9.3-4**). Complex I (NADH-coenzyme Q reductase), electrons are passed from NADH to the electron transport chain, where they flow through the remaining complexes. NADH is oxidized to NAD in this process. Complex II (succinate CoQ dehydrogenase) oxidizes FADH2, getting more electrons for the chain. At complex III (coenzyme Q–cytochrome c reductase), no additional electrons enter the chain, but electrons from complexes I and II flow through it. At complex IV (cytochrome oxidase) electrons are transferred to a molecule of oxygen, where oxygen gains electrons and it is reduced to water. The movement of electrons through complexes I-IV causes protons (hydrogen atoms) to be pumped out of the intermembrane space into the cell cytosol resulting in an electrochemical gradient due to the net negative charge (from the electrons) in the matrix space and the net positive charge (from the proton pumping) in the intermembrane space. Complex V, ATP synthase, uses the energy stored in a proton gradient across a membrane to drive the synthesis of ATP from ADP and phosphate (Pi). This phosphorylation reaction is an equilibrium, which can be shifted by altering the proton-motive force. When the proton-motive force is high, the reaction is forced to run in the opposite direction; it proceeds from left to right, allowing protons to flow down their concentration gradient and turning ADP into ATP. In the absence of a proton-motive force,

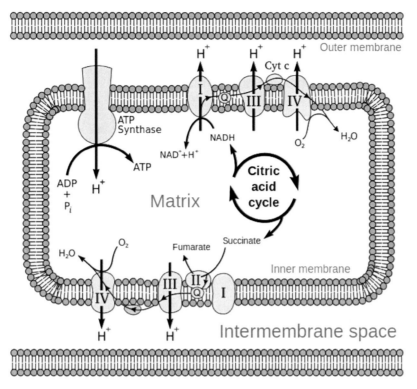

Figure 9.3-4: Electron transport and oxidative phosphorylation.
From: http://en.wikipedia.org/wiki/Electron_transport_chain

the ATP synthase reaction will run from right to left, hydrolyzing ATP and pumping protons out of the matrix across the membrane [34].

In total, the process started through the glycolysis of one glucose molecule yields about 32 ATP in oxidative phosphorylation [1,35].

9.4. Metabolic function of fructose

Fructose is a carbohydrate, which is processed by incorporation into carbohydrate metabolism, with fructose metabolic function to affect the increase in the intermediates of carbohydrate metabolism. Most of the metabolic effects of fructose are due to its rapid utilization in the liver influencing carbohydrate and lipid metabolism [36,37].

As in the most hexose sugars, hexokinase will catalyze the phosphorylation of fructose, however, phosphorylation of fructose is inhibited by glucose in physiological concentration. In liver, fructose rapidly phosphorylated to form fructose 1-phosphate, a reaction that is catalyzed by fructokinase (ketohexokinse enzyme, specific for fructose). Another important

enzyme, in carbohydrate metabolism is the enzyme fructose-bisphosphate aldolase, which cleaves both fructose 1-phosphate and the intermediates of glycolysis fructose 1,6-bisphosphate. There are three genetically distinct isoforms of this crucial enzyme: aldolase A in muscle, aldolase B in liver, and aldolase C in brain. People with a lack of aldolase B cannot metabolize fructose properly (hereditary fructose intolerance). In the liver, aldolase B splits fructose 1-phosphate into glyceraldehyde and dihydroxyacetone phosphate, intermediates of the glycolysis pathway. Glyceraldehyde is phosphorylated by triokinase. Triosephosphate isomerase converts dihydroxyacetone phosphate into glyceraldehyde 3-phosphate, which can then continue along the glycolytic pathway or contributes to gluconeogenesis depending on existing conditions [36,37].

9.5. Brief summary

The energy requirements of many tissues (e.g., brain, red blood cells, and exercising skeletal muscle cells) depend on continuous flow and metabolism of glucose. Most of the usable energy obtained from the breakdown of glucose is derived by oxidative phosphorylation, which takes place within mitochondria. First the breakdown of glucose by glycolysis and the TCA cycle yields a total of four molecules of ATP, ten molecules of NADH, and two molecules of FADH2. Then electrons from NADH and FADH2 are transferred and coupled to molecular oxygen, through the electron transfer chain, and 32 molecules of ATP are formed by oxidative phosphorylation. Glucose metabolic pathways (e.g., glycolysis and gluconeogenesis) are influenced by fructose metabolism. Fructose metabolism in liver affects the glucose metabolism by increasing the amount of some glucose metabolic intermediates.

Alterations in factors that control food intake (e.g., high fructose intake has been shown to cause dyslipidemia and to impair hepatic insulin sensitivity) and regulate glucose and energy metabolism are related to well-known pathological conditions such as obesity, type 2 diabetes and the metabolic syndrome, and some types of cancer. Hence, more studies need to be done concerning factors that control food intake and regulate glycose and energy metabolism, such as well-known hormones like insulin [25,38,39].

9.6. Literature cited

1. Gropper S, and Smith, J. Advanced Nutrition and Human Metabolism, Sixth Edition: 79- 81, 2013.

2. Institute of Medicine of the National Academies. (2005). "Dietary Carbohydrates: Sugars and Starches". Dietary Reference Intakes for Energy, Carbohydrate, Fiber, Fat, Fatty Acids, Cholesterol, Protein, and Amino Acids, (265-337) Washington, DC: Thw National Academics Press.

3. Horton, R. A., Horton, L. M.,Ochs, R. S., Rawn, J. D., Scrimgeour, K. G. (2002). Principles of Biochemistry Upper Saddle River: Prentice Hall

4. Boron, W..F., Boulpaep, E. L. (2012). Medical Physiology Philadelphia: Saunders

5. Otten JJ, Hellwig JP, Meyers L. Dietary Reference Intakes: The Essential Guide to Nutrient Requirements. The National Academies; 2006. Available from http://www.nap.edu/catalog/11537.html.

6. Kreitzman S.N, Coxon Y. A, Szaz K.F. (1992) Glycogen storage: illusions of easy weight loss, excessive weight regain, and distortions in estimates of body composition,. Amer J Clin Nutr, 56(1): 292-3.

7. Armstrong J.L, Bonavaud S.M, Toole B.J, and Yeaman S.J. (2001) Regulation of glycogen synthesis by amino acids in cultured human muscle cells, J BIOL CHEM 276(2): 952-6.

8. Bowtell J.L., Gelly J, Jackman L.M. (2001) Effect of oral glutamine on whole body carbohydrate storage during recovery from exhaustive exercise, J Applied Physiol 86(6): 1770-6.

9. Miller, B.M., Larner, J. (1973). "Mechanism of control of hepatic glycogenesis by insulin". J. Biol. Chem. 248, 3483-3488.

10. Cadefau, J., Bollen, M., Stalmans, W. (1997). "Glucose-induced glycogenesis in the liver involves the glucose 6-phosphate dependent dephosphorylation of glycogen synthase." J. Biochem. 322, 745-750.

11. Green, A.R., Aiston, S., Greenberg, C.C., Freeman, S., Poucher, S.M., Brady, M.J., Agius, L. (2004). The Glycogenic action of protein targeting to glycogen in hepatocytes involves multiple mechanisms including phosphorylase inactivation and glycogen synthase translocation. J. Biol. Chem. 279, 46474-46482

12. Lomako J, Lomako WM, and Whelan WJ. (1993) Glycogen synthesis in the astrocyte: from glycogenin to proglycogen to glycogen, FASEB J, 7(14): 1386-93.

13. Martin, W.H., et. al. (1998). "Discovery of a human liver glycogen phosphorylase inhibitor that lowers blood glucose in vivo." Proc. Natl. Acad. Sci. U.S.A. 95, 1776- 1781.

14. Lomako J, Lomako WM, and Whelan WJ. (1991) Proglycogen: a low-molecular-weight form of muscle glycogen. FEBS Lett 279: 223–228.

15. Shearer J, Wilson RJ, Battram DS, Richter EA, Robinson DL, Bakovic M, and Graham TE. (2005) Increases in glycogenin and glycogenin mRNA accompany glycogen resynthesis in human

skeletal muscle. Am J Physiol Endocrinol Metab 289: E508–E514.

16. Escott-Stump S. (2015) Nutrition & Diagnosis-Related Care. 8th ed. Philadelphia: Wolters-Kluwer. pp.156-7.

17. Peeter, A., Baes, M. (2010). Role of PPARα in hepatic carbohydrate metabolism. PPAR Research. 1-12. doi: 10.1155/2010/572405

18. Heinbecker, P. (1982). "Studies on the metabolism of Eskimos". J. Biol Chem 80, 461- 475.

19. Meyer, C., Dostov, J.M., Welle, S.L., Gerich, J. E. (2002). "Role of human liver, kidney, and skeletal muscle in postprandial glucose homeostasis." Am. J. of Physiol Endocrinol Metab. 282, E419-E427.

20. Bier D.M., Leake, R.D., Haymond, M.W., Arnold, K.J., Gruenke, L.D., Sperling, M.A., (1977). "Measurement of true glucose production rates in infancy and childhood with 6,6-dideuteroglucose." Diabetes, 26, 1016-1023.

21. Dekaban, A.S., Sadowsky, D. (1978) "Changes in brain weights during the span of human life: Relation of brain weights to body heights and body weights." Ann. Neurol 4, 345-356.

22. Dashty M., 2013. A quick look at biochemistry: Carbohydrate metabolism, Clinical Biochemistry, 46, p. 1339–1352.

23. Cox, S., 2005. Energy/Metabolism ,Encyclopedia of Human Nutrition,. Four-Volume Set, Second Edition, Elsevier Academic Press, Oxford, UK. p. 106-114.

24. Mckee T., Mckee J., 2011. Biochemistry: The Molecular Basis of Life, Chapter 8. Charbohydrate Metabolism, Oxford University Press, USA; 5 edition, New York, NY U.S.A.

25. Nature, 2013. Nutrient utilization in humans. http://www.nature.com/scitable/topicpage/dynamic-adaptation-of-nutrient-utilization-in- humans-14232807. Accessed on November 26th, 2013.

26. Fernie A.R. Carrari1 F. Sweetlove J., 2004. Respiratory metabolism: glycolysis, the TCA cycle and mitochondrial electron transport, Current Opinion in Plant Biology, 7, p.254–261.

27. Kim J., Dang C. V., 2005. Multifaceted roles of glycolytic enzymes, TRENDS in Biochemical Sciences, Vol. 30 No.3, p. 142-150.

28. Wu C., Khan S.A., Lange A.J., 2005, Regulation of glycolysis—role of insulin, Experimental Gerontology 40, p. 894–899.

29. Themedicalbiochemistrypage, 2013. The Pyruvate Dehydrogenase Complex and TCA cycle. http://themedicalbiochemistrypage.org/tca-cycle.php. Accessed on November 26th, 2013.

30. Harris R.A., Bowker-Kinley M.M., Huang B., Wu P., 2002. Regulation of the activity of the pyruvate dehydrogenase complex, Advance Enzyme Regulation, 42, p. 249–259.

31. Robinson Jr. J.B., Serre P.A., 1985. Organization of Krebs Tricarboxylic Acid Cycle Enzymes, BIOCHEMICAL MEDICINE 33, p. 149-157.

32. Wan B., LaNoue K. F., Cheung J. F., Scaduto Jr R. C., 1989. Regulation of Citric Acid Cycle by Calcium, The journal of Biological Chemistry, Vol. 264, No. 23, p. 13430-13439.

33. Nunes-Nesi A., Araujo W. L., Obata T., Fernie A.R., 2013. Regulation of the mitochondrial tricarboxylic acid cycle, Physiology and metabolism, Current Opinion in Plant Biology, Volume 16, Issue 3, p. 335–343.

34. Hatefi Y., 1985. The mitochondrial electron transport phosphorylation system, Annual review biochemistry, 54, p.1015-1069.

35. Dean, W. 2013. Mitochondrial dysfunction, nutrition and aging. Nutrition Review, http://nutritionreview.org/2013/09/mitochondrial-dysfunction/. Accessed on November 30th, 2013.

36. Kohlmeier M., 2003. Nutrient Metabolism, Fructose. Food Science and Technology International Series, Academic Press, 1 edition. Oxford, UK, p. 210-216.

37. Lustig R.H., 2010. Fructose: Metabolic, Hedonic, and Societal Parallels with Ethanol, J Amer Dietetic Assoc, 110(9): 1307-1321.

38. Feinman R.D., Fine J.E., 2013. Fructose in perspective, Nutrition & Metabolism,, 10(1): 10-45.

39. Tappy L., Le K. A, 2010. Metabolic effects of fructose and the worldwide increase in obesity. Physiol. Rev. 90(1): 23–46.

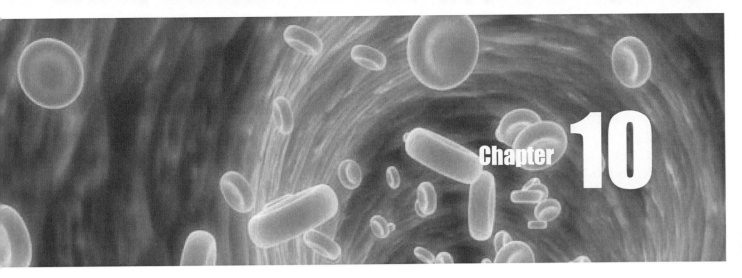

Chapter 10

Lipid Storage, Metabolism, and Body Structure

Learning Objectives

After completing this chapter, you should be able to:

1. Identify sites of lipid storage in the body

2. List the functions of stored lipids in the body and complications associated with improper lipid storage

3. Explain the function and metabolic roles of cholesterol

4. Outline fatty acid oxidation from transport into the mitochondria and the four steps of β-oxidation needed to produce acetyl CoA.

5. Explain fatty acid biosynthesis

6. Identify important functions of cholesterol

7. Explain how the structure of omega-3 and omega-6 fatty acids impacts the metabolic pathway to synthesize eicosanoids

8. Identify the three basic parts in the structure and functioning of phospholipids and sphingolipids

Introduction

Lipids are a diverse class of macromolecules that can be difficult to define. According to the American Heritage Dictionary, lipids are "any of a group of organic compounds, including the fats, oils, waxes, sterols, and triglycerides, that are insoluble in water but soluble in nonpolar organic solvents, are oily to the touch, and together with carbohydrates and proteins, constitute the principal structural material of living cells [1]." Lipids are used in many different forms in body systems but the most important function is their role as an energy source.

The most basic lipids are fatty acids, composed of a carboxylic acid group attached to a hydrocarbon chain. Three fatty acids are attached to a glycerol backbone to make a triglyceride. Fatty acids serve as an energy source in the body in when free fatty acids are degraded in the mitochondria. Long chain fatty acids, those with 16 or more carbons, are the most physiologically active. Tissue energy needs can be met from fatty acids when liver and muscle glycogen stores have been depleted [2]. Fatty acid oxidation is an important metabolic pathway; so important that heart and liver cells gain 80% of their total energy from this pathway. In order for the body to use this source of energy, triglycerides are first sent out of fat stores and then fatty acids are cleaved off the glycerol backbone. This cleavage reaction is facilitated by lipoprotein lipase in lipoproteins and hepatic lipase in the liver [2]. Fatty acids are released in the endothelial walls of capillaries and at the liver cell surface.

Lipids can possess hydrophilic heads (polar) and hydrophobic tails (non polar). Lipids are important because they provide energy, and have other metabolic and structural functions. Storage of lipids begins with the formation of chylomicrons, which transport dietary lipids from the intestine to other body structures. Adipose tissue can help to maintain body heat and cushion internal organs. There is also a hormonal function of adipose tissue. Leptin is an adipose hormone that regulates hunger and appetite. Low leptin levels can lead to over-eating and possibly obesity. The liver also plays an important role in lipid storage and lipid recirculation.

10.1. The First Stage of Lipid Storage: Chylomicron Formation & Lipoprotein Transport

After the digestion and breakdown of dietary lipids and the formation of micelles for absorption across the enterocyte membrane, triacylglycerols, cholesterol, and glycerophospholipids must be re-synthesized. These re-synthesized products, along with fat soluble vitamins, are collected at the endoplasmic reticulum where globules are coated with apolipoproteins in order to stabilize the structure in the aqueous environment of the cytoplasm and blood stream. These protein covered globules proceed to the Golgi Apparatus. Here carbohydrates are attached to the apolipoproteins and the completed chylomicron is moved on to the cell membrane (**Figure 10.1-1**). Exocytosis of the chylomicron into the lymphatic system carries the lipid particle though the body where it can eventually enter the bloodstream through the left subclavian vein [3].

10.1.1. Chylomicrons in Circulation

The chylomicron particle might be considered a short term storage form of lipids. In order to increase their stability while in circulation, chylomicrons are arranged with more polar lipoproteins such as phospholipids and cholesterol molecules at the surface, while the more hydrophobic lipoproteins, such as triacylglycerols and cholesterol esters are completely contained in the interior of the membrane (**Figure 10.1-2**). As they circulate in the vascular system, chylomicrons can exchange lipoproteins absorbed from exogeneous sources with target tissues and other circulating lipid molecules.

10.1.2. Supporting Players in Lipoprotein Storage: Apolipoproteins and Lipoprotein Lipase

Before going any further, we must first consider how circulating lipid molecules such as chylomicrons, are recognized by other lipoproteins and their targets in order for lipoproteins to be exchanged and delivered. In addition to phospholipids and cholesterol in the membranes, a class of molecules called apolipoproteins is a key factor in lipoprotein solubility and recognition.

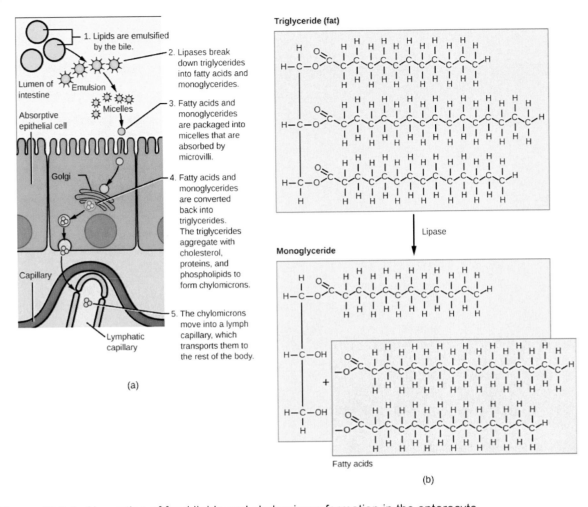

Figure 10.1-1: Absorption of food lipids and chylomicron formation in the enterocyte.
From http://cnx.org/resources/101d636c67ee72ba83800b9eedf008b7/Figure_34_03_03.jpg

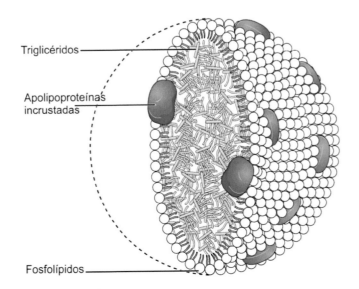

Figure 10.1-2: Chylomicron Structure/ Composition. "2512 Chylomicrons Contain Triglycerides Cholesterol Molecules and Other Lipids" by OpenStax College-Anatomy & Physiology, Connexions Web site. http://cnx.org/content/col11496/1.6/, Jun 19, 2013.. Licensed under Creative Commons Attribution 3.0 via Wikimedia Commons -

http://commons.wikimedia.org/wiki/File:2512_ Chylomicro ns_Contain_Triglycerides_ Cholesterol_Molecules_and_Ot her_Lipids.jpg

https://upload.wikimedia.org/wikipedia/ commons/c/cb/2512_Chylomicrons_ Contain_Triglycerides_Cholesterol_ Molecules_and_Other_Lipids_gl.jpg

Present in chylomicrons as well as the lipoprotein particles of the liver, apolipoproteins confer specificity to the lipoprotein depending on its site of synthesis and target tissues for deposition. Specifically apolipoprotein B is incorporated in both the hepatic and enteric lipoproteins, and has important ligand binding functions in both particles, however the isomer differs depending on the site of synthesis. Chylomicrons contain the shorter apoB-48, while liver lipoproteins are identified by apoB-100 [4]. Others in the family have enzyme activating activity that assists in the breakdown and release of lipid components when bound at the target tissue. A table of important apolipoproteins illustrates their full range of function. (**Table 10.1.-1**).

Another important player in lipoprotein recognition at target tissues is the enzyme lipoprotein lipase, which can be found in the vascular endothelium of non-hepatic target tissues. This enzyme is capable of cleaving triacylglycerols into free fatty acids, monoacylglycerols, and diacylglycerols for uptake by adipose and muscle tissue. Apoliproteins at the surface of circulating lipid particles not only assist in the binding of these particles to the target tissue, but also in the activation of lipoprotein lipase to begin cleavage. The blood vessels around the liver do not contain this enzyme, but instead have a hepatic lipase. Hepatic lipase is synthesized and secreted by the liver and binds to ligands on the cell surface of hepatocytes and endothelial cells. Hepatic lipase also exists in the bloodstream around the liver when stimulated by the hormone heparin [5].

10.1.2.1. Circulation of Lipoproteins for Storage in Adipose Tissue

Chylomicrons are the primary mode of transport for dietary lipids out of the intestinal enterocytes to peripheral tissues, making further absorption possible [4]. In healthy individuals much of the triacylglycerol deposited in muscle is used as an energy substrate within the short term, whereas adipose tissue is the site of long term lipid storage; as much as 85 percent of the volume of an adipose cell is taken up by triglycerides [3].

By the action of lipoprotein lipase, triacylglycerols are cleaved and free fatty acids and monoacylglycerols are taken up by the fat cell with the help of apolipoproteins, which are recognized by receptors on the membrane. Once inside, triacylglycerols are constantly being turned over, undergoing lipolysis and subsequently re-esterification so the resulting triacylglycerol contains a different arrangement of fatty acid chains than the original molecule. Lipolysis and re-esterification are under separate regulatory signals, primarily insulin and leptin, and respond differently to nutritional and hormonal signals they receive from the body [6].

Table 10-3: Apolipoprotein Location and Function

Apolipoprotein	Lipoprotein	Function
apoA 1	HDL, Chylo	Activator of Lecithin Cholesterol Acetyltransferase. Ligand for HDL Receptor
apoA-2	HDL, Chylo	Inhibitor of Lipase, Possible inhibitor of LCAT?
apoA-4	Secreted with Chylo but transfers to HDL	Formation of triacylglycerol rich lipoproteins
apoB-100	LDL, IDL, VLDL	Ligand for LDL receptor
apoB-48	Chylo, Chylo Remnant	Ligand binding interactions
apoC-1	VLDL, HDL, Chylo	Inhibitor of Lipase, Possible activator of LCAT
apoC-2	VLDL, HDL, Chylo	Activator of Lipoprotein Lipase
apoC-3	VLDL, HDL, Chylo	Inhibitor of Lipoprotein Lipase
apoD	HDL	Associated with LCAT
apoE	VLDL, HDL, Chylo, Chylo Remnant	Ligand for chylomicron remnant receptor in liver and LDL receptor.

10.1.3. Hormonal Control of Triacylglycerol Storage: Insulin

The pancreatic hormone insulin, a postprandial signal for high blood glucose, controls the uptake of fatty acids into adipocytes by stimulating lipoprotein lipase action, which encourages lipid storage after a meal. Insulin also encourages the entry of carbohydrates, as glucose, into adipose cells. Glucose is subsequently converted to glycerol phosphate through acetyl coenzyme A intermediate. The mono- and diacylglycerol products of lipoprotein lipase digestion are taken into the adipose cell, along with the glycerol phosphate from glucose. These molecules provide glycerol backbones for triacylglycerol re-synthesis and storage. Insulin further acts to favor triacylglycerol storage by inhibiting intracellular hormone sensitive lipase, which hydrolyzes stored triacylglycerols during lipolysis [7].

10.1.3.1. Function of Triacylglycerol as an Energy Substrate

Triacylglycerols are a rich source of energy, providing as much as 9 kilocalories per gram of lipid consumed. To look more closely at their structure, the trihydroxy alcohol, glycerol serves as a backbone to 3 fatty acid molecules, each connected by an ester bond (**Figure 10.1-3**).

During lipolysis, hydrolysis by lipoprotein lipase in the vascular endothelium, as well as hepatic and hormone sensitive lipases in liver and adipose tissue respectively, initiate triacylglycerol breakdown and yield a glycerol backbone and between 1 and 3 fatty acids [8]. The liberation of fatty acids occurs in a specific order depending on the enzyme; commonly either the first or third fatty acid is cleaved before the fatty acid attached in the middle at the 2 position. To be used for energy free fatty acids are released

in a non-esterified form and carried by albumin in the blood stream to various tissues for oxidation [9]. Because fatty acids are highly reduced, they undergo more oxidation than proteins or carbohydrates. Beta oxidation, the cyclic process of removing two carbon units from the fatty acid chain produces a significant amount of ATP per fatty acid molecule. (**Figure 10.1-3**). The fatty acyl-CoA formed in the final step becomes the substrate for the next round of β-oxidation. β-oxidation continues until acetyl-CoA removal yields beta hydroxybutyrate.

Another product of lipase cleavage is glycerol. Free glycerol cannot be used in adipose tissue because it cannot be phosphorylated, however recall the product of glucose metabolism in adipocytes is glycerol phosphate. Instead, free glycerol is circulated to the liver where it is phosphorylated by glycerol 3 kinase. Phosphorylated glycerol in the liver and other tissues can then enter the glycolytic pathway and either be oxidized for energy or be used in the synthesis of new glucose molecules by gluconeogenesis [3] (**Figure 10.1-4**).

10.1.4. Triacylglycerols Store Essential Fatty Acids

Certain fatty acids are necessary in growth and development but cannot be synthesized in animal cells. These so called essential fatty acids must therefore be acquired from plant foods and stored in the body as a component of triacylglycerols or phospholipids. The two essential fatty acids are linoleic acid and alpha linolenic acid. Linoleic acid is an omega 6 fatty acid with 18 carbons and 2 double bonds at carbons 9 and 12 when counting from the carboxylic end. Alpha linolenic acid is an omega 3 fatty acid, which also has 18 carbons, but has 3 double bonds at carbons 9, 12,

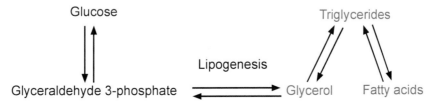

Figure 10.1-3: Formation of glycerol backbone for triglycerides from glucose.
Web image: http://www.elu.sgul.ac.uk/rehash/guest/scorm/168/package/content/lipid_metabolism.html

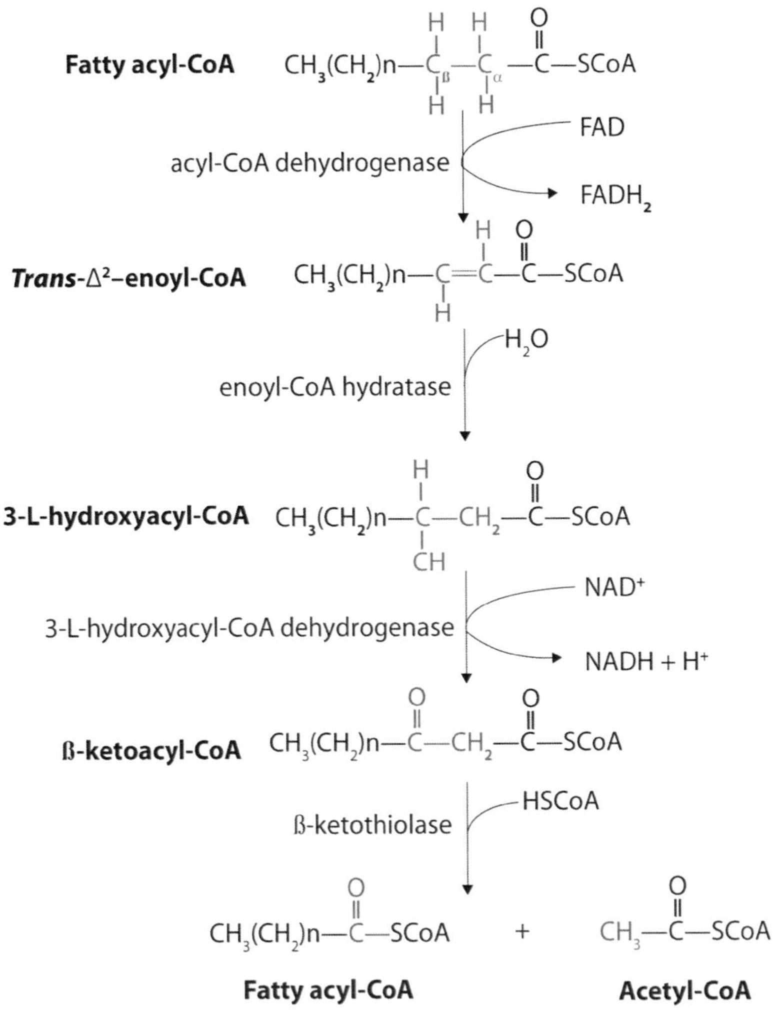

Figure 10.1-4: Fatty acid Beta Oxidation. Steps numbered 1-4 are 1. Oxidation, 2. Hydration, 3.Oxidation, 4. Thiolysis. Modified

From http://2012books.lardbuck et.org/books/introduction- to-chemistry-general- organic-and-biological/ s23- 06-stage-ii-of-lipid- catabolism.html (Creative Commons)

and 15 from the carboxylic end. Linoleic and alpha linolenic fatty acids are essential because humans lack the desaturase enzymes that puts double bonds at the 12 and 15 positions. Since humans are unable to desaturate fatty acid chains past the 9th carbon, the essential fatty acids are also necessary to form longer chain omega 3 fatty acids, such as eicosapentanoic acid, docohexanoic acid. Eicosapentanoic acid (EPA) has 20 carbons and 5 double bonds at carbons 5, 8, 11, 14 and 17. Docohexanoic acid (DHA), as its name suggests, has 22 carbons and 6 double bonds at positions 4, 7, 10, 13, 16, and 19. Although not essential, arachadonic

acid is also an important omega 6 polyunsaturated fatty acid with 20 carbons and 4 double bonds at carbons 5, 8, 11, and 14 (**Figure 10.1.5**).

These fatty acids are all important components of cell membranes, as can be seen in the development of dermatitis when the diet of both infants and adults is deficient.

Formulas are now being supplemented with these long chain fatty acids, eicosapentanoic acid and docohexanoic acid, in an attempt to prevent a deficiency state due to insufficient metabolism in infants and young children [10].

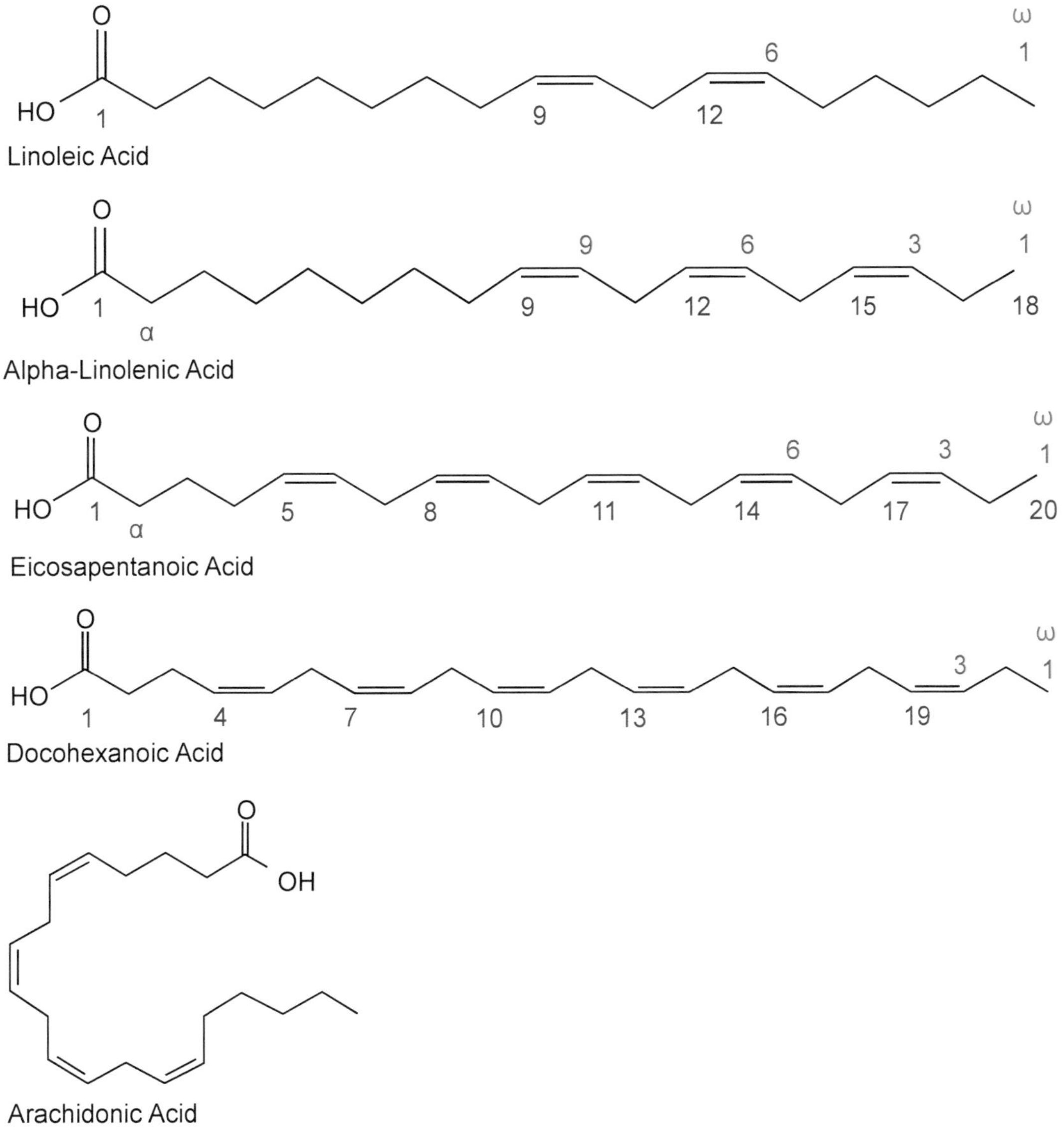

Linoleic Acid

Alpha-Linolenic Acid

Eicosapentanoic Acid

Docohexanoic Acid

Arachidonic Acid

Figure 10.1-5: Essential Fatty Acids
Web image: http://commons.wikimedia.org/wiki/File:Linoleic_acid.png
http://commons.wikimedia.org/wiki/File:Linolenic acid.png
http://commons.wikimedia.org/wiki/File:EPA.png
http://commons.wikimedia.org/wiki/File:DHA.png
http://commons.wikimedia.org/wiki/File:Arachidonic acid.png

10.1.5. Functions of Essential Fatty Acids

Beside their function in cell membrane structure and fluidity, the omega 3 fatty acids, which include linolenic, eicosapentanoic, and docohexanoic acids, are of extra interest because of their reported hypolipidemic and antithrombotic effects.

Eicosapentanoic acid as well as arachadonic acid are precursors to eicosanoid synthesis; which are fatty acid structures composed of 20 carbon atoms with added oxygen, and include prostaglandins, thromboxanes, and leukotrienes [11] (**Figure 10.1.6**).

Prostaglandins and thromboxanes have a wide range of effects throughout the body, including inducing fever and inflammation, lowering blood pressure, as well as causing blood platelet aggregation, dieresis, and smooth muscle contraction. Additional effects are also observed in the immune, nervous, and gastric systems. Although they may have hormone-like functions, these eicosanoids are not circulated to target tissues from one specific area of synthesis, and instead are synthesized in many different tissues and effect only the cells where they are made. Leukotrienes also have a role in the contraction of respiratory, vascular, and intestinal smooth muscle. They are implicated in asthma and anaphylactic shock due to their effects on the respiratory system, causing constriction of the bronchi and increased mucus secretion.

10.1.6. Phospholipids as Storage

Triacylglycerols are not the only site of essential fatty acid storage. Although their presence in membranes is important, when sufficient amounts of essential fatty acids cannot be hydrolyzed from stored triacylglycerols for eicosanoid synthesis, the body must draw from membrane phospholipids. These membrane phospholipids are also called glycerophosphotides, and have fatty acids esterified to positions one and two of the glycerol backbone. The third carbon differs from triacylglycerols however with the esterification of a phosphoric acid. There are a number of different glycerophosphatides depending on the phosphatidic acid, such as choline, serine, insoitol, and ethanolamine. (**Figure 10.1-7**).

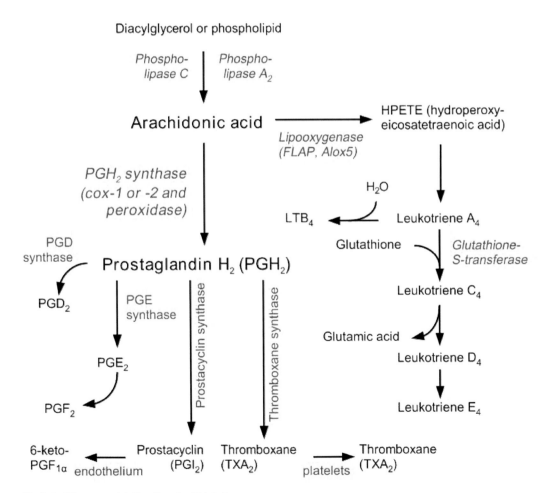

Figure 10.1-6: Eicosanoid Synthesis. Web Image:
From: http://upload.wikimedia.org/wikipedia/commons/4/40/Eicosanoid_synthesis.svg

Phosphatidylcholine and phosphatidylinositol are the two main glycerophosphotides from which omega 3 fatty acids are liberated for leukotriene synthesis [11].

10.1.7. Functions of Phospholipids

Because of their polar nature due to the addition of the phosphate group, phospholipids are commonly found on the surface of blood borne lipids to stabilize them in an aqueous environment. They are also a major component of cell and organelle membranes. An important structural component, they form a bilayer that allows for the passage of both water and fat soluble particles across the membrane. Phospholipids have an amphipathic character having a hydrophilic head and a hydrophobic tail, which allows phosphatidylinositol also to serve as an anchor for membrane proteins such as antigens when the proteins are covalently attached to the lipid [11]. This binding property of phosphatidylinositol is especially important in insulin response. The cleavage of tri-phosphorylated inositol from the diacylglycerol by phospholipase C in the presence of insulin stimulates the release of calcium ions and activates a number of calcium dependent enzymes and hormonal responses. The free diacylglycerol also stimulates the enzyme protein kinase C, which phosphorylates a number of proteins in the cytoplasm and alters their activity in response to insulin.

10.1.8. Hepatocyte Absorption of Chylomicron Remnants

After circulation through the body to target tissues and deposition of triacylglycerols, phospholipids, and cholesterol into adipose tissue and other peripheral tissues, the remaining contents of the chylomicrons return to the liver. This reduced chylomicron particle is called a chylomicron remnant and is relatively rich in cholesterol esters and lipid soluble vitamins (**Figure 10.1-8**).

Hepatocytes, like adipocytes, have a receptor on their surface that recognizes apolipoprotein B and E in chylomicron remnants and liver lipoproteins, so these particles are taken up to be stored or re-circulated. Cholesterol esters are stored for such functions as conversion into bile salts or they may also be incorporated into VLDL or HDL along with the newly synthesized triglycerides from carbohydrate metabolism, and released into the plasma.

The fate of the chylomicron remnant depends on the diet because in the fed state, the concentration of glucose, amino acids, and short chain fatty acids,

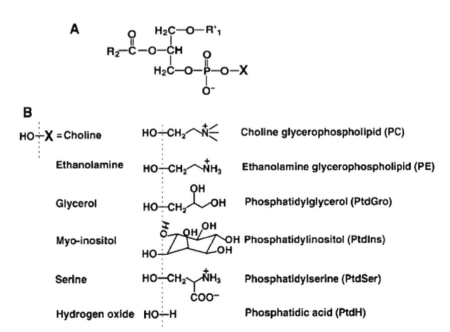

Figure 10.1-7: Phospholipid Head Groups. Web Image:
From: http://msr.dom.wustl.edu/Research/images/Lipodomics_Figure_2.jpg

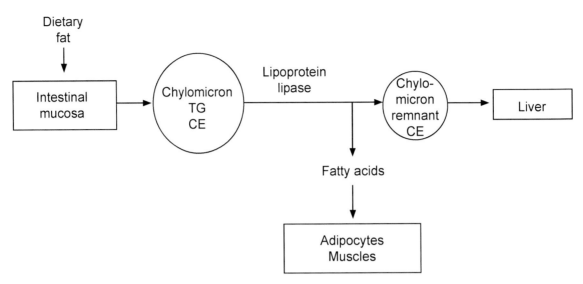

Figure 10.1-8: Progression to Chyolmicron Remnants.
Web Image: http://web.campbell.edu/faculty/nemecz/308_lect/lect3/lecture_3.html

which do not get circulated in chylomicrons, go directly to the liver to meet energy needs as well as replenish glycogen stores after a fasting period. However, excess glucose, as we discussed earlier, can be converted to glycerol phosphate for triacylglycerol synthesis. Storage in hepatocytes keeps some triacylglycerols in the liver, and more is absorbed from chylomicron remnants [12].

10.1.9. Recirculation of Lipids in the Liver

In healthy individuals, to prevent excess lipid buildup in the liver, hepatocytes make a lipoprotein similar to the chylomicron of the enterocyte. This lipoprotein, called Very Low Density Lipoprotein and abbreviated to VLDL, is smaller than chylomicrons however its components are the same, being an aggregation of phospholipids, cholesterol, cholesterol esters, as well as triacylglycerides. They have a very low density due to their high concentration of triglycerols, although less than chlyomicrons. As they circulate to non-hepatic tissues and deposit the triglycerols by binding at specific receptors on cell membranes, the density of the lipoprotein molecule increases. VLDL's also contain cholesterol and cholesterol esters as well as fat-soluble vitamins, which remain in the lipoprotein molecules as it progresses from a VLDL to an Intermediate Density Lipoprotein (IDL) and then to

a Low Density Lipoprotein (LDL). VLDL, IDL, and LDL are considered bad cholesterol (**Figure 10.1-9** and **Table 10.1-2**).

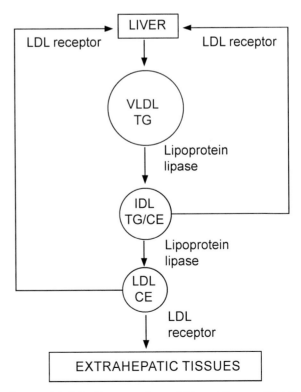

Figure 10.1-9: Progression of Liver **Figure 10.1-9**. Lipoproteins Web Image: http://web.campbell.edu/faculty/nemecz/308_lect/l ect3/lecture_3.html

Table 10-11: Lipoproteins Lipids and Functions.

Lipoprotein Class	Major Core Lipids	Major Apoproteins	Origin of Apoproteins	Transport Function	Mechanism of Lipid Delivery
Chylomicrons	Dietary triglycerides	A-1, A-2, A-4, B-48	Small intestine	Dietary triglyceride	Hydrolysis by lipoprotein lipase
Chylomicron remnants	Dietary cholesteryl esters	B-48, E	Chylomicrons	Dietary cholesterol	Receptor-mediated endocytosis in liver
VLDL	Endogenous triglycerides	B-100, C, E	Liver and small intestine	Endogenous triglyceride	Hydrolysis by lipoprotein lipase
IDL	Endogenous cholesteryl esters and triglycerides	B-100, E	VLDL	Endogenous cholesterol	Receptor-mediated endocytosis in liver (50%) or conversion to LDL (50%)
LDL	Endogenous cholesteryl esters	B-100	IDL	Endogenous cholesterol	Receptor-mediated endocytosis in liver or extrahepatic tissues
HDL	Endogenous cholesteryl esters	A-1, A-2	Liver and small intestine	Facilitates removal of cholesterol from extrahepatic tissues	Cholesteryl ester transfer to IDL cholesterol and LDL

10.1.10. Controlling Cholesterol: High Density Lipoproteins

High Density Lipoproteins (good cholesterol), HDL, function in opposition to LDL. Instead of depositing cholesterol to tissues, HDL in the bloodstream removes unesterified cholesterol from cells and other lipoproteins, returning it to the liver and excreting it into the bile (**Figure 10.1-10**).

HDL binds at the same sites at LDL on the cell surface and competes with LDL for receptor binding since LDL receptor recognizes both apo B-100 and apoE [5]. Another key apolipoprotein component

of HDL is apolipoprotein A1. ApoA1 stimulates the action of Lecithin Cholesterol Acyltransferase (LCAT), which stimulates the esterification of free cholesterol molecules of cell membranes or other lipoproteins by adding transferring fatty acids from C2 of phosphatidylcholine to free cholesterol. Apolipoproteins and cholesterol ester products are more easily exchanged between lipoproteins, and therefore will promote a net transfer of cholesterol out of non-hepatic cells and other lipoproteins [5]. Cholesterol esters can now be transported directly to the liver in association with HDL or indirectly with LDL. Once returning to the liver, cholesterol esters are hydrolyzed

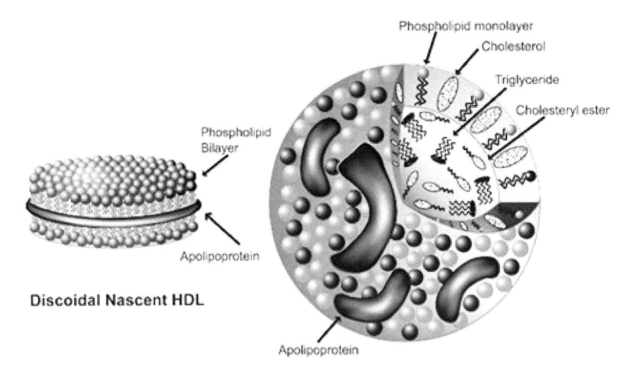

Figure 10.1-10: Structural and Compositional Features of HDL (adapted from Ueda et al. Journal Clinical Ligand Assay (2005) 4:28:216-32.)
Web Image: http://www.bhlinc.com/clinicians/clinical-references/reference-manual/chapter8

by cholesterol esterase, and free cholesterol is then free to be converted to bile and excreted. This function of HDL is how it came to be marketed as the "good" cholesterol, since the removal of cholesterol from peripheral tissues lowers the risk of plaque formation and atherosclerosis.

10.1.11. Improper Lipid Storage-Obesity

The majority of the body's energy comes from carbohydrate and fat. Carbohydrate is used preferentially for energy, and excess is then used to replenish stores of glycogen in the liver and muscles. When these needs are met, excess glucose can be converted to fatty acids and circulated from the liver to the adipocyte for storage. Additionally, as long as carbohydrates are being used for energy fewer fatty acids are being oxidized. This means that, in addition to the de novo synthesis of

fatty acids from the liver, storage of dietary fatty acids is also high while the rate of lipolysis is inhibited by insulin in the presence of high blood glucose. These dietary triacylglycerols are taken up for storage without demanding much additional energy. As long as the energy imbalance continues the adipocytes continue to take on more triacylglycerols and become larger. More adipocytes can be produced to accept the additional triacylglycerols. This proliferation occurs most rapidly in late childhood, however, it can continue throughout the life cycle. This is not a reversible process. When body fat is lost, adipocytes do not disappear; they only become smaller [3].

In cases of chronic obesity, when circulating glucose and triglyceride levels are elevated, the development of insulin resistance is common. This stimulates the pancreas to compensate for decreased sensitivity in tissues with much higher levels of the hormone in an attempt to maintain normal glucose concentrations. Insulin resistance in adipose tissue means that inhibition of lipolysis is lost, and perpetuates the cycle of high circulating levels of glucose as well as triacylglycerols. As long as the liver and kidney retain their sensitivity to insulin however there is stimulation of liver triacylglycerol synthesis. Increased TAG synthesis causes increased TAG levels in the liver, a contributor to the development of non-alcoholic fatty liver disease [12].

10.1.12. Lipids Contribution to Cardiovascular Disease

Atherosclerosis, the degeneration of blood vessels and the buildup of clotting factors, especially cholesterol; decreases the elasticity and volume of the vein, artery, or capillary. Tears in the walls of blood vessels are generally repaired by recruitment of monocytes and T lymphocytes. These cells are responsible for the secretion of cytokines, which in turn attract phagocytic cells to the area resulting in some inflammation. However when the concentration of LDL and cholesterol esters in the blood stream is high, such as the case of obese individuals, there is a risk for exaggerated inflammation while phagocytic cells take up LDL and become engorged with lipids. The accumulating lipids become oxidized, progressing into lipid laden foam cells on the basal side of the endothelium that cause smooth muscle cells to also take on oxidized LDL. The damage caused by the infiltration of foam cell macrophages into the smooth muscle lining of the blood vessel perpetuates the cycle, recruiting more macrophages that eventually also take on enough lipids to become foam cells. All of this inflammation and aggregation of lipids causes fatty plaque formation and the occlusion of the blood vessel.

Changing the diet to avoid long chain saturated fatty acids, which seem to increase the LDL cholesterol ratio could be one step in preventing cardiovascular problems. Additionally incorporation of more omega 3 and omega 6 fatty acids, which are most active at decreasing the ratio of cholesterol to LDL, could have a role in preventing further atherosclerotic build-up [20]. Atherogenic effects of hypercholesterolemic fatty acids, like saturated fatty acids, cholesterol, and trans fats, are still an area of active research. These nutrients could function by enhancing the synthesis of cholesterol and LDL, either by reducing the degree of control exerted over cholesterol synthesis or affecting the synthesis of apolipoprotein B in the enterocyte or liver. Alternatively, they could also retard LCAT activity or receptor mediated uptake of LDL, causing more lipoprotein to be present in circulation. Finally, they may act as regulators of gene expression in multiple steps of lipid metabolism.

10.2. Lipids: Molecular Structures and Metabolism

10.2.1. Fatty acid oxidation

10.2.1.1. Fatty Acid Transport

In order to begin β-oxidation of fatty acids to obtain energy, the free fatty acids first must be transported across the membrane of liver and muscle cells into the blood stream, which require transporters. Carnitine (β-hydroxy gamma- trimethylaminobutyric acid) is critical for long chain fatty acids to be transported into the mitochondria [17]. On the outer mitochondrial membrane, ATP dependent acyl-CoA synthetases convert non-esterified fatty acids to acyl-CoA esters. When the body is in a fasting state and glycogen levels decline, carnitine palmitoyl transferase I (CPT I) is upregulated to increase the formation of long chain acyl-carnitine from acyl-CoA and carnitine. This reaction by CPT I is a rate-limiting step in long chain fatty acid transport into the mitochondria. **Figure 10.2-1** depicts CPT I catalyzing carnitine and acyl-CoA into long chain acyl-carnitine. The acyl-carnitine molecule is transported across the inner mitochondrial membrane by carnitine- acylcarnitine translocase [CACT]. Inside the inner mitochondrial membrane, CPT II reforms acyl-CoA and carnitine. The carnitine is released and recycled for another use by CACT [17]. Medium and short chain fatty acids (12 or less carbons) enter the mitochondria on their own, and do not have to rely on these enzymes for transport.

10.2.1.2. β-oxidation

Once the acyl CoA molecule is inside the inner mitochondrial membrane, β- oxidation can begin. The β-oxidation process requires many sets of enzymes to produce one molecule of acetyl CoA from the initial fatty acid substrate from each turn of the four step cycle [2]. The four-step cycle is shown in **Figure 10.2-1**. With each complete β-oxidation cycle, the fatty acid is shortened by two carbons, which become the two-carbon molecule, acetyl CoA. The first reaction involves an acyl-CoA dehydrogenase enzyme, which is an oxidoreductase that requires flavin adenine dinucleotide (FAD) to function. Specifically, very long chain acyl-CoA dehydrogenase (VLCAD) catalyzes a reduction reaction at the 2,3 position of the acyl-CoA to produce 2,3-enoyl-CoA. VLCAD is responsible for reducing acyl-CoAs of 12 to 18 carbons in length while medium chain and short chain acyl-CoA dehydrogenases (MCAD and SCAD) are used for medium (6 to 10 carbons) and short chain (4 and 6 carbons) acyl-CoA molecules. The electrons are transferred via electron transfer flavoprotein (ETF) to ETF-coenzyme Q oxidoreductase (ETF-QO). The electrons will eventually enter the oxidative phosphorylation pathway where the energy is ultimately derived in the form of adenosine triphosphate (ATP) [2].

The second reaction involves hydrating the double bond at the 2,3 position which creates L-3-hydroxyacyl-CoA. This reaction is catalyzed by long chain enoyl-CoA hydratase (LHYD), which is part of a membrane associated trifunctional enzyme complex called the mitochondrial trifunctional protein (TFP). Assembly of this complex is essential to the transport across the membrane and for catalytic stability of the individual enzymes [2]. Crotonase catalyzes the same hydrolysis reaction for medium and short chain fatty acids as LHYD does for long chain fatty acids.

The third step involves reducing at the L-3 hydroxy position to produce 3- ketoacyl-CoA by long chain L-3 hydroxyacyl-CoA dehydrogenase [LCHAD] [2].

Also, medium and short chain fatty acids use MCHAD and SCHAD, respectively, to carry out this reaction to form their subsequent 3-ketoacyl-CoA species. Lastly, the fourth reaction involves a thiolytic cleavage. The 3-ketoacyl-CoA is cleaved to yield acetyl CoA and an acyl CoA which has been shortened by two carbons. The enzyme responsible for this final reaction of β-oxidation is long chain 3-ketoacyl-CoA thiolase (LKAT) and it is part of the TFP [2]. MKAT

and SKAT are used respectively for medium chain and short chain fatty acids in the cycle.

10.2.1.3. Ketone Body Formation

During the fasting state, ketone bodies can be produced as an alternative fuel to using fatty acids. The liver can use the fatty acid oxidation pathway to produce the ketones 3-hydroxybutyrate and acetoacetate. Certain tissues need ketones to survive during starvation, especially the brain [2]. When glucose is available, the brain has a very high affinity for using glucose exclusively for fuel. However, when the body is in a fasting state or starvation and glucose is not accessible, the brain adapts to using ketones for energy. It does not adapt to using fatty acids or other sources of fuel and this is why ketone production is critical for maintenance and function of brain tissue.

To form ketones, the pathway starts with acetyl CoA, one of the products of the β-oxidation pathway [2]. 3-Hydroxy-3-methyl-glutaryl-CoA synthetase (HMG- CoA) takes one molecule of acetyl CoA and one molecule of acetoacetyl CoA and forms HMG-CoA. Subsequently, HMG-CoA is cleaved by HMG-CoA lyase to yield acetoacetate. Acetoacetate is in redox equilibrium with D-3-hydroxy butyrate, which is the more prevalent ketone species. Ketones are then distributed through the bloodstream to tissues that cannot use β-oxidation. In the tissues, acetoacetate-succinyl CoA transferase converts acetoacetate back to its active form, acetoacetyl CoA [2]. This molecule is then thiolytically cleaved to create two molecules of acetyl CoA, which enter the Kreb's Cycle to continue to make energy.

10.2.2. Fatty acid and triglyceride biosynthesis

10.2.2.1. Fatty Acid Biosynthesis

In the human body, biochemical pathways usually operate in both forward and reverse directions in order to maintain homeostasis. Just as fatty acids are broken down and energy yielded in β-oxidation, fatty acids can be synthesized as well. Saturated fatty acids are relatively simple molecules but a complicated pathway is required to construct them [13]. Palmitate (C16:0) is the main

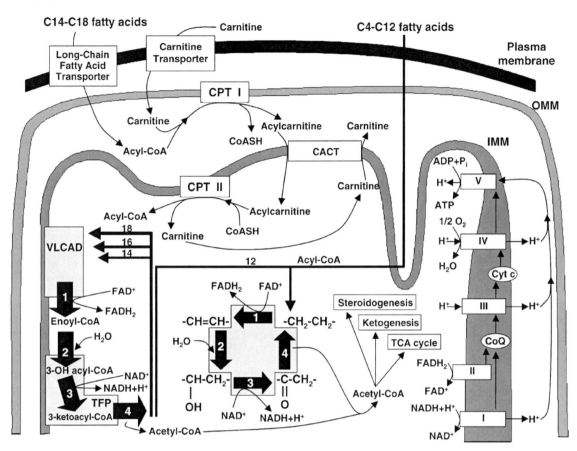

Figure 10.2-1: Long chain fatty acid transporters transport of long chain fatty acids across the plasma membrane into the mitochondria. CPT I creates acylcarnitine from acyl-CoA and carnitine. CPT II then regenerates acyl-CoA and carnitine from acylcarnitine. Acyl CoA enters β-oxidation inside the inner mitochondrial membrane. Acetyl CoA is produced and then enters other energy yielding pathways. Beta-oxidation is represented by the arrows marked 1, 2, 3 and 4, which represent the oxidation, hydration, oxidation, and thiolase reactions described in the text. From reference [2].

fatty acid produced because all of the long chain fatty acids, both saturated and unsaturated, can be derived from it [14]. The primary site of fatty acid biosynthesis is the liver [15]. Other tissues can synthesize fatty acids that will become triglycerides. These tissues include sebaceous glands where fatty acids are created and then secreted as ester waxes and triglycerides that act as lubricants [15].

Fatty acid synthases are the enzymes responsible for building fatty acids starting with the two-carbon precursor molecule, acetate. There are two main reactions in fatty acid synthesis, the first using acetyl CoA synthetase. This enzyme is biotin-dependent and converts acetate into malonate, which is the first committed step in this pathway [14]. Malonate

undergoes rounds of chain extension where one carbon is added each round. Each cycle requires five enzymes: an acyl transferase (MAT), ketosynthase (KS), and three reductive enzymes, ketoreductase, dehydratase, and enoyl reductase. Throughout this pathway, the growing chain is secured to a non-catalytic acyl carrier protein (ACP), which prevents the molecule from diffusing away in the cell. At the end of the synthesis reactions, the molecule is complete and thioesterase releases the fatty acid chain from ACP [14].

10.2.2.2. Triglyceride Formation

After the fatty acids are synthesized, they will be attached to glycerol to become triglycerides. First, a triacylglycerol molecule must be constructed before the fatty acids are added. There are two distinct pathways for synthesizing triacylglycerol: the phosphatidic acid pathway and the monoacylglycerol pathway. In the phosphatidic acid pathway, glycerol 3-phosphate and dihydroxyacetone phosphate, three-carbon intermediates from glycolysis, are acylated to phosphatidic acid [3]. Phosphatidic acid is then hydrolyzed to sn-1,2-diacylglycerol (DAG) and then finally acylated to triacylglycerol. Alternatively, phosphatidic acid may be formed from DAG via the ATP dependent DAG kinase. DAG is released from phosphatidic acid by phosphohydrolase and then acylated by DAG acyltransferase to form triacylglycerol. In comparison, the monoacylglycerol pathway is much simpler. Monoacylglycerols are converted to diacylglycerols in the first step [3]. This reaction is catalyzed by monoacylglycerol acyltransferase. The diacylglycerol is then acylated by diacylglycerol acyltransferase. Fatty acids can now be attached at the sn-1, 2, and 3 positions to be a fully formed triglyceride.

10.2.3. Cholesterol metabolism

Sterols constitute another class of lipids. Cholesterol, which is a flat, planar, multi-ring molecule necessary for life, is the most abundant sterol in animals (**Figure 10.2-2**) [16]. Cholesterol is found in plasma membranes and serves as a precursor for steroid hormones and bile. Cholesterol can be ingested through the diet or can be synthesized by the liver. Exogenous forms of cholesterol are digested, absorbed, and then carried through the blood in lipoproteins because of their inherent hydrophobicity, which makes them insoluble in the aqueous environment of the body.

If one's diet is deficient of cholesterol, the liver will synthesize the amount the body needs. The initial steps in endogenous cholesterol synthesis from the liver include the formation of acetoacetyl CoA, β-hydroxyl β-methyl glutarate (HMG-CoA), and mevalonic acid [17]. The conversion of HMG-CoA to mevalonic acid is the rate- limiting step. Through several condensation reactions, mevalonic acid is changed into squalene, a long chain hydrocarbon. In another sequence of reactions, squalene is converted into a ring structure and transformed into cholesterol.

After cholesterol is synthesized, it can be transformed to bile salts in the liver, secreted

directly into bile, or it can be secreted into the plasma with lipoproteins [17]. These various fates of cholesterol are depicted in **Figure 10.2-3**. For the bile salt pathway, the cholesterol is first changed into 7-alpha- hydroxycholesterol, which is the rate-limiting step for the production of both cholic acid and chenodeoxycholic acid. These acids are conjugated with glycerol or taurine and then secreted into bile through the biliary duct into the duodenum of the small intestine. When cholesterol is secreted directly into bile instead of being incorporated into bile acid molecules, the lower solubility can result in gallstone formation [17]. Normally, cholesterol that is destined to be secreted directly into bile is packaged in mixed micelles. However, if the amount of cholesterol exceeds the solubility capacity of the micelle, then it will crystallize in the gall bladder and form a gallstone.

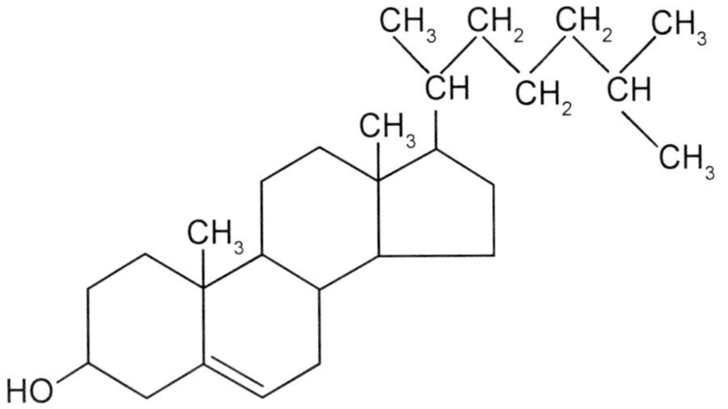

Figure 10.2-2: Structure of cholesterol. The four rings give cholesterol a flat, planar structure. The hydrocarbon atoms provide hydrophobicity. From reference [15].

A portion of cholesterol made by the liver is secreted into the bloodstream for utilization by other tissues in the body. Cholesterol must be carried by lipoproteins, usually very low density lipoprotein (VLDL). VLDL has a membraneous coat consisting of specific apoproteins, phospholipids, and free cholesterol [16]. The nonpolar core contains mostly triglycerides and small amounts of cholesterol esters. After transport through the tissues, lipoprotein lipase will degrade the lipoprotein to release free fatty acids and glycerol in the capillary.

Cholesterol synthesis in the liver is regulated by negative feedback inhibition by cholesterol specifically on the conversion of HMG-CoA to mevalonic acid by

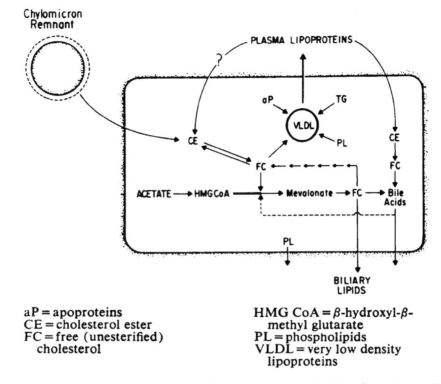

aP = apoproteins
CE = cholesterol ester
FC = free (unesterified)
    cholesterol

HMG CoA = β-hydroxyl-β-
    methyl glutarate
PL = phospholipids
VLDL = very low density
    lipoproteins

Figure 10.2-3: Hepatic metabolism of cholesterol. Cholesterol enters the liver from the small intestine in the chylomicron and goes through a series of reactions to be transformed into bile acids. Cholesterol may also be packaged into very low density lipoproteins (VLDL) for export into the bloodstream to be transported to tissues. From Reference [16].

HMG-CoA reductase [16]. The activity of HMG-CoA reductase in the cholesterol synthetic pathway largely has to do with the amount of exogenous cholesterol being consumed in the diet. Food intake is always varying so the amount of cholesterol being taken in also changes, impacting how much cholesterol needs to be synthesized by the liver. For example, if a person's diet includes very little cholesterol from food, the HMG-CoA reductase activity will be high and therefore their endogenous cholesterol synthesis will be increased. On the other hand, if someone has a diet rich in cholesterol, HMG-CoA reductase will be down-regulated and the liver will not make as much endogenous cholesterol.

Other than cholesterol impacting its own synthesis through regulatory pathways, bile acids also play a role in the regulation of cholesterol formation. Bile acids, and therefore the cholesterol in them, help to increase the rate of digestion of lipids. An increase in bile acid production would increase cholesterol absorption through the diet because there are more

bile acids to digest lipids, including cholesterol, and therefore decrease liver cholesterolgenesis [16]. Bile acids also decrease their own synthesis independent of cholesterol. When bile acids inhibit their own production there will be less cholesterol being digested and absorbed from the diet. Therefore, the liver must produce more endogenous cholesterol.

10.2.4. Conversion of fatty acids to Eicosanoids

Some essential long chain fatty acids (20 carbons or more), from the omega-3 and omega-6 fatty acid families, can produce molecules known as eicosanoids. The multiple cis double bonds of these long chain fatty acids induce bending in the molecule, which allows hairpin formation and then enzymatic transformation to eicosanoids [18]. This bent structure is shown in **Figure 10.2-4** [19]. Eicosanoid is a term used to encompass several classes of molecules, which include prostaglandins, thromboxanes, and leukotrienes [18]. Eicosanoids are considered local hormones because their plasma concentration is very low and they are not synthesized from a specific endocrine gland but are formed in most tissues [18]. Eicosanoids' effects on the tissues of the body include inflammation and thrombotic properties.

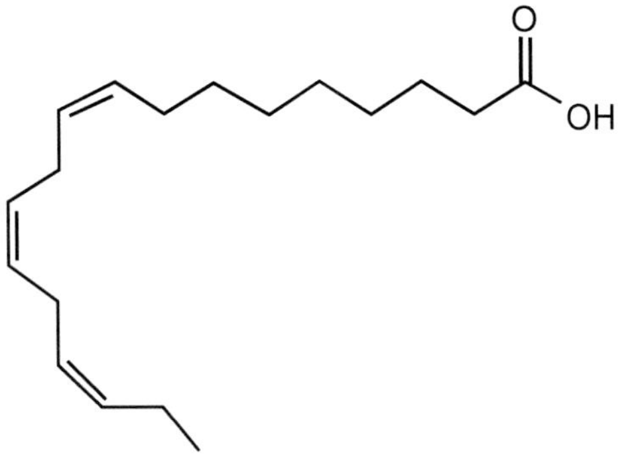

Figure 10.2-4: α-Linolenic acid (C18:9,12,15), an essential fatty acid. The cis double bonds at the 9, 12, and 15 positions induce turns in the molecule, which gives these fatty acids unique characteristics. These long chain fatty acids will eventually be metabolized into eicosanoids [19].

The initial step in the pathway to synthesize eicosanoids is thought to be an influx of calcium ions causing cytoplasmic phospholipase A2 to be recruited to the membrane of the cell [22]. This enzyme then hydrolyzes the fatty acid, arachidonic acid (C20:4) in the sn-2 position. The activity of phospholipase A2 is increased by cytokines such as interleukin 1 as well as tumor necrosis factor (TNF). A series of reactions ensue as seen in Figure 9.8. Regardless of starting with omega-3 or omega-6 fatty acids, the pathways use most of the same enzymes. The products of the omega-3 pathway are docosahexaenoic acid (DHA, C22:6) and eicosapentaenoic acid (EPA C20:5). The omega-6 pathway produces arachadonic acid (AA, C20:4) and docosapentaenoic acid (DPA C22:5) (**Figure 10.2-5**). When phospholipase A2 cleave glycerophospholipids containing these fatty acids, the free fatty acids can be further metabolized to eicosanoids by various enzymes [18].

Free EPA and free arachidonic acid can both be used in a variety of pathways depending on the tissue type. For example, platelets and other tissues such as the kidney, can further metabolize arachidonic acid to

thromboxanes which are powerful vasoconstrictors and inducers of platelet activation. However, characteristics of the eicosanoids change based on whether or not EPA or arachidonic acid is used as a precursor [20]. If EPA is used, thromboxane A3 is produced which is a much weaker vasoconstricter than the thromboxanes produced from arachidonic acid. In the endothelial lining of capillaries, however, EPA and arachidonic acid create products with almost the same properties, prostaglandins I2 and I3, which are both potent vasodilators and inhibitors of platelet aggregation [20]. Eicosanoids as a class of compounds are important because they affect many systems of the body at once including, but not limited to, effects on intermediary metabolism, muscle tone, and cell growth [21]. Therefore, long chain fatty acid transformations into eicosanoids have profound impacts on the body.

10.2.5. Structure and function of phospholipids

Phospholipids are also important biological molecules, making up cell membranes as well as having roles in cell signaling. Phospholipids are comprised of two fatty acyl molecules esterified at the sn-1 and sn-2 positions on glycerol. They also contain one of several possible polar head groups, which is linked by a phosphate residue at the sn-3 position of the glycerol backbone (**Figure 10.2-6**) [21]. The fatty acyl groups give the molecule hydrophobic properties that contrast with the hydrophilic properties of the polar phosphate group. Therefore, phospholipids are amphipathic molecules.

This amphipathicity provides the basis for the compartmentalization of cells via biological membranes. Besides maintaining membranes, phospholipids help to stabilize membrane proteins, facilitate the active conformational structure of proteins, and act as cofactors in enzymatic reactions [21]. Phospholipids are also crucial for the digestion and absorption of lipids because they are secreted in bile. Lastly, phospholipids act as a reservoir for signaling molecules such as arachidonic acid and inositol triphosphate.

The three most prevalent phospholipids are phosphatidylcholine, phosphatidylethanolamine, and phosphatidylserine [21]. In order to synthesize phospholipids, lysophosphatidic acid is first formed when a fatty acyl CoA (usually saturated) donates the

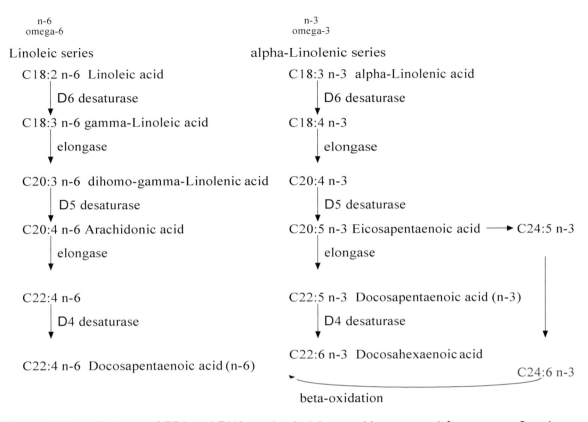

n-6 omega-6	n-3 omega-3

Linoleic series

alpha-Linolenic series

C18:2 n-6 Linoleic acid

C18:3 n-3 alpha-Linolenic acid

D6 desaturase

D6 desaturase

C18:3 n-6 gamma-Linoleic acid

C18:4 n-3

elongase

elongase

C20:3 n-6 dihomo-gamma-Linolenic acid

C20:4 n-3

D5 desaturase

D5 desaturase

C20:4 n-6 Arachidonic acid

C20:5 n-3 Eicosapentaenoic acid ⟶ C24:5 n-3

elongase

elongase

C22:4 n-6

C22:5 n-3 Docosapentaenoic acid (n-3)

D4 desaturase

D4 desaturase

C22:4 n-6 Docosapentaenoic acid (n-6)

C22:6 n-3 Docosahexaenoic acid

C24:6 n-3

beta-oxidation

Figure 10.2-5: Pathway of EPA and DHA synthesis (eicosanoid precursors) from omega-6 and omega-3 fatty acids. Even though the pathways have different starting materials (omega-6 versus omega-3 fatty acids), most of the same enzymes are used. Eicosapentaenoic acid (EPA) and docosahexaenoic acid (DHA) are produced from this pathway and will be transformed further into eicosanoids such as prostaglandins, leukotrienes, and thromboxanes [23].

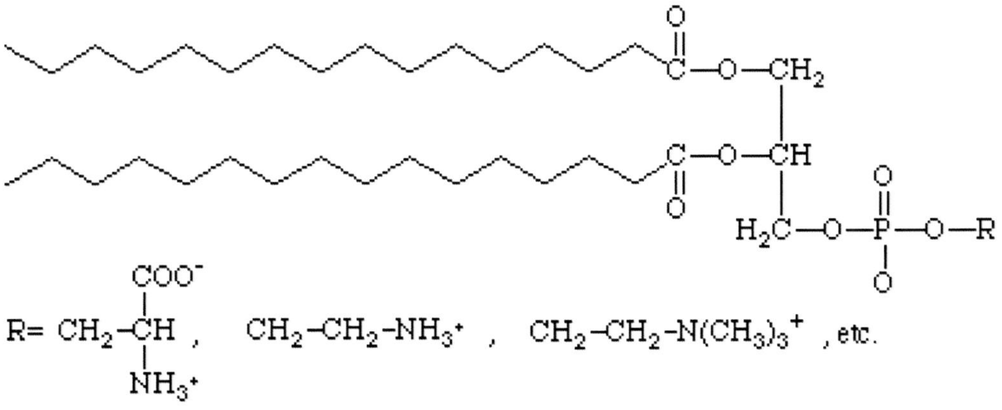

Figure 10.2-6: Basic structure of phospholipids. Fatty acid chains are attached to a glycerol backbone with a phosphate group in the sn-3 position. A polar head group is attached to the phosphate. The long hydrocarbon tails from the fatty acids coupled with the charged head group give the phospholipid its important property of amphipathicity [21]. Image credit: http://users.humboldt.edu/rpaselk/C438.S10/C438Notes/C438nLec03.htm

fatty acid to glucose 3-phosphate at the sn-1 position. This reaction is catalyzed by glycerol 3-phosphate acyltransferase and is rate limiting for phosphatidic acid synthesis. Acylglycerol 3-acyltransferase then catalyzes the formation of phosphatidic acid by attaching another fatty acyl CoA, which is usually unsaturated, to lysophosphatidic acid at the sn-2 position [27]. Phosphatidic acid can undergo hydrolysis of the phosphate group to yield diacylglycerol (DAG). DAG is used to synthesize phosphatidylcholine and phosphatidylethanolamine, with a new phosphate coming from a nucleotide.

Phosphatidylcholine is the most abundant phospholipid in mammalian membranes and is synthesized via the CDP-choline pathway [21]. Choline enters the cell and is phosphorylated by choline kinase to create phosphocholine. Next CTP-phosphocholine cytidylyltransferase (CT) converts phosphocholine to CDP- choline. Lastly, CDP-choline 1,2-DAG cholinephosphotransferase (CPT) adds CDP- choline to DAG, which forms phosphatidylcholine.

Phosphatidylethanolamine (PE) has a relatively small head group that can accommodate the insertion of proteins within the membrane while still maintaining the integrity of the membrane. Phosphatidylethanolamine also has the ability to form non-bilayer structures [21]. This feature allows it to form new membranes and vesicles as well as participate in membrane fusion and budding processes. PE is synthesized by the CDP-ethanolamine pathway in which ethanolamine is phosphorylated by ethanolamine kinase in the cytosol.

Phosphatidylserine (PS) is found in the most abundance in the inner face of the plasma membrane. Externalization of phosphatidylserine to the outer layer of the membrane is important in cell signaling for blood clotting as well as inducing phagocytosis of apoptotic cells. The head group of PS is a zwitterion, with both positive and negative charges. This negative charge allows for contact with positively charged groups such as certain proteins and may help facilitate contact between proteins and their membrane bound receptors [21]. Also, during signal transduction processes, PS stimulates protein kinase C which is an important molecule in signal transduction. In mammals, PS is made from PC or PE where the choline or ethanolamine group, respectively, is exchanged for serine. This reaction is catalyzed by phosphatidylserine synthase-1 (PSS-1) and PSS-2, which is responsible for ethanolamine-serine exchange. Both of these enzymes are found in parts of the endoplasmic reticulum (ER) that are in close contact with the mitochondrial membrane [21]. This location shows it may help the transport of PS into the mitochondria where phosphatidylserine carboxylase regenerates PE.

10.2.6. Structure, synthesis and function of Sphingolipids

Sphingolipids are lipid molecules related to phospholipids that have important roles in cell growth, signaling, programmed cell death, and stress responses [23]. The molecule's structure is one of a long fatty acid tail, usually 18 or 20 carbons in length, which may be saturated or unsaturated. This chain has an alcohol on the terminal carbon (C1) and an amine at C2. A fatty acid can attach at the amine with an amide bond to produce a ceramide. From here, the molecule may be glycosylated in a variety of ways, have double bonds added, or have polar head groups added which changes the biochemistry of the molecule and impacts its function [23].

The pathway to synthesize sphingolipids starts with a condensation reaction between palmitoyl-CoA and serine [23]. This forms 3-ketodihydrosphingosine, also known as sphingonine. This first reaction is catalyzed by serine palmitoyl transferase, which is pyridoxal 5' phosphate dependent. It is very specific for palmitoyl CoAs over other acyl CoAs at a ratio of 5:1. Sphingonine is then reduced to dihydroceramide by an oxidoreductase, 3-ketoshinganine reductase which requires NADPH for catalysis. In the final step, ceramide is formed through an acylation reaction of dihydroceramide by dihydroceramide desaturase. The steps of ceramide formation are shown in **Figure 10.2-7**. Ceramide serves as an intermediate, which can be modified for making many types of sphingolipids as seen in **Figure 10.2-8** [22].

Sphingolipids regulate several pathways that have various effects on cell functions. Ceramide and sphingosine-1-phosphate (S1P) are the most biologically active sphingolipids [23]. The structure of ceramide and S1P is pictured in **Figure 10.2-8**. Ceramide activates protein phosphatases to regulate cell growth, differentiation, proliferation, and apoptosis.

Ceramide has also been found to regulate protein kinase C, which affects the level of phosphorylation during the signal transduction process [23]. S1P has been found to have tumor promoting properties. S1P is involved in cell growth, proliferation, inflammation, angiogenesis, and resistance to apotosis in cancer cells.

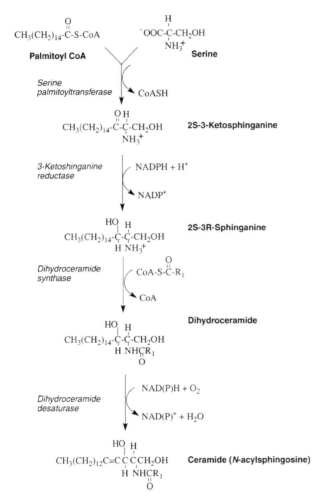

Figure 10.2-7: Pathway of ceramide synthesis. Ceramide acts as a critical precursor for sphingolipid synthesis. From reference [22].

10.2.7. *Importance of Lipids in the Diet*

Lipids have many physiological roles in the body and they have unique functions that reflect their various structures. Triglycerides and fatty acids are long hydrocarbon molecules that provide much energy because of the many covalent carbon-carbon bonds.

Cholesterol, being a multi-cyclic ring molecule is essential for maintaining the fluidity of membranes and playing a role in digestion through bile. Eicosanoids act as hormones and have impacts across many systems, such as blood pressure and coagulation of blood. Phospholipids also play critical roles in cell membranes as well as in cell signaling through lipases that release the eicosanoid precursors.

Since lipids play so many roles in multiple systems of the body, lipids serve as essential components of nutrition. Lipids are categorized as a macronutrient because a large amount of lipids is needed in the diet everyday to meet physiological functions. According to the Dietary Reference Intakes, 20-35% of a person's diet should be fat, or triglycerides and essential fatty acids. This amount of fat will properly enable lipid functioning in the body. Despite the important functioning of lipids, fat has had negative connotations in the American diet for years; many Americans still believe fat should be low in the diet or even eliminated. While one should avoid eating too much fat, fat has an important role in the diet and should be regarded as a vital nutrient to fulfill key physiological functions in the body.

10.3. Other Actions of Adipose Tissue

Most of our storage of triglycerides for energy occurs in what we refer to as white adipose tissue (WAT). However, at least two other types of adipose tissue that exist in humans, and to a greater extent in other animals, are brown adipose tissue (BAT) and beige adipose tissue. BAT exists as a separate type of tissue that is in higher amounts in human babies than adults, and is also found in rodents and hibernating animals. Beige adipose cells are interspersed within white fat tissue and seem to be induced by cold exposure and a cycle of release of various cytokines that activate the cells to produce heat [24]. Beige cells are activated by a norepinephirine-induced elevation of cyclic AMP, along with a protein called Early-B-cell factor-2 (EBF2) [25]. As we have discussed above, cAMP also stimulates hormone stimulated lipase in WAT to release free fatty acids. Brown and beige adipocytes have an abundance of mitochondria that can catabolize free fatty acids to

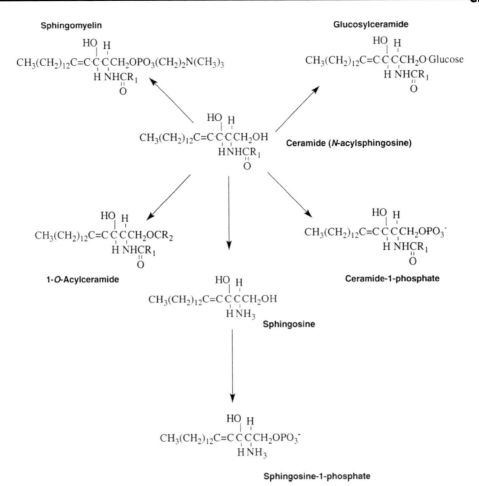

Figure 10.2-8: Basic structure of phospholipids. Fatty acid chains are attached to a glycerol backbone with a phosphate group in the sn-3 position. A polar head group is attached to the phosphate. The long hydrocarbon tails from the fatty acids coupled with the charged head group give the phospholipid its important property of amphipathicity [21]. From: http://users.humboldt.edu/rpaselk/C438.S10/C438Notes/C438nLec03.htm

release the stored energy by oxidation. The fatty acids are subject to beta-oxidation and the resulting acetyl-CoA is processed through the Krebs cycle. However, the mitochondria in BAT express an uncoupling protein (UCP1) that allows the reduced NADH and FADH to become oxidized without generating ATP because the UCP1 dissipates the proton gradient in the intermembrane space that mitochondria use for ATP synthesis. Instead of the energy charge in these cells blocking the continued beta-oxidation of fatty acids, the cells release energy as heat [26]. Beige adipose cells also release heat from a futile cycle of synthesis and hydrolysis of creatine-phosphate, the compound the muscle cells use to increase stored ATP-equivalents. Animals that have a greater amount of BAT or induced

beige adipose tissue are resistant to weight gain and obesity-related symptoms when fed a high fat diet [24].

In addition to secretion of hormones like leptin and adoponectin, adipose tissue releases metabolites that have biological impacts on other tissues. One example is the branched fatty acid esters of hydroxy fatty acids (FAHFAs), or specifically, palmitic-acid-9-hydroxy-stearic-acid, 9-PAHSA, a molecule that improved glucose homeostasis by increasing adipocyte glucose uptake, increased insulin secretion, and reduced inflammation. This metabolite is decreased in insulin resistant individuals [27]. Adipose tissue can also be the major site of synthesis of plasma uridine in fasting animals. Elevating this metabolite lowers body temperature, directly affects oral glucose tolerance, and may have a significant impact on energy balance [28]. While excess adipose tissue in the majority of Americans is recognized as a health crisis, this tissue has functional roles that are critical for the homeostasis of many metabolites.

10.4. SUMMARY

Chylomicrons are the first stage of lipid storage of exogenous lipids in circulation. For stability in an aqueous environment, they are arranged with the polar phospholipids and cholesterol molecules at the surface, while non-polar triacylglycerols and cholesterol esters are packed within. From the enterocyte, they are released into the lymph system and then into circulation where they make their way to target tissues, such as muscle or adipose.

Apolipoproteins in the membrane help the recognition and binding of chylomicrons, as well as liver lipoproteins, in peripheral tissues. Once bound, triacylglycerols and cholesterols are digested by lipases to transfer free fatty acids across the cell membrane where they are used for energy or stored.

Chylomicrons eventually make their way to the liver as chylomicron remnants, which are much smaller than when they left the enterocyte, and relatively rich in cholesterol esters. Remnants are degraded by hepatic lipase in the liver and the remaining lipids are stored or re- circulated. The liver makes 2 lipoproteins, Very Low Density Lipoprotein, which functions like the chylomicron to bring endogenous lipids to peripheral tissues, and High Density Lipoprotein. High Density Lipoprotein works oppositely to VLDL by bringing cholesterol from peripheral sites back to the liver for excretion as bile.

Stored triacylglycerols are very good sources of energy and are metabolized by tissues when carbohydrate sources are not present. Fatty acids of triacylglycerols can also be incorporated in phospholipids, which have an important role in building and maintaining cell membranes. Cholesterol is also an important contributor to cell membranes for maintaining fluidity. In addition, cholesterol in the skin is converted to active vitamin D, while cholesterol in the liver is used to make bile salts, necessary for digestion and further lipid absorption. Excess lipid storage can be harmful however. When control over lipid storage

is lost the prevalence of obesity, insulin resistance, and cardiovascular disease risk all increase drastically.

10.5. LITERATURE CITED

1. Rinaldo, P., Matern, D., Bennett, M. J. [2002]. *"Fatty acid oxidation disorders."* Annual Review of Physiology, 64(3), 477-502.

2. Weissman, K. J., [2008]. *"Taking a closer look at fatty acid biosynthesis."* Chembiochem: European Journal of Chemical Biology, 9[18], 2929-2931.

3. Gropper S, and Smith, J. Advanced Nutrition and Human Metabolism, Sixth Edition: 79- 81, 2013. Otten JJ, Hellwig JP, Meyers L. Dietary Reference Intakes: The Essential Guide to Nutrient Requirements. The National Academies; 2006. Available from http://www.nap.edu/catalog/11537.html.

4. Chatterjee C, Sparks DL. Hepatic lipase, high density lipoproteins, and hypertirglyceridemia. Am J Pathol. 2011 Apr;178(4):1429-33.

5. Marcelin G, Chua SJ. Contributions Of Adipocyte Lipid Metabolism To Body Fat Content And Implications For The Treatment Of Obesity. Curr Opin Pharmacol. 2010 October; 10(5): 588–593.

6. Ahmadian M, Duncan RE, Sul HS. Skinny on Fat Metabolism: Lipolysis and Fatty Acid Utilization. Trends Endocrinol Metab. 2009 November; 20(9): 424–428.

7. Duncan R, Ahmadian M, Jaworski K, Sarkadi-Nagy E, Sul HS. Regulation of Lipolysis in Adipocytes. Annu Rev Nutr. 2007 August; 27(1): 79–101.

8. van der Vusse GJ. Albumin as fatty acid transporter. Drug Metab Pharmacokinet. 2009;24(4):300-7.

9. Boehm G, Borte M, Böhles HJ, Müller H, Kohn G, Moro G. Docosahexaenoic and arachidonic acid content of serum and red blood cell membrane phospholipids of preterm infants fed breast milk, standard formula or formula supplemented with n-3 and n-6 long- chain polyunsaturated fatty acids. Eur J Pediatr. 1996 May;155(5):410-6.

10. Lands WEM. Biochemistry and physiology of n-3 fatty acids. FASEB J. 1992 May; 6(8): 2530-2536.

11. Nagle CA, Klett EL, Coleman RA. Hepatic triacylglycerol accumulation and insulin resistance. J Lipid Res. 2009 April; 50(1): S74-S79.

12. Allayee H, Roth N, Hodis HN. Polyunsaturated Fatty Acids and Cardiovascular Disease: Implications for Nutrigenetics. J Nutrigenet Nutrigenomics. 2009 October; 2(3): 140– 148.

13. Volpe, J. J., Vagelos, P. R. [1973]. *"Saturated fatty acid biosynthesis and its regulation"*. Annual Review of Biochemistry, 42(1), 21-60.

14. Lehner, R., & Kuksis, A. [1996]. *"Biosynthesis of triacylglycerols"*. Progress in Lipid Research,35(2), 169-201.

15. Carnegie Mellon University. "Biology Animations." *Department Of Biological Sciences, Carnegie Mellon University*. Department Of Biological Sciences, Carnegie Mellon University, 2006. Web. 25 Nov. 2012. <http://telstar.ote. cmu.edu/biology/MembranePage/index2.html>.

16. Grundy, S. M. [1978]. *"Cholesterol metabolism in man"*. Western Journal of Medicine, 128(1), 13-25. Retrieved from: http://www.ncbi.nlm. nih.gov/pmc/articles/PMC1237959/pdf/ westjmed00257-0049.pdf

17. De Caterina, R., Basta, G. [2001]. *"N-3 fatty acids and the inflammatory response — biological background"*. European Heart Journal Supplements, 3, 42-49. Retrieved from: http://eurheartjsupp. oxfordjournals.org/content/3/suppl_D/D42. full.pdf

18. Legg, K. [2011] *"Alpha Linolenic Acid."* *Lipidomics Gateway*. Nature Publishing Group, 2011. Retrieved from: <http://www.lipidmaps. org/update/2011/110901/full/lipidmaps.2011.23. html>.

19. Smith, W. J. [1989]. *"The eicosanoids and their biochemical mechanisms of action"*. The Biochemical Journal, 259(2), 315-324. Retrieved from: http://www.ncbi. nlm.nih.gov/pmc/articles/PMC1138513/pdf/ biochemj00209-0011.pdf

20. Cook, J. A. Eicosanoids. Critical Care Medicine [Internet]. 2005 [cited 2012 Dec 5];33(12):488-491. Retrieved from: doi:10.1097/01. ccm.0000196028.19746.42

21. Kelly, K., Jacobs, R. [2011]. "Phospholipid biosynthesis" Edmonton (AB), Canada: University of Alberta, Department of Food and Nutritional Science. Retrieved from: http://lipidlibrary.aocs. org/animbio/phospholipids/index.htm

22. Shayman, J. A. [2000] *"Sphingolipids"*. Kidney International, 58, 11-26. Retrieved from: http://www.nature.com/ki/journal/v58/n1/ pdf/4491650a.pdf

23. Bartke, N., Hannun, Y. A. [2009]. *"Bioactive sphingolipids: Metabolism and function"*. Journal of Lipid Research, 50, 91-96. Retrieved from: http://www.ncbi.nlm.nih.gov/pmc/articles/ PMC2674734/

24. Stine, RR Shapira, SN Lim, H- Ishibashi, Harms, Won, K-J Seale, P. (2016)_EBF2 promotes the recruitment of **beige** adipocytes in white **adipose tissue.** Molecular metabolism, 01/2016, 5(1): 57-65.

25. Kissig M, Shapira SN, and Seale P (2016) SnapShot: Brown and Beige Adipose Thermogenesis Cell *166*: 258-9. DOI http://dx.doi.org/10.1016/j. cell.2016.06.038

26. Fan W, Evans R. (2016) The Quest to burn fat, effortlessly and safely. Science 353(6301):749-50.

27. Yore, M.M., Syed, I., Moraes-Vieira, P.M., Zhang, T., Herman, M.A., Homan, E.A., Patel, R.T., Lee, J., Chen, S., Peroni, O.D., Dhaneshwar, A.S., Hammarstedt, A., Smith, U., McGraw, T.E., Saghatelian, A., Kahn, B.B.,. (2014). Discovery of a class of endogenous mammalian lipids with anti-diabetic and anti-inflammatory effects. *Cell, 159*(2), 318-332. doi:10.1016/j.cell.2014.09.035

28. Scherer, P. E. (2016). The multifaceted roles of adipose tissue-therapeutic targets for diabetes and beyond: The 2015 Banting lecture. *Diabetes, 65*(6): 1452-61.

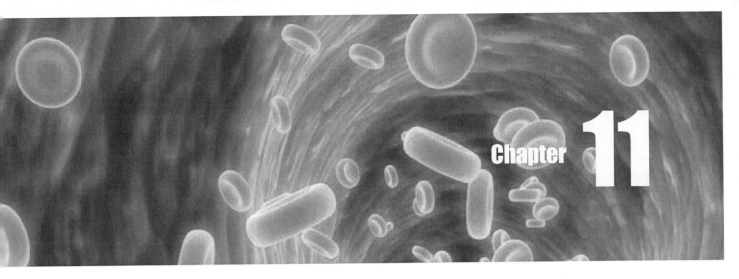

Chapter 11

Selected functions of vitamins and minerals

Roles in differentiation, growth and development, antioxidants, and energy and protein metabolism

By Neel Shah, Kyle Emery, Charles Giamberadino, Katie Shiraishi, Meaghan Bethea, Weston Bussler, Christina Inserillo, Nazish Durrani, Natalia Smith, Anita Williams, Stephanie, Dill, and Jonathan Allen

11.1. Introduction

Vitamins are organic nutrients required by organisms to perform vital functions. Some are synthesized in the body, and others require dietary intake to fulfill human needs. Vitamins required in humans are divided into water and fat soluble categories. Water soluble vitamins dissolve in water and are generally not stored in the body as are the fat soluble vitamins, in tissues such as adipose. Regular consumption of water soluble vitamins is required as they are readily excreted, and toxicity occurs more often in fat soluble vitamins due to their storage.

Vitamins have many different functions in the body (**Figure 11.1.1.**). The largest number is associated with enzymes as cofactors in metabolic reactions, such as in energy metabolism. Vitamins also play major roles in growth, development, and cellular differentiation.

Some vitamins are antioxidants; others have roles in vision, immune function, nerve function, among many others. These wide-ranging functions will be discussed in this chapter for water soluble and fat soluble vitamins.

11.1.2. Vitamin C

Vitamin C or ascorbic acid (Figure 11.1.1.) has many important functions in the body as an antioxidant or reducing agent. Vitamin C has roles in the synthesis of collagen, carnitine, tyrosine, and some neurotransmitters. Other biological functions have been inconsistently linked to vitamin C as well, such as boosting the immune system, fighting cancer, reducing heart disease, and maintaining eye health. Many animals have the ability to synthesize vitamin C. However, humans lack the gulonolactone oxidase enzyme that is needed to make the vitamin [1].

11.1.2.2. *Vitamin C, the Reducing Agent*

Vitamin C is a water-soluble vitamin important in the formation and structural integrity of collagen, which is a component of connective and epithelial tissues. Vitamin C serves to reduce the iron cofactor in reactions leading to the generation of collagen, thus aiding in wound healing and maintaining blood vessels, bones, and teeth (**Figure 11.1.2.**).

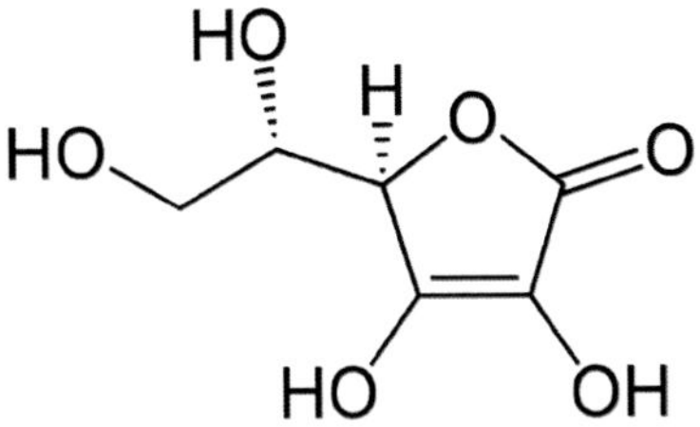

Figure 11.1- 1: Vitamin C (Ascorbic Acid). http://upload.wikimedia.org/wikipedia/co mmons/ thumb/e/e7/L- Ascorbic_acid.svg/200px-L- Ascorbic_acid. svg.png

Carnitine is a nitrogen containing compound involved in the transport of fatty acids for beta oxidation. In the synthesis of carnitine, vitamin C again reduces iron from the ferric to the ferrous state [1]. Vitamin C is also a reducing agent in several reactions necessary to synthesize and catabolize tyrosine.

Neurotransmitters such as norepinephrine and serotonin are also synthesized through vitamin C dependent reactions. Vitamin C reduces the copper atoms required for making norepinephrine from dopamine. In synthesizing serotonin from tryptophan, vitamin C is involved in regenerating the cosubstrate tetrahydrobiopterin [1].

11.1.2.2. *Vitamin C, the Antioxidant*

Vitamin C can donate and accept hydrogen atoms with ease, and thus offers protection against oxidation of nucleic acids, lipids, and proteins in cells, thereby preventing cell damage. Vitamin C reduces various reactive oxygen species, including hydroxyl radicals, hydroperoxyl radicals, superoxide radicals, alkoxyl radicals, and peroxyl radicals. In addition, vitamin C works in tandem with vitamin E, regenerating it as they scavenge free radicals [1].

Additionally, vitamin C plays a critical role in the function of the immune system. The vitamin has the ability to stabilize reactive oxygen species used by phagocytes to destroy foreign microbes. Further studies are needed to determine the role of vitamin C in preventing and treating the common cold, some forms of cancer, and heart disease, and promoting eye health [2].

11.1.2.3. *Preventing Vitamin C Imbalance*

Vitamin C deficiency results in a condition known as scurvy. The common symptoms are generally related to vitamin C's role in collagen synthesis and include bleeding gums and a decrease in wound healing. Bruising can occur more easily and the skin can turn

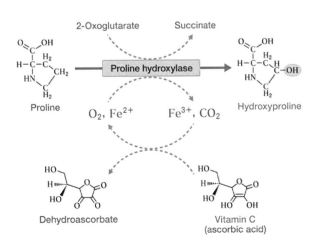

Figure 11.1- 2: Mechanism: Hydrollation of Amino Acids Involved in Collagen Synthesis.
Source: http://csls-text3.c.u-tokyo.ac.jp/active/11_05.html

dry and rough. There may be sore bones and joints as well, along with an increase in infection. Certain conditions call for an increase in Vitamin C intake, such as environmental stress, smoking, fever and infection, healing of wounds, use of certain drugs (such as oral contraceptives), and growth (such as children and pregnant women).

There is little risk of Vitamin C toxicity, as several large doses are required before symptoms occur. Vitamin C overdoses may result in bloating, cramps, diarrhea, and an increased chance of kidney stones, particularly for people with kidney disease. In addition, there may be a rebound of scurvy when high doses of Vitamin C are discontinued.

The RDA for Vitamin C is 90 mg/day for men and 75 mg/day for women (**Table 11.1.1.**). Higher intake is needed in certain circumstances, such as during pregnancy and for smokers.

TABLE 11.1.1: RDA of Vitamin C . From University, O. S. (2001-2011, March 26th). *Linus Pauling Institute*. Retrieved December 3rd, 2012, from Micronutrient Research for Optimum Health: http://lpi.oregonstate.edu/infocenter/vitamins/vitaminC/

Age	Male	Female	Pregnancy	Lactation
0–6 months	40 mg*	40 mg*		
7–12 months	50 mg*	50 mg*		
1–3 years	15 mg	15 mg		
4–8 years	25 mg	25 mg		
9–13 years	45 mg	45 mg		
14–18 years	75 mg	65 mg		115 mg
19+ years	90 mg	75 mg		120 mg
Smokers	Individuals who			35 mg/day

more vitamin C than nonsmokers.

11.1.3. Vitamin E as an antioxidant

Vitamin E is well known for its antioxidant functions. Vitamin E prevents the oxidation of unsaturated fatty acids present in phospholipid bilayer membranes of cells by reactive oxygen species. Cells membranes of some cells, such as red blood cells, are highly susceptible to destruction by oxygen free radicals. Free radicals are produced in the body as a result of several biological stresses, for example, infection, inflammation and exposure to environmental pollutants. The destructive reaction by free radical occurs in three steps - initiation, propagation and termination [1].

During initiation, a free radical takes away the electron from a lipid membrane which results in the destruction of polyunsaturated lipids of the cell membrane and the formation of alkyl radicals. During propagation, these lipid alkyl radicals react with additional free radicals to form lipid peroxyl radicals which are responsible for cell membrane lipid peroxidation. Finally vitamin E terminates this chain reaction. The vitamin E chromanol ring system donates hydrogen, reduces the peroxyl radicals and hence terminates these oxidation reactions. Other antioxidants, such as vitamin C and glutathione, reduce vitamin E so that it can again prevent membrane oxidation. In addition to termination reactions, vitamin E can quench singlet oxygen, also preventing cellular damage [1].

11.1.3.1. Vitamin E and gene expression

Besides playing an important role of an antioxidant, vitamin E has been shown to have various other outstanding therapeutic effects by influencing gene expression. It is via influencing the gene expression and formation of new proteins that vitamin E conducts its remarkable functions of preventing cardiovascular diseases, decreasing the development of various types of cancers and inhibiting the inflammatory processes within the body.

11.1.3.2. Cardio protective role of vitamin E

Cardiovascular diseases are the major cause of death in both men and women in the U.S.. Epidemiological studies show the link between lower incidence of CVD with high vitamin E intake in diet [3]. In six studies identified in a meta-analysis, vitamin E reduced risk for fatal and non-fatal coronary heart disease and all cause mortality, whereas 2 studies observing myocardial infarction as the end-point did not find a vitamin E effect. The process of atherosclerosis begins with the oxidation of LDL lipids by oxygen free radicals. The cardio protective role of vitamin E could be due in part to the antioxidant effect of this vitamin by preventing LDL oxidation by free radicals. Another possible mechanism is the role of vitamin E in gene expression of the protein coding for CD 36 receptors. The CD 36 receptor is a type of receptor present on macrophages and is sensitive to oxidized LDL lipids. It is due to the presence of this receptor that the oxidized LDL's are phagocytosed by macrophages which later form foam cells, which are linked to atherosclerotic plaque formation. Vitamin E decreases CD 36 gene expression, resulting in reduced formation of this receptor protein [3]. This reduces the oxidized LDL ingestion by macrophages, diminishing fat deposition in the vessel wall which helps to prevent atherosclerosis.

11.1.4. Carotenoids

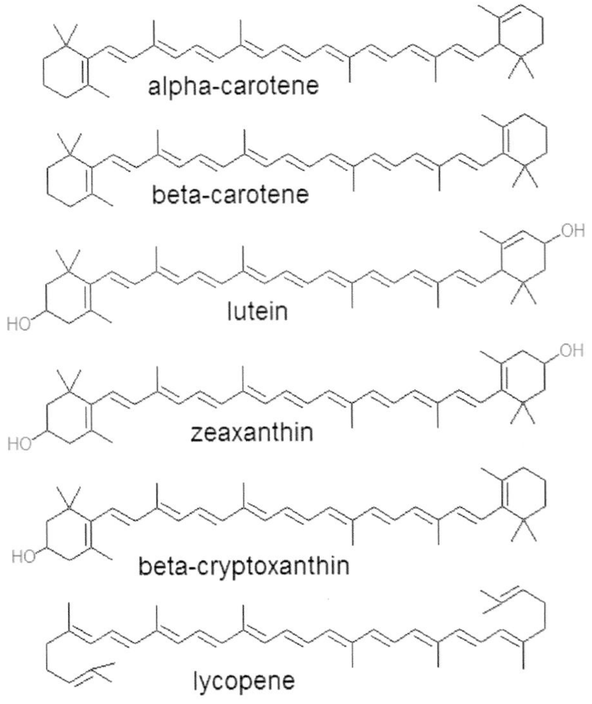

Figure 11.1-3: Common carotenoids.
From: http://en.citizendium.org/wiki/File:Carotenoids2.png

Carotenoids consist of some compounds that can be converted to vitamin A, but many of these and others have separate physiological functions as

antioxidants and as regulators of cell proliferation, growth, and differentiation. Examples of carotenoids are β-carotene, α-carotene, β-cryptoxanthin, lycopene, lutein, and zeaxanthin (**Figure 11.1.3.**).

11.1.4.1. Carotenoids as antioxidants

Carotenoids help protect organic molecules from oxidation through their ability to quench molecules such as singlet oxygen. In addition, carotenoids protect against peroxyl radicals to prevent peroxidation of lipids. Though unclear, some studies have shown that carotenoids can reduce the risk of macular degeneration and atherosclerosis and heart disease [1].

11.1.5. Selenium

Selenium was not a known trace mineral until 1979 when Chinese scientist discovered a link between selenium levels and the cardiac condition of the children living in Keshan providence, a rural areas where the selenium content was low in foods. It was observed that the cardiac condition, congestive cardiomyopathy now named Keshan disease, could be prevented with the increased intake of Selenium [1]. Keshan disease is characterized by heart deterioration caused by a collection of fatty acid peroxides in the heart. Selenium functions by eliminating the peroxides prior to deposit in the heart. Any fatty acid peroxides collected on the heart during selenium deficiency cannot be reversed [4]. Therefore, it is vital to maintain appropriate levels of selenium. Since this discovery, additional research has shown patients suffering from acute myocardial infractions have significantly lower concentrations of selenium [4]. In addition to cardiac function, selenium has many metabolic functions as a trace mineral.

One of the primary functions is its role in the glutathione perioxidase system. In this system, selenium plays a vital role in preventing lipid perioxidation and cell membrane damage caused by free radicals. The glutathione perioxidases, or GPx, are antioxidant enzymes that break down peroxides, such as hydrogen peroxide, in the extracellular and intracellular fluid. These peroxides are neutralized, with the help of selenoproteins acting as a cofactor for GPx, into less toxic alcohol derivatives and water before they can form free radicals [1]. The selenoproteins are proteins containing the amino acid, selenocysteine, which is a cysteine amino acid analog with a selenium atom in place of sulfur. The enzymatic action of GPx is directly proportional to the amount of selenium intake [4]. In this role, Selenium spares Vitamin E to attend to other antioxidant functions.

Another key function of selenium is its effects on thyroid hormone metabolism. Another type of selenoproteins is deiodinase enzyme. Deiodinase I, or 5'DI is found mainly in the thyroid, liver, and kidneys. In thyroid metabolism, Deiodinase converts the inactive thyroxine into active 3,3'-5'triiodothyronine [4]. By modulating thyroxine metabolism via insulin mimetic mechanisms, selenium may actually contribute to type II diabetes [5].

Selenium is found in various organs in the body including large amounts in the spleen, liver, and lymph nodes as a part of an immune response. Research evidence shows selenium promotes antibody growth along with stimulating the activity of the helper T cells, cytotoxic T and Natural Killer cells, all cells that are essential in immune response [4]. Additionally, selenium may play a vital role in decreasing the risk of prostate, lung and other cancers due to evidence that selenium deficiency is potentially a cancer-promoting factor [1, 4]. Further research is being conducted to better understand and confirm this linkage.

11.2. Functions of Water Soluble Vitamins Serving as Cofactors in Metabolism

Water soluble vitamins have an important role in the growth, function, and maintenance of body tissues. Unlike fat-soluble vitamins, these vitamins are not stored in the body and are readily discarded through the kidneys. Therefore, they need to be replaced daily through dietary sources [1]. The water soluble vitamins include vitamin C (ascorbic acid) and the B-complex vitamins. B-complex vitamins include: thiamin, riboflavin, niacin, vitamin B_6, vitamin B_{12}, folate, pantothenic acid, and biotin. The B vitamins primarily function as coenzymes in energy metabolism pathways, though some are also involved in red blood cell synthesis and other functions relation to a normal

appetite, good vision, and healthy skin and nervous system. A discussion of the functions and metabolic roles of the B involved in energy metabolism follows.

11.2.1. Thiamin (Vitamin B_1)

Thiamin, also known as B_1 or aneurine, is a water-soluble B vitamin. It functions as a coenzyme in energy metabolism and in the synthesis of pentoses and NADPH and also functions in nerve conduction. Its coenzyme function is seen in the pyruvate dehydrogenase complex, α-ketoglutarate complex, and the branched chain α- ketoglutarate acid dehydrogenase complex. The structure of thiamin consists of a carbon attached to a nitrogen-containing ring and a sulfur ring (**Figure 11.2.1.**). The coenzyme form, thiamin pyrophosphate (TPP), also known as thiamin diphosphate (TDP), is formed when two phosphate groups are added to the vitamin and requires adenosine triphosphate (ATP) and thiamin pyrophosphokinase [1].

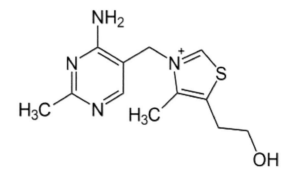

Figure 11.2-1: Thiamin structure commons.wikimedia.org

11.2.1.1. Functions of Thiamin: Coenzyme and Noncoenzyme

TPP is a key coenzyme in the pyruvate dehydrogenase complex, necessary to remove carbon dioxide from pyruvate in glucose metabolism. This decarboxylation transforms the pyruvate into acetyl-CoA, which then enters into the citric acid cycle (TCA). TPP also assists in the conversion of alpha- ketoglutarate into succinyl-CoA in the TCA cycle and the metabolism of the branched-chain amino acids isoleucine, leucine, and valine [6].

The pyruvate reaction begins with the removal of carbon dioxide from pyruvate to form hydroxyethyl-TDP (Figure 11.2.2.). Then acetyl lipoamide is formed by attaching the hydroxyethyl group to lipoic acid bound to dihydrolipoyl transacetylase (oxidized lipoamide). The acetyl lipoamide then reacts with coenzyme A forming acetyl CoA [6]. The decarboxylation of alpha-ketoglutarate follows a similar process to generate succinyl-CoA. TPP also serves as a coenzyme in the decarboxylation of α-keto acids after transamination from branched-chain amino acids, thereby preventing accumulation in the blood [7].

In the pentose phosphate pathway, glucose is converted to a 5 carbon sugar in order to generate nucleic acids and NADPH. TPP functions as a coenzyme to transketolase carrying active aldehyde to xylulose. Transketolase then hydrolyzes and transfers the carbons to an aldose receptor. This process is used to form ribose phosphate to make nucleic acids and also NADPH [8]. The reactions involved in the synthesis of pentoses are Mg^{2+} dependent.

Thiamin triphosphate (TTP) is the form of thiamin that is involved in noncoenzyme functions. The role of TTP in the nervous system is not fully understood at this time. However, studies show that TTP is released in response to nerve stimulation and is also an activator of chloride channels in nerve membranes [9].

11.2.1.2. Thiamin Imbalance

The need for thiamin in the diet was established in the 1800's by C. Eijkman. Eijkman observed that consumption of polished rice resulted in neurological problems, which are now known as beriberi [6]. Beriberi results in peripheral neuropathy and cardiovascular problems. Thiamin deficiency affects the cardiovascular, muscular, nervous and gastrointestinal systems. The earliest symptoms of beriberi include anorexia, fatigue, depression, irritability, poor memory and the inability to concentrate. Advanced deficiency results in peripheral neuropathy [1].

Several types of beriberi exist, including dry, wet, cerebral, and infantile. Dry beriberi results in peripheral polyneuritis, paralysis and muscle atrophy. Wet beriberi symptoms include congestive heart failure, cardiac dilation, and edema due to heart muscle damage. Infantile beriberi leads to cardiac failure and occurs due to thiamin deficiency in mothers. Cerebral beriberi may lead to Wernicke's encephalopathy, which is a neuropsychological complication found in those with alcoholism and AIDS. In alcoholism, there is a decreased intake of the vitamin due to decreased food consumption. In addition, alcohol inhibits thiamin absorption, while also increasing necessary intake due

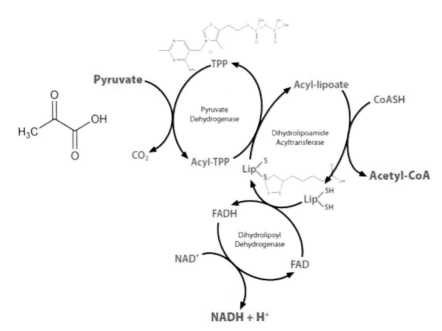

Figure 11.2-2: Five steps in Decarboxylation of Pyruvate, using the cofactors thiamin dihosphate, lipoic acid, coenzyme A, FAD ana dAD. Modified from http://www.abcam.com/?pageconfig=resource&rid=13857

to liver damage. Patients receiving parental nutrition that is high in dextrose and low in or lacking thiamin can also develop Wernicke's encephalopathy [1].

Severe thiamin deficiency has been linked to various other conditions, such as impaired cardiac function and congestive heart failure. It can also result in dementia and possibly Alzheimer's, as thiamin plays an important role in maintenance of brain function [8]. Thiamin deficiency may be related to cataract formation as well. Thiamin deficiency has also been observed in some cancer patients with rapidly growing tumors.

Thiamin toxicity is not determined. A tolerable upper level (UL) has not been set due to lack of well-established toxic effects due to excess thiamin. Life-threatening anaphylactic reactions have been observed with large intravenous doses of thiamin, as well as symptoms such as headache, convulsions, and cardiac arrhythmias [10].

The recommendation by the Food and Nutrition board is 1.2 mg of thiamin/day for men and 1.1 mg/day for women (**Table** 11.2.1.). A varied diet and/or a multivitamin with 100% of the Daily Values will ensure an intake of at least 1.5 mg of thiamin/day. Presently, there is no evidence that the requirement for thiamin is increased in older adults, but some studies have found inadequate dietary intake and thiamin insufficiency to be more common in elderly populations [11].

TABLE 11.2-1: RDA of Thiamin

Recommended Dietary Allowance (RDA) for Thiamin			
Life Stage	Age	Males (mg/day)	Females (mg/day)
Infants	0-6 months	0.2 (AI)	0.2 (AI)
Infants	7-12 months	0.3 (AI)	0.3 (AI)
Children	1-3 years	0.5	0.5
Children	4-8 years	0.6	0.6
Children	9-13 years	0.9	0.9
Adolescents	14-18 years	1.2	1.0
Adults	19 years and older	1.2	1.1
Pregnancy	all ages	-	1.4
Breastfeeding	all ages	-	1.4

11.2.2. Riboflavin (Vitamin B$_2$)

Riboflavin's main function is as a coenzyme through its derivatives, flavin mononucleotide (FMN), and flavin adenine dinucleotide (FAD) **(Figure 11.2.3.).** As hydrogen atom acceptors, these flavins can take part in many oxidation-reduction reactions. There are a large number of such reactions in which the flavins serve, including in the electron transport chain, the decarboxylation of pyruvate and α-ketoglutarate, the formation of fumarate from succinate, the synthesis of active folate, among many others [1].

TABLE 11.2-2: RDAs for Riboflavin Reference [10]

Daily Riboflavin Requirement		
Age	RDA*	Upper Limit
Children 1-3 years	.5 mg	N/A**
Children 4-8 years	.6 mg	N/A**
Children 9-13 years	.9 mg	N/A**
Teen boys 14-18 years	1.3 mg	N/A**
Teen girls 14-18 years	1.0 mg	N/A**
Adult men 19-70	1.3 mg	N/A**
Adult women 19 -70	1.1 mg	N/A**
Adult men 70 +	1.3 mg	N/A**
Adult women 70 +	1.1 mg	N/A**
Pregnancy	1.4 mg	N/A**
Breastfeeding	1.6 mg	N/A**
*RDA= average daily nutrient intake level sufficient to meet the nutrient requirement of 98% of healthy individuals		
**N/A indicates that NIH has not published this information		

The current RDAs for riboflavin are 1.3. and 1.1 mg/day for men and women, respectively (Table 3). Deficiencies in riboflavin are uncommon in the western world, and deficiencies are usually accompanied by other nutritional inadequacies. Symptoms include swelling and lesions in and around the mouth, anemia, and neuropathy. No reports of toxicity have been reported, even with large doses; thus no UL has been set [1].

11.2.3. Niacin (Vitamin B$_3$)

The B vitamin niacin is contained in the two cofactors nicotinamide adenine dinucleotide (NAD) and nicotinamide adenine dinucleotide phosphate (NADP) **(Figure 11.2.4.)**, which function as electron acceptors and hydrogen donors in enzymatic reactions [12]. The primary role of NADH is to ultimately produce ATP through its role as an electron carrier in the

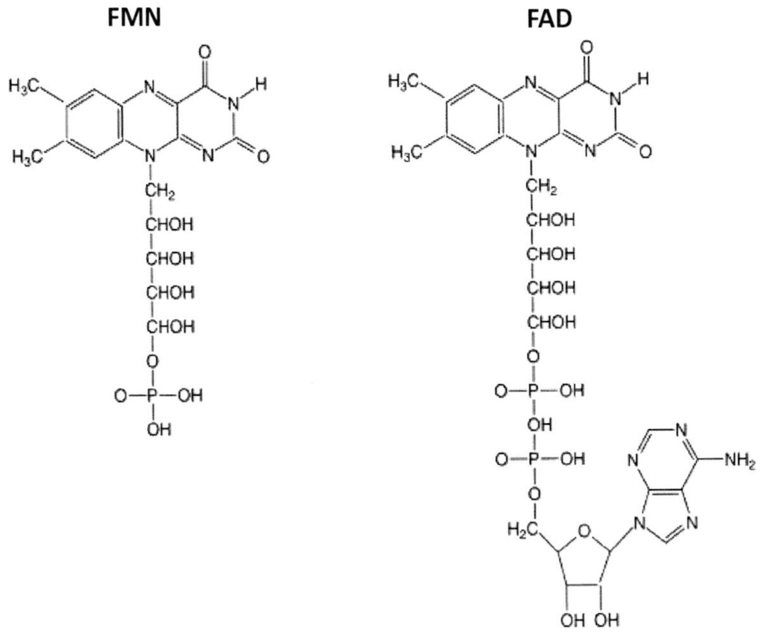

Figure 11.2-3: FMN and FAD structures.

electron transport chain. NADH is formed from NAD during a number of other processes, including glycolysis, decarboxylation of pyruvate, the TCA cycle, β-oxidation of fatty acids, and ethanol oxidation. NADH carries the reducing power and equivalent energy of metabolic fuels to the electron transport pathway to produce ATP. NAD also functions as a donor of adenosine diphosphate ribose (ADP-ribose) in protein modification and ADP-ribose cyclization [1].

NADPH is a reducing agent in fatty acid, cholesterol, and steroid hormone synthesis. It also serves in a reductive role in the oxidation of glutamate, synthesis of DNA precursors, regeneration of several antioxidants, and in folate metabolism [1]

11.2.3.1 Niacin Imbalance

The RDAs for niacin are 16 and 14 mg/day for men and women, respectively (**Table** 11.2.3.). If niacin is not absorbed in adequate amounts into the body it can result in a condition called pellagra. This condition causes skin, neurological and gastrointestinal problems, and if untreated, death. Nicotinic acid has been used to reduce lipids in the blood, including cholesterol, triglycerides, and low-density lipoproteins. In addition, it has been shown to increase levels of

high-density lipoprotein. However, these benefits are not without side effects, such as gastrointestinal problems, vasodilation, liver damage, and increased plasma glucose. As a result of these effects, a UL of 35 mg/day was set [1].

TABLE 11.2- 3: Niacin RDAs [10]

Daily Niacin Requirement		
Age	**RDA***	**Upper Limit**
Children 1-3 years	6 mg	10 mg
Children 4-8 years	8 mg	15 mg
Children 9- 13 years	12 mg	20 mg
Teen boys 14-18 years	16 mg	30 mg
Teen girls 14-18 years	14 mg	30 mg
Adult men	16 mg	35 mg
Adult women	14 mg	35 mg
Pregnant teens	18 mg	30 mg
Pregnant women	18 mg	35 mg
Breastfeeding teens	17 mg	30 mg
Breastfeeding women	17 mg	35 mg
*RDA= average daily nutrient intake level sufficient to meet the nutrient requirement of 98% of healthy individuals		

nutrimentumfood.com

11.2.4. Pantothenic Acid

Pantothenic acid is used to synthesize Coenzyme A (CoA) (**Figure 11.2-5**). CoA plays a role in a wide

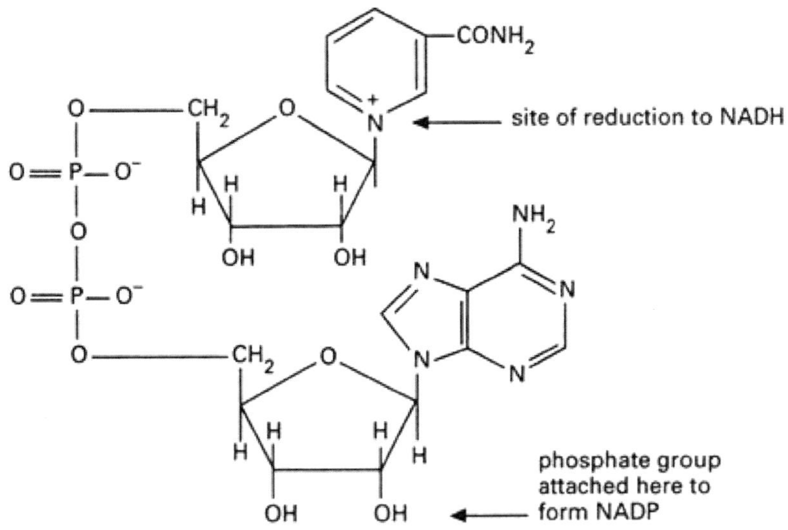

Figure 11.2-4: NAD structure, From www.answers.com

range of nutrient metabolism, including that of carbohydrates, lipids, and proteins. CoA also donates acetyl groups to proteins, sugars, and other molecules to affect their function. For example, some enzymes are acetylated, thereby turning them on or off (**Figure 11.2-6**) [1].

The AI for adults is 5 mg, and deficiencies can result in "burning feet syndrome," which results in numbness and burning in the feet. Other symptoms of pantothenic acid deficiency include vomiting, weakness, and irritability. Toxicity is unusual, with symptoms including gastrointestinal problems [1].

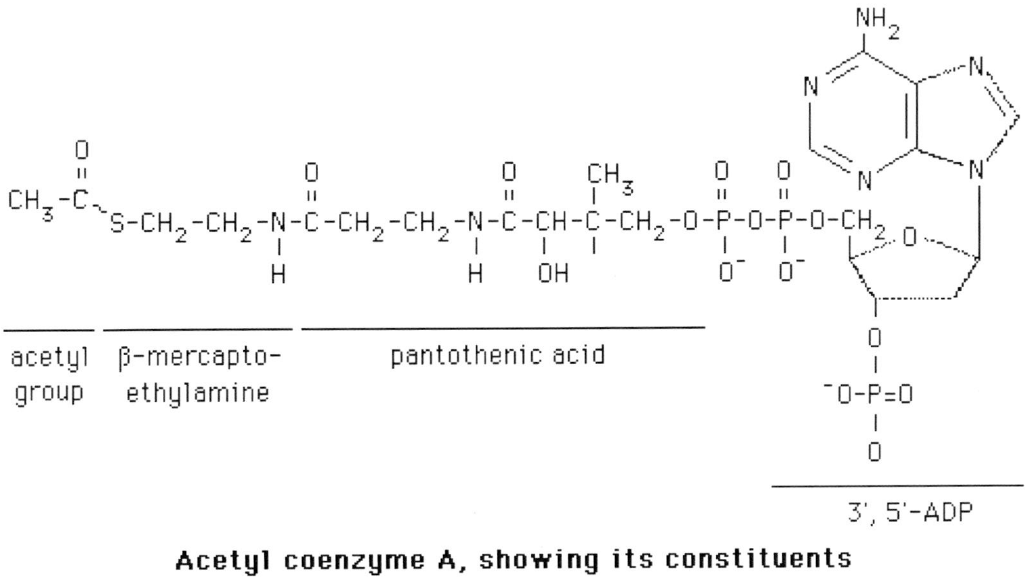

Acetyl coenzyme A, showing its constituents

Figure 11.2-5: Coenzyme A with its constituents labeled. From library.med.utah.edu

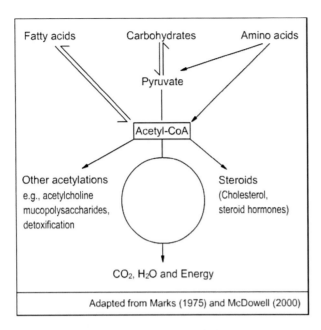

Figure 11.2-6: Coenzyme A' in metabolism.
Source: www.dsm.com

11.2.5. Vitamin B₆

Vitamin B_6 has several different structural forms: pyridoxal, pyridoxamine, and pyridoxine (**Figure 11.2-7**). Pyridoxal phosphate is the active coenzyme form of vitamin B_6, with roles in more than 100 enzymatic reactions, most of which are involved in amino acid metabolism. Vitamin B_6 also has non-coenzyme functions to modulate the action of steroid hormones, though these functions are not as well described as its coenzyme functions [1].

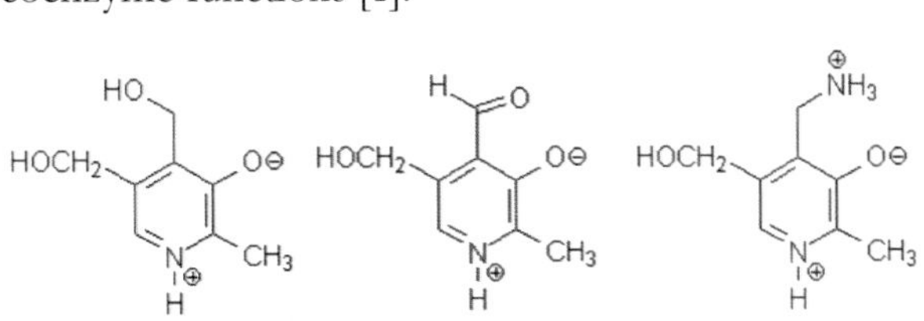

Figure 11.2-7: Vitamers of vitamin B6.
From https://noexcuseshealth.files.wordpress.com/2013/03/vitamin-b6-structure.gif

11.2.5.1. Vitamin B₆ Functions

As a coenzyme, vitamin B_6 has many roles in a variety of types of reactions. Transamination reactions in

the production of amino acids require vitamin B_6 in the form of pyridoxamine and pyridoxal phosphates. Vitamin B_6 also is important in decarboxylation reactions in the synthesis of hormones and neurotransmitters from amino acids, such as serotonin from 5-hydroxytryptophan, γ-aminobutyric acid (GABA) from glutamate, and dopamine from tyrosine (**Figure 11.2-8**). Pyridoxal phosphate is involved in transulfhydration and desulfhydration reactions that produce cysteine from methionine and pyruvate from cysteine, respectively. Deamination or dehydration reactions that result in the release of ammonia or ammonium may use pyridoxal phosphate. In addition, pyridoxal phosphate is required for the cleavage and transfer of the hyroxylmethyl group of serine to tetrahydrofolate to form glycine and to switch between D- and L- amino acids. Pyridoxal phosphate is involved in many other cellular processes, including the synthesis of heme, sphingolipids, niacin, carnitine, and taurine, as well as the breakdown of glycogen [1].

11.2.5.2. Vitamin B6 Imbalance

The daily requirement of vitamin B_6 for adults is 1.3 mg, and this value rises after the age of 50. Deficiency of vitamin B_6 is rare in the western diet. Symptoms include drowsiness, fatigue, and sores and cracking in and around the mouth in adults and neurological problems in infants. Though vitamin B_6 has been used to treat a variety of conditions, such as carpal tunnel syndrome and depression, large doses may result in neuropathies that can affect movement and sensory perception [1].

11.2.6. Biotin

Biotin's major functions are both coenzyme and non-coenzyme roles. As a coenzyme, biotin is linked to one of four carboxylases: acetyl CoA carboxylase, pyruvate carboxylase, propionyl CoA carboxylase, and β-methylcrotonyl CoA carboxylase (**Figure 11.2-9**). Pyruvate carboxylase converts pyruvate to oxaloacetate needed for the TCA cycle or for gluconeogenesis. Acetyl CoA carboxylase forms malonyl CoA from acetyl CoA for fatty acid synthesis. Propionyl CoA carboxylase forms methylmalonyl CoA from propionyl CoA for amino acid and fatty

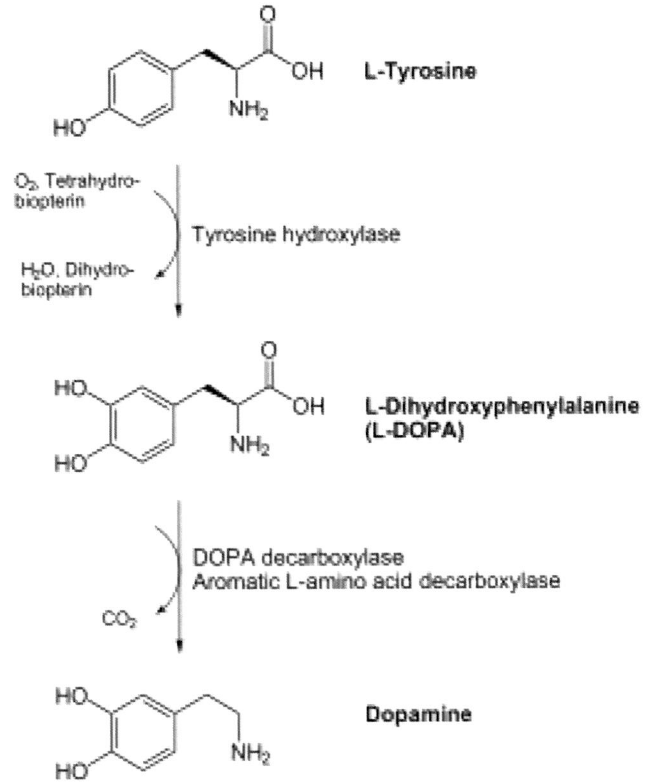

Figure 11.2-8: Production of dopamine from tyrosine. Pyridoxal phosphate is a coenzyme in the decarboxylation step.

acid metabolism. β-methylcrotonyl CoA carboxylase converts β-methylcrotonyl CoA to β-methylglutaconyl CoA during leucine catabolism [1].

Biotin's non-coenzyme roles are not as well delineated, and they include cell proliferation and gene expression. Biotin attached to histones is correlated with increased cell proliferation and affects the cell's reaction to DNA damage. In addition, biotin regulates gene expression at the level of transcription and translation [1].

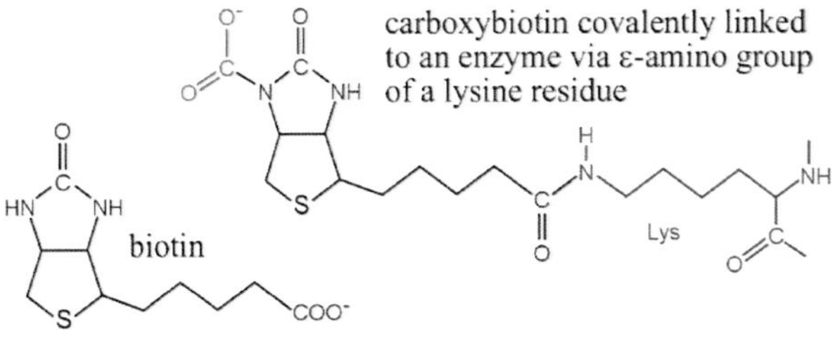

Figure 11.2-9: Structure of biotin and its linkage to a carboxylase guweb2.gonzaga.edu

11.2.6.1. Biotin Imbalance

The AI for biotin is 30 μg per day for adults and is essential in the diet. Biotin deficiency results in a variety of symptoms, including lethargy, depression, pain, anorexia, nausea, alopecia, and dermatitis. Inadequate biotin reduces the function of biotin-dependent enzymes, and urinary excretion of its metabolites increases. Large doses of biotin have no reported side effects, thus there is no established UL [1].

11.2.7. Copper

Copper is an essential element required for the function of many cellular enzymes including: superoxide dismutase, tyrosinase, peptidyl-α-monooxygenase, and lysyl oxidase [13]. Two diseases associated with copper intake are Menkes and Wilson's disease. Menkes disease is a lethal neurodegerative disorder resulting from a defect in a copper transporter [14]. Wilson's disease is a problem of excess copper due to a mutation in another copper transporter, causing motor dysfunction and liver disease [15]. Like iron, copper is critical for mitochondrial function and oxidative phosphorylation. Copper availability can shift cancer cells toward anaerobic respiration [16].

11.2.8. Chromium

Chromium is required for normal glucose metabolism. Deficiencies in chromium can occur in patients receiving parenteral nutrition. The result is a reversible diabetes that can be treated with chromium [17]. The trivalent form of chromium is the biologically valuable form for humans, originally thought to function as part of a complex of amino acids called glucose tolerance factor [1]. More recently an oligopeptide called apochromodulin has been identified. Four Cr^{3+} ions bind to the peptide. The resulting chromodulin complex increases the enzymatic activity of the insulin receptor cascade [1]. Thus, chromium is able to regulate insulin signaling by modulating the activity of intracellular kinases, enhancing the insulin signal [18].

Nutritional supplement companies often tout the ability of chromium to promote muscle growth and increase metabolism. There is some evidence for their claims, though *in vitro* data with rat cells should not compel any novice body builders to increase their chromium levels. In muscle cells, chromium increases the amount of IGF-1 and the IGF1-receptor after insulin treatment, and an increase in anabolic metabolism [19]. Other animal data supports the idea the chromium could be useful in conjunction with treatments for obesity and type II diabetes. One study found that rats fed a high fat diet with chromium-histidinate supplementation had lower blood glucose than the rats fed only a high fat diet [20].

In humans, the effects of chromium supplementation appear to be less dramatic. In a study following overweight women undergoing a moderate exercise regimen, supplementation with chromium picolinate did not have an effect on blood glucose, insulin, serum cholesterol, high-density lipoprotein, body weight, or fat mass [21]. A meta-analysis of all studies with humans and various forms of chromium supplementation failed to find any effect of chromium with respect to blood glucose, insulin sensitivity, lipid profiles, and several other metabolic measures [22].

Overall, there is very strong evidence that chromium is essential for normal glucose metabolism but little evidence that it has potential as a treatment for either diabetes or obesity. It is difficult to exclude chromium from human diets to the extent that deficiency symptoms can be measured.

11.2.9. Molybdenum

Molybdenum is considered to be one of the essential "trace" or minor minerals required for human health and with an RDA of 45 µg for most adults [23]. Some dietary sources of molybdenum include legumes, green leafy vegetables, milk, and whole grains. The content within plants varies greatly, because the content depends on the amount within the soil to which the plants were grown [24].

Molybdenum is essential for the function of three enzymes: xanthine oxidase, aldehyde oxidase, and sulfite oxidase by acting as a cofactor. Molybdenum cofactor, or Moco, is made up of Mo covalently bonded to two sulfur atoms from a unique pterin that is then referred to as molybdopterin. The synthesis of the molybdenum cofactor utilizes GTP and can be divided into four steps. During Moco synthesis, research suggests that Copper acts as a placeholder for the subsequent insertion of Molybdenum into the cofactor [25]. The enzymes that Molybdenum is a cofactor for catalyze oxidation-reduction reactions within the human body. Xanthine oxidase has two molybdenum atoms per enzymatic unit and catalyzes the oxidation of hypoxanthine to xanthine and then further to uric acid. This enzyme is additionally associated with the catabolism of purines [26]. The activity of xanthine oxidase is proportional to the concentrations of molybdenum, but only when molybdenum is at low levels. Once the levels of molybdenum increase over a certain concentration, molybdenum may have an inhibitory effect on xanthine oxidase. Sulfite oxidase is responsible for the last step in the oxidative reduction of sulfur-containing amino acids and lipids and oxidizes sulfite to sulfate, [26]. Aldehyde oxidase functions by oxidizing certain aldehydes, pyrimidines, pteridines, and purines [24].

Molybdate (MoO_4^{-2}) is the bioavailable form of molybdenum [26]. Molybdenum is absorbed within the small intestine, and the uptake during digestion is extremely efficient considering the relatively low amounts consumed within food products. There is no storage site for molybdenum but high concentrations of the metal are found within the small intestine, skin, liver, bones, and kidneys, [24]. Molybdenum is excreted through bile and through urine, while more than half of the daily intake of Mo is excreted in urine. Under the normal dietary intake of molybdenum, its content within tissues is generally between 0.1-1.0 micrograms per gram [27]. A recent study has demonstrated that unlike other essential minerals, molybdenum intake can be measured through plasma levels. The plasma levels of molybdenum can indicate a high or low dietary intake of molybdenum over a relatively short amount of time of fourteen days, [28].

Molybdenum deficiency within humans has not been properly established, although there have been various experimental studies regarding this phenomena. The results of these experimental studies show that molybdenum deficiency leads to headaches, lethargy, coma, and decreased xanthine oxidase activity, among other symptoms. There is however a deficiency characterized by the complete loss of sulfite oxidase, xanthine oxidase, and aldehyde oxidase activity called human Moco deficiency (MoCD – Molybdenum cofactor deficiency). Patients who are diagnosed with MoCD are characterized by their progressive neurological damage and the symptoms are mainly due to the elevated sulfite levels within the body, [26]. Molybdenum cofactor deficiency is generally seen in infants and is an inherited autosomal-recessive deficiency disease, which generally leads to early death [29].

Although rare, molybdenum deficiencies can be deadly. Without adequate molybdenum to act as a cofactor for sulfite oxidases, the brain and other organs are damaged by sulfite. Sulfite is generated from the breakdown of sulfur containing amino acids. Sulfite oxidases convert this metabolite to sulfate [26]. Molybdenum is also a component of xanthine oxidase, an enzyme involved with amino acid metabolism. Its critical importance with respect to sulfur containing amino acid metabolism could implicate other roles for this nutrient.

Molybdenum toxicity has rarely occurred, although one study described a population in Armenia, which had large daily intakes of molybdenum. Within this study, adults generally consumed about 10-15 mg of molybdenum per day were noted to have symptoms that resembled gout and hyperuricemia. These villagers were diagnosed with joint pain, edema and even joint deformity as well [27].

11.2.10. Manganese

The use of oxygen in cellular respiration generates a constant supply of reactive oxygen species (ROS) inside the mitochondria. The ROS can damage mitochondrial DNA leading to destruction of the mitochondria, which can eventually lead to cell death. Manganese super oxide dismutase (Mn-SOD) breaks down the ROS and allows the mitochondria to continue generating ATP [30]. Manganese has roles in the urea cycle, carbohydrate and protein metabolism, and acts as a cofactor for various enzymes [1].

A major metabolic question with cancer cells involves their switch from aerobic to anaerobic metabolism, which is often called the Warburg Effect. There is evidence that Mn-SOD controls glucose metabolism and regulates the cell cycle [31]. There is also evidence that cancer cells have lower levels of Mn-SOD, and artificially elevating these levels can slow cell growth [32]. While none of this work is conclusive, it does suggest a potential role for manganese in preventing defects in cellular metabolism.

11.2.11. Potassium

There are 245 grams of potassium in the human body. Its functions involve water and electrolyte balance, glucose metabolism, muscle function, and acid base balance. Potassium is also known for its ability to lower blood pressure and to decrease the risk of stroke.

The intake of potassium is known to promote sodium excretion and calcium retention. This results in less bone resorption because of low serum calcium and an increase in bone mineral density. Increased excretion of sodium also leads to lower blood volume and reduced blood pressure. In contrast, low intakes of potassium can make an individual sensitive to minor intakes of sodium causing hypertension (a rise in blood pressure). On the other hand, an increase in dietary potassium or intake of potassium supplements has been shown to reduce hypertension [33]. Supplementation of potassium and magnesium together significantly lowered blood pressure in rats. The mechanism may be an increase in the sodium potassium ATPase activity, diuresis, and natriuresis [34].

Potassium also has a role in the metabolism of glucose. Low intakes of potassium or hypokalemia can negatively affect insulin secretion by the pancreas and promote insulin resistance. Martini, et al., concluded that low intakes of potassium leads to the activation of the renin-angiotensin-aldosterone system, and negative effects on insulin secretion. In contrast, lowering hypertension and increasing potassium intake can have beneficial effects on glucose metabolism and reduce the risk of insulin resistance [35].

Lastly, potassium has a role in pH balance [33]. Foods that are rich in potassium provide more strong cations and fewer anions, which will increase the concentration of bicarbonate and lower the serum pH. In response to acidosis, there is an increase of potassium in the extracellular fluid in exchange for hydrogen, in effect, balancing the serum pH [36].

11.2.12. Sodium

There are 105 grams of sodium in the human body, thirty percent of which is found on the bone with the remaining found circulating in the blood. The sodium found on the bone can be utilized when sodium intakes are low. Sodium is important in fluid balance, nerve function, and muscle contraction. Sodium also affects the amount of calcium in the body. An increase in the intake of sodium results in increased calcium excretion [1].

A majority of sodium is found in the extracellular fluid. High intakes of sodium are correlated with an increase in blood pressure. Some individuals are more sensitive to this increase than others. This sensitivity can be influenced by the intake of other macro- minerals such as potassium and magnesium, which increase the excretion of sodium. (See previous section). Low sodium intakes will result in a drop in blood pressure. This activates the renin-angiotensin-aldosterone system that allows for the reabsorption of water and sodium by the kidneys. This function is to maintain blood pressure and water balance [33]. Conversely, during times of high sodium intake, blood pressure

rises and therefore sodium excretion is enhanced. A rise in sodium intake results in hypertension in some individuals, but not all. Hypertension is influenced by genetic and environmental elements. Dietary treatments for hypertension such as reduction in sodium intake and increase in potassium intake seem to vary. This is thought to be due to the genetic factors involved in hypertension. Responses to low sodium intake were similar among family members, linking genetic makeup with salt sensitivity and hypertension. A dietary intervention that simultaneously lowered sodium intake while increasing potassium intakes had a similar result [37]. Further research on this subject may be able to determine the exact genes that indicate a predisposition towards hypertension as it relates to sodium and potassium.

Sodium gradients are created by the sodium potassium ATPase pump in the cell membrane. The sodium enters the cell as the hydrogen exits. Then in exchange for sodium, potassium enters the cell as the sodium exits. The latter exchange uses ATP, and generates energy in the form of the concentration gradient that can serve as a signal in the nerve cell's membrane, or for coupled transport of other molecules against their concentration gradient [1].

11.3.1. Protein accretion functions in growth and development

Proteins are ubiquitous in the human body, serving in a variety of critical functions that are essential to life. These functions include structural, catalytic, transportation, signaling, hormonal, and other roles. Body composition analysis has played an important role in helping to understand the distribution of proteins in the body, with different models and analytical techniques contributing to this growing body of knowledge. Wang et. al suggested a five-level model (**Figure 11.3.1**) to guide body-composition research that analyzes the body at the following levels: atomic (e.g. oxygen, carbon, hydrogen, nitrogen, etc.), molecular (protein, lipid, water, etc.), cellular (within cells, extracellular fluids and solids), tissue-systems (adipose, blood, bone, muscle, other), and the whole body level [38].

**Basic Model
2-Compartment**

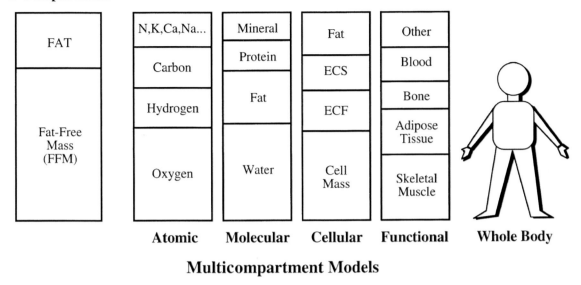

Figure 11.3-1: Five-level model for organizing body-composition research.
From: http://physrev.physiology.org/content/physrev/80/2/649/F1.large.jpg?width=800&height=600&carousel=1

11.3.1.1. Protein Composition in Humans

In Vivo Neutron Activation Analysis (IVNA) is a technique that has been used to analyze the body composition at the element-level (Level I in Table 11.3.1) [39]. Briefly, this technique exposes the whole body to radiation, changing the nuclear state of some element upon absorption of the neutron. Measuring the decay of radioactive atoms and comparing to a known radioactive half-life allows for the quantification of certain elements and is considered an accurate technique for measuring Total Body Nitrogen (TBN).

Total Body Protein (TBPro) can then be calculated from TBN using a ratio of 16% nitrogen content in protein, which has been validated in cadaver studies [40]. The downside of IVNA is both the whole-body exposure to radiation, as well as the limited availability of IVNA facilities to scientists [39], therefore other methods have been explored for quantifying TBPro. Wang et al. [41] proposed a model for estimating TBPro using three variables: Total Body Potassium (TPK) which is measured using a non-invasive whole body counter that measures the naturally occurring ^{40}K isotope; Total Body Water (TBW) which is measured using a tracer dose of labeled water; and bone mineral,

TABLE 11-18: Applying the 5-level model of body composition to protein analysis [38, 41,42].

Level 1 – Atomic (% body weight)	**Level 2 – Molecular** (% of body weight)	Level 3 – Cellular (% of TBPro)	Level 4 – Tissue (% TBPro)
Oxygen (61%)	Water (60%)	Cellular (75-79%)	Skeletal muscle (43%)
Carbon (23%)	Lipids (17%)	Extra-cellular solids (19-23%)	Skin (15%)
Hydrogen (10%)	Protein (15%)	Extra-cellular fluids (2%)	Blood (15%)
Nitrogen (16%)	Mineral (5%)		Liver & kidney (10%)

which is measured with dual-energy X-ray absorption (DXA). This model correlated highly with the results found using IVNA in healthy women, healthy men, and in men with AIDS (r=0.92, P < 0.001). Other in vivo techniques for measuring different aspects of body composition include anthropometric measurements (e.g. skin-fold thickness), underwater weighing, bioelectrical impedance and magnetic resonance imaging. Information regarding this can be found in an excellent review article by Ellis [40].

Applying the five-level model of body composition to protein analysis provides an interesting snapshot of protein composition and compartmentalization within the human body (**Table 11.3.1**). At the molecular level, in a 70 kg man, protein represents about 10.5 kg of total body weight (TBW), with the main source being skeletal muscles (approximately 40% of TBPro). Four proteins that are ubiquitous in humans – ***myosin*** and ***actin***, the contractile proteins in skeletal muscles; ***collagen***, the structural protein in connective tissues; and ***hemoglobin***, the oxygen carrying protein in blood, make up almost 50% of TBPro [42].

Among the most abundant proteins in the body are the contractile proteins, actin and myosin. Both of these are ATP-dependent motor proteins, which compose a majority of the contractile protein category. The roles of actin, myosin, tropomyosin and troponin in muscle were described in section 6.3. Actin and myosin are present in nearly all cells and can contribute to cell motility and movement of intracellular organelles or vesicles through the microfilaments and microtubules that contain these proteins.

11.3.1.2. Fibrous proteins

The most abundant fibrous proteins are collagen, elastin, and keratin [42]. Collagen is abundant in the extracellular matrix of connective tissue around the body [43]. The extracellular matrix is important because it surrounds active cells and has cell receptor specificity [43]. Collagen found in connective tissues surrounds organs such as the digestive system and helps with structural stability to ensure the organ does not collapse [43]. Collagen structure varies throughout the body, but one commonality for all the different forms is a right-handed triple helix composed of three α-chains [43]. Collagen has several different types that include,

Collagen Type I, II, III, V, XI, IV, VI, VII, X, IX, XII, XIV, XIX, XX, XXI, XIII, and XVII. Each one of these collagen types is found in different structures throughout the body. Collagen Type I is known to be of the greatest abundance in the body and it falls under the family known as "the fibril-forming collagens" [43]. Type I is found in bones, tendons, skins, ligaments, cornea, and many interstitial connective tissues. Collagen makes up more over 90% of the protein component of bone. Other collagen types which fall under the family of fibril-forming collagens are Type II, III, V, and XI. Hyaline cartilage which is found primarily on joint surfaces is composed of 80% type II collagen [43]. Another family of collagen proteins is "the FACIT collagens", which consists of collagen types IX, XII and XIV [44]. The other families of collagen proteins are a microfibrillar collagen, short chain collagens and the collagen of basement membranes [43]. The collagen type IV is characterized under the family of collagen of basement membranes, which is important due to the basement membrane's role in the body as a barrier to foreign substances [43].

Collagen research has questioned if any of the different types of collagen can aid in reversal of any chronic diseases. One such study looks at the effects of Collagen Type VII on Dystrophic Epidermolysis Bullosa (DEB) [45]. DEB is a genetic condition where those affected experience widespread blistering in mild cases and in more serious cases vision loss and disfigurement [45]. Collagen type VII has similar function to collagen type IV in that both are present in the basement membrane [44]. DEB creates mutations in the expression of this type of collagen and Woodley et al. were able to demonstrate how an injection of type VII collagen into the basement membrane can lead to reversal of DEB [45].

11.3.1.3. Protein and Amino Acid-Derived Hormones

Proteins are heavily involved in hormone synthesis and function throughout the body. One example is thyroglobulin, which is a precursor for synthesis of thyroid hormone [42]. Thyroid hormones (T4 and the more active form, T3) are derived from the iodinated tyrosine residues of thyroglobulin, and are vital in lipid and carbohydrate metabolism.

The tyrosine residue is important for activation of a family of proteins, including receptor tyrosine kinase (RTK), non-receptor tyrosine kinase (NRTK), and protein tyrosine kinase (PTK) [46]. The RTK family is important because it consists of important receptors for hormones needed for growth and metabolism such as insulin and epidermal growth factor [46]. PTK family is known to work in association with protein-tyrosine phosphatases (PTPs), in order to monitor cell function mediated by phosphotyrosine signaling [47]. Mice without PTPs demonstrate alterations in embryo fibroblasts and decreased proliferation, cell adhesion and cell metabolism [47]. Because the insulin receptor is a part of RTK protein family [46], poor insulin function leading to type II diabetes may involve the tyrosine phosphorylation cascade.

11.3.1.4. Protein's role in organ development

Proper organ and tissue development for the embryo are dependent on the tyrosine phosphatase protein, Pez, among others. Pez and TGF-beta work in conjunction with each other for epithelial-mesenchymal transition (EMT) to occur [48]. EMT is important for proper embryonic development, and is known to be a pre-requisite for proper organ formation [48]. It aids in formation of germ layers and endocardial cushions of the atrio-ventricular (A-V) canal in heart tissue [48]. Additionally, EMT is essential in proper bone and cartilage formation [48].

The role of proteins in various body functions include muscular contraction, hormone function, and proper organ development in an embryo. Improper protein intake may lead to a decreased quality of life in adults and malformed embryos. Complications due to inadequate protein intake are easily preventable with a healthy diet. Protein is an essential part of the diet that should be emphasized, especially during pregnancy, since inadequate protein may lead to problems with the embryo, and could put the mother at a health risk as well.

11.3.2. Vitamin A in Growth and Differentiation

Vitamin A is the term collectively used for three active forms of retinoids, named retinol (alcohol), retinal (aldehyde) and retinoic acid (**Figure 11.3-2**). Vitamin A performs various important metabolic and physiological functions in the body. It mediates night vision and controls cell differentiation and proliferation. It is becoming increasingly evident that Vitamin A plays a major regulatory role in the normal development and growth of cells and also modulates innate and cell mediated immunity.

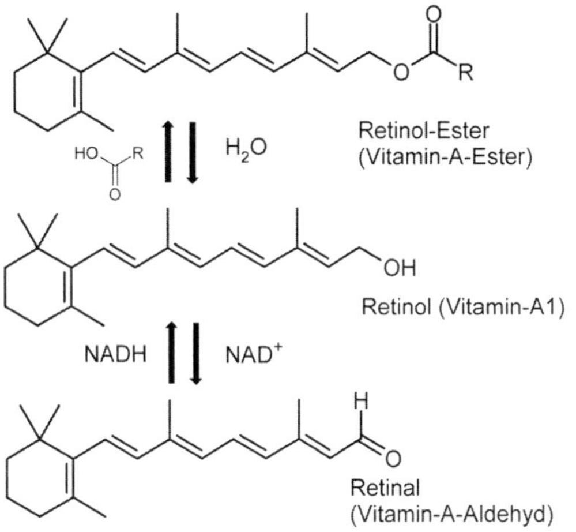

Figure 11.3-2: Active forms of vitamin A commons. wikimedia.org

11.3.2.1. Vitamin A controls cell differentiation

Retinoic acid participates in cell proliferation and differentiation of various types of cells, converting undifferentiated cell into a more mature cell. Retinoic acid helps to differentiate many types of cells but especially epithelial linings of the respiratory system, gastrointestinal tract and skin. It also regulates the differentiation of blood cell precursors (myeloid precursor cells). In addition, vitamin A promotes the growth of epithelial cells through increasing the number of growth factor receptors and gap junctions in the cells [1].

The cell proliferation regulatory effects of retinoic acid are conducted via the process of gene expression. 9-cis retinoic acid and all-trans retinoic acid first bind with cellular retinoic acid binding protein (CRABP) for transport into the nucleus. They bring about their effects by binding to the nuclear receptors for retinoic acid (**Figure 11.3.3.**). These receptors belong to the steroid hormone, thyroid hormone receptor

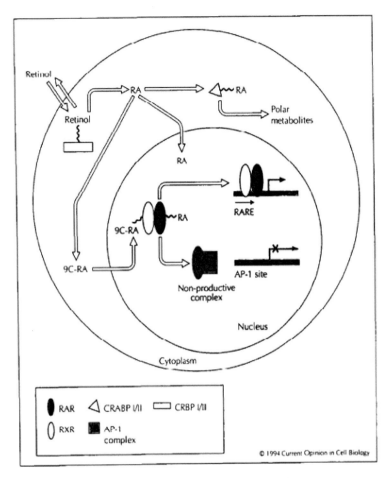

A representation of the proposed mechanism of action of retinoic acid. The locations and proposed interactions of the cytoplasmic binding proteins and the nuclear retinoid receptors (with RA and 9C-RA [9-cis-retinoic acid] bound) involved in the RA signalling pathway are designated.

Figure 11.3-3: From Vitamin A, differentiation and cancer, by Love, Jane M and Gudas, Lorraine J, Current Opinion in Cell Biology, ISSN 0955-0674, 1994, 6(6):825 – 831

and vitamin D binding receptor family [49]. The vitamin A-receptor complex (which also interacts with other proteins and factors) impacts the process of transcription by attaching itself to special region of DNA composed of vitamin A responsive genes. Data suggests that retinoic acid alters the cell differentiation by regulating the genes coding for various enzymes, and growth and transcription factors [1].

11.3.2.2. Vitamin A reduces infections and modulates immunity

Vitamin A augments immunity in several ways. The mucosal barrier lining the body cavities is one of the major components of innate immune system. Vitamin A maintains the integrity of the mucosal lining, and

the mucosal barrier of the respiratory, intestinal and urogenital tracts in deficient individuals becomes disrupted (**Figure 11.3.4**).

Mucus secreted by goblet cells is another essential part of innate immunity. Mucus traps the microorganisms entering the body cavity and later sweeps them away, moving them out of the body. Vitamin A stimulates the conversion of epithelial cells (keratinized) into the formation of mucus producing cells (goblet cells) [1].

Vitamin A also stimulates T cell activation via the process of gene expression. Retinoic acid binds to the retinoic acid nuclear receptors (RAR) of T lymphocytes. The retinoic acid receptor complex interacts with other receptors to form heterodimers and homodimers. These receptor complexes stimulate retinoic acid response element genes (RARE) that are present on a

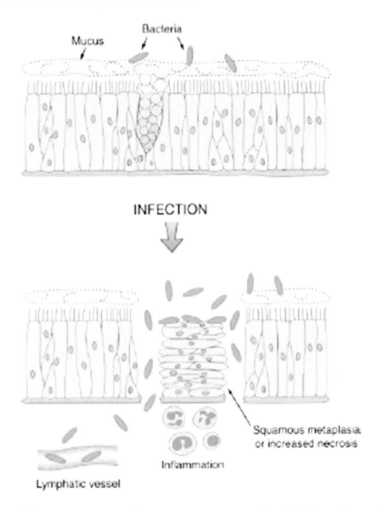

Figure 11.3-4: Vitamin A deficiency converts columnar to squamous epithelial cells, with greater risk for bacterial penetration and resulting inflammation. From Annual Review of Nutrition, VITAMIN INFECTION, AND IMMUNE FUNCTION*, Vol. 21: 167-192 (2001) DOI: A, 10.1146/annurev.nutr.21.1.167

specific promoter region of DNA. Stimulation of RARE results in the formation of adhesion molecules which up regulate T cell activation markers on T lymphocyte cell surface. This process results in enhanced T cell activation. Retinoic acid also augments the release of cytokines such as IL-2 from TH-1 cells and collectively increases cell-mediated immunity [50].

11.3.2.3. Vitamin A regulates the development of stem cells

Myeloid stem cells (present in bone marrow) are the precursor cells of granulocytes (neutrophils, eosinophils and basophils). Retinoic acid exerts its effects on neutrophil proliferation via retinoic acid

nuclear receptors (RAR). Retinoic acid binds to the nuclear receptors of these cells, affects gene expression and alters the proliferation and differentiation of granulocytes (especially neutrophils). The well pronounced action of vitamin A on the normal differentiation of myeloid stem cells is evident by the fact that retinoic acid therapy can increase the effectiveness of treatment of acute promyelocytic leukemia patients [51]. Also, vitamin A plays an important role in the normal function of neutrophils.

11.3.2.4. Vitamin A as an anti-inflammatory agent

Vitamin A exerts its anti-inflammatory effects in two ways; first it reduces the population of monocytes in lymphoid organs and bone marrow. In addition, retinoic acid decreases the transcription of interleukin 12 (IL-12), which is a pro-inflammatory cytokine produced by monocytes and macrophages [51]. IL-12 activates TH1 Helper T cells release interferon gamma, another pro inflammatory cytokine that increases activation of macrophages and their recruitment at the site of infection. Vitamin A also increases the transcription of anti-inflammatory cytokines such as interleukin 10 (IL-10).

11.3.3. Folate

Folate's main function is as acceptors and donators of one-carbon groups in its active form as tetrahydrofolate (THF) (**Figure** 11.3-5). Structurally, folate and THF are made of three parts: pteridine, para-aminobenzoate, and glutamate. As a coenzyme, THF serves in reactions in two major categories: amino acid metabolism and nucleotide metabolism.

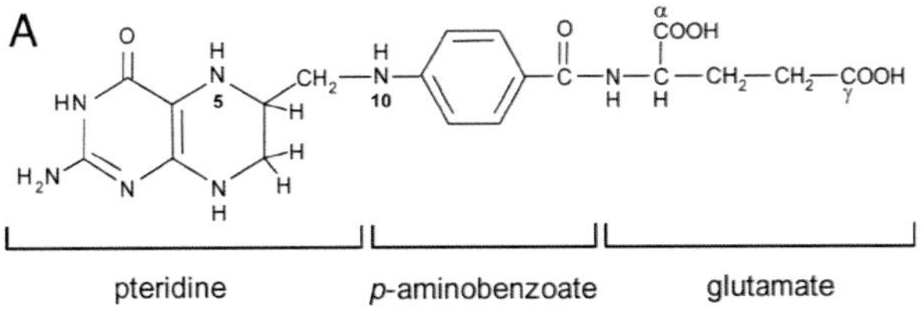

Figure 11.3-5: Structure of tetrahydrofolate pnas.org

11.3.3.1. Functions of folate

Metabolism of several amino acids, including histidine, serine, glycine, and methionine, require THF or one of its derivatives. THF receives the formimino group from and intermediate during the synthesis of glutamate (**Figure 11.3-6**). In the synthesis of serine from glycine, 5,10-methylene THF donates a hydroxylmethyl group. Glycine is also produced from serine with the aid of THF. Glycine degradation as well as its synthesis from choline also require THF. 5-methyl THF is necessary along with vitamin B_{12} in a series of reactions that result in methylation of substrates that affect nucleic acids, myelin, polyamine, carnitine,and catecholamine synthesis, and others. Folate's role is as a coenzyme in the regeneration of methionine from homocysteine by transferring a methyl group to vitamin B_{12}, which then acts as a coenzyme to transfer the methyl group to homocysteine, resulting in methionine. Methionine is then used to generate

S-adenosyl methionine (SAM), which methylates a number of other substrates (**Figure 11.3-7**) [1].

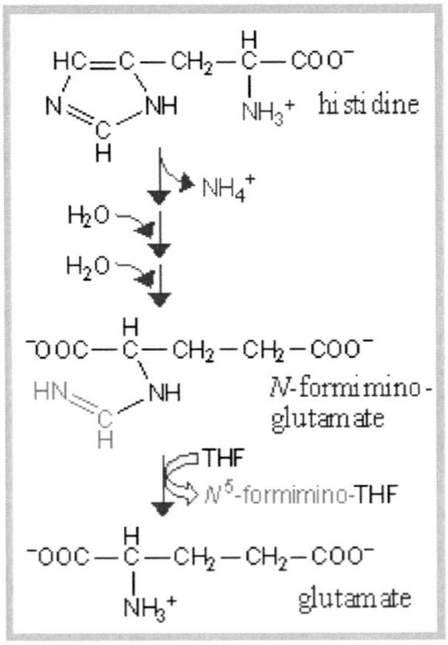

Figure 11.3-6: Folate's role in glutamate synthesis. From histidine From www.rpi.edu

Folate also functions in the synthesis of nucleotides, both purines and pyrimidines. A critical methyl acceptor is the nucleotide thymine because inadequate synthesis of this nucleotide has adverse clinical outcomes in blood formation and development. 5,10-methylene THF is required as a coenzyme in the conversion of deoxyuridine monophosphate to thymidine monophosphate to be used in the production of DNA. Another form of THF, 10-formyl THF, is required for the ring formation in purines [1]. The role of folate deficiency as a cause of birth defects, such as anencephaly and neural tube defects, has been studied in mice and observed in humans [52].

11.3.3.2. Folate imbalances

The RDA for folate is 400 μg/day dietary folate equivalents for adults, with higher levels necessary in women who are or may become pregnant to protect against neural tube defects in the fetus. Dietary folate equivalents are used instead of units of folate, as supplemental folate is more bioavailable than folate from food sources. A variety of disease states are related to folate deficiency, the clearest link being to megaloblastic macrocytic anemia. It is a common condition occurring in people with low folate status

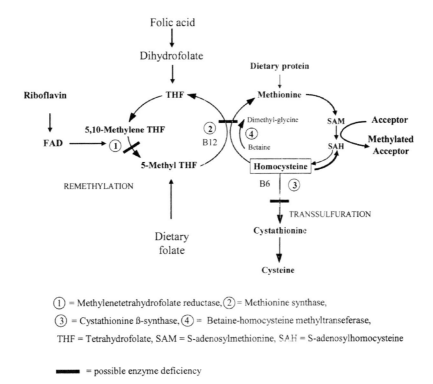

$\textcircled{1}$ = Methylenetetrahydrofolate reductase, $\textcircled{2}$ = Methionine synthase,

$\textcircled{3}$ = Cystathionine ß-synthase, $\textcircled{4}$ = Betaine-homocysteine methyltranseferase,

THF = Tetrahydrofolate, SAM = S-adenosylmethionine, SAH = S-adenosylhomocysteine

▬▬ = possible enzyme deficiency

Figure 11.3-7: Folate (THF) and Vitamin B$_{12}$ in the regeneration of methionine from homocysteine, a reaction necessary for the methylation of many biologically important substrates.
From sciencedirect.com

because of folate's role in DNA synthesis. Red blood cells are unable to divide properly, though translation of protein products continues, leading to the presence in the blood of large cells that have failed to become mature erythrocytes. White blood cells are also impacted, falling in number and failing to mature. Cells may incorporate uracil instead of thymidylate and be unable to correct the errors, resulting in breaks in the DNA. Symptoms of megaloblastic macrocytic anemia include weakness, fatigue, headaches, problems concentrating, irritability, and shortness of breath [1] (see chapter 8)

Folate's role in DNA synthesis may also affect the development of cancer, as thymidylate and methylation levels are low in cases of folate deficiency. In addition, low folate levels result in an increase in homocysteine, as it cannot be methylated back to methionine. Increases of homocysteine are associated with cardiovascular disease and dementia. These diseases may relate back

to folate deficiency, though the mechanisms are not yet known [1].

Folic acid toxicity is not common; however, possible symptoms include insomnia, moodiness, and gastrointestinal problems. Folic acid supplementation can mask a vitamin B$_{12}$ deficiency, so the UL is set at 1,000 µg/day of supplemental folate or fortified foods to prevent neurological damage from a lack of vitamin B12 [1].

11.3.4. Vitamin B$_{12}$

Vitamin B12, also known as cobalamin, consists of a group of compounds with a complex structure. Each compound has the same basic structure, with the exception of one group attached to the cobalt at the center of the corrin ring (**Figure 11.3-8**). Once absorbed, cells of the body convert other forms of vitamin B12 to 5'cyanocobalimin and methylcobalamin, the two active forms of the vitamin. Each of these vitamers has been linked with one enzymatic reaction in the human body [1].

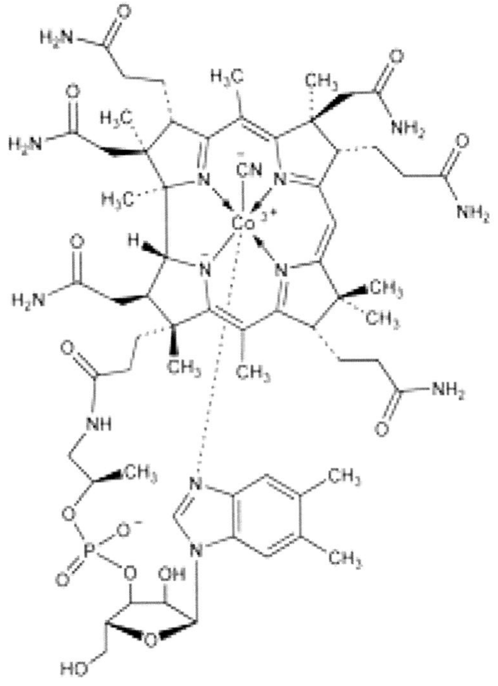

Figure 11.3-8: Structure of cyanocobalamin. The CN group is replaced in other forms of the vitamin.
From https://www.rsc.org/Merck-Index/

the event of deficiency or genetic defect, this mutase enzyme does not function and results in the buildup of methylmalonic acid and methylmalonyl-CoA [1].

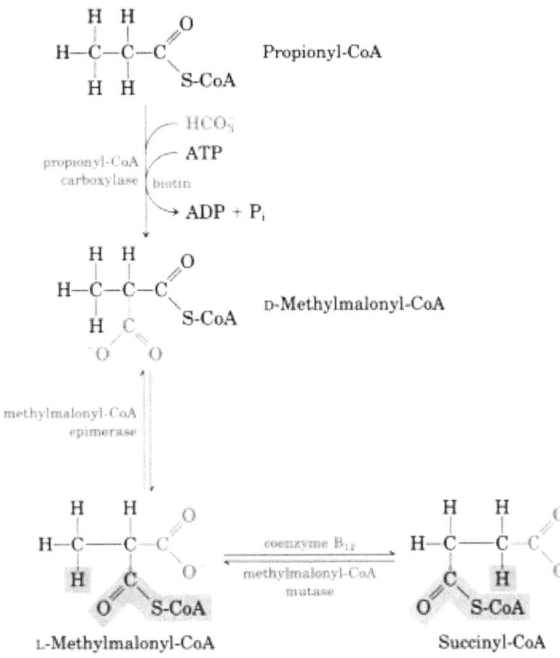

Figure 11.3-9: Role of vitamin B12 in the conversion of methylmalonyl-CoA to succinyl-CoA.
From www. bioinfo.org.cn

11.3.4.1. Functions of Vitamin B12

Methylcobalamin functions in the conversion of homocysteine into methionine as discussed in the section on folate functions (**Figure 11.3-7**). In the cytosol of the cells cobalamin binds to homocysteine methyl transferase and picks up a methyl group from 5- methyl tetrahydrofolate (THF). Then, methionine synthase releases the methyl group to homocysteine converting it to methionine and cobalamin [52].

Vitamin B12 is needed in the form of adenosylcobalamin in the conversion of methylmalonyl-CoA to succinyl-CoA (**Figure 11.3-9**). Two molecules of adenosylcobalamin are required for methylmalonyl-CoA mutase to function properly in the conversion of L-methylmalonyl-CoA to succinyl-CoA, which is an intermediate in the TCA cycle [52]. B12 is the only water soluble vitamin that can be stored in the body for an extended period of time. However, in

11.3.4.2 Vitamin B12 Imbalances

The RDA for adults is 2.4 μg/day, with increases necessary for pregnant or lactating women. Deficiency of vitamin B results in megaloblastic macrocytic anemia, as in the case of folate deficiency. Blood cell production is hampered, and the resulting blood cells are large and immature. Symptoms of vitamin B12 deficiency include fatigue, shortness of breath, insomnia, numbness or tingling in the extremities, and neurological problems such as loss of memory and concentration and trouble with movement. Also, as with folate, Vitamin B12 deficiency results in a high level of homocysteine that is associated with cardiovascular disease. Vitamin B12 deficiency may be due to lack of absorption rather than intake, which can be the problem in pernicious anemia, which is a lack of intrinsic factor, reduced stomach acidity, increased intestinal acidity, and other absorption deficiencies.

There is no evidence of vitamin B12 toxicity, and no UL has been established [1].

11.3.5. Sulfur

Sulfur is a macro-mineral that can be located within the hair, skin and nails, and is produced by the metabolism of the proteins cysteine and methionine. Macro-minerals are essential for homeostatic function of the human body. The main functions of macro-minerals include vitamin metabolism, energy production, bone mineralization, electrolyte and pH balance, digestion, and maintenance of the osmotic pressure of extracellular fluid. Although essential amino acids are not the only source of sulfur in our diet, they are the main sources. Other minor forms include food and drinking water. Sulfur is used in the body as a part of the structure of certain molecules, specifically the vitamins: thiamin and biotin [1].

Due to the fact that the majority of sulfur comes from the metabolism of essential proteins methionine and cysteine, metabolism of sulfur amino acids can result in the production of homo-cysteine and S-adenosylmethionine (SAM), the latter of which is a methyl donor necessary for multiple reactions. The methyl group in this molecule comes from a series of reactions involving vitamin B12 and folate [53].

Sulfur containing antioxidants play an important role in protecting our bodies from oxidative stress. More specifically, glutathione is an antioxidant that neutralizes free radicals that are products of various cellular functions. Glutathione shields the cell by preventing reactions between the reactive oxygen species and the cell's components including DNA synthesis and cell structure [54].

11.3.6. Carotenoids and cell proliferation, growth, and differentiation

Some carotenoids have inhibitory effects on cell proliferation, growth and differentiation. The mechanisms behind these effects are not known, but could be related to the effects of vitamin A on gap junctions as well as increasing connexin proteins between cells. Studies have not shown that increases in carotenoids result in reduced cancer risk [1].

11.3.7. Vitamin E as an inhibitor of oncogenesis

Vitamin E has been recently receiving more attention in the scientific community for its therapeutic role in preventing certain types of cancers [55]. Two possible roles have been postulated for Vitamin E in this anti-cancer effect: as an antioxidant decreasing the damage caused by free radicals and as a modulator of gene expression for cancer producing genes. Cyclin D1 is a protein that interacts with tumor suppressor factors and regulates the cell cycle. Studies have shown that overexpression of cyclin D1 is associated with carcinogenesis. Gamma tocopherol has been shown to decrease gene expression and synthesis of cyclin D1 [3]. By using this underlying mechanism, vitamin E regulates the cell cycle and exerts its cancer-preventing effects.

11.3.7.1. Vitamin E Imbalances

The RDA for adult men and women is 15 mg of alpha tocopherol. Due to the higher levels of reactive oxygen radical production in smokers, their vitamin E requirement is slightly higher than the general population, although separate recommendations have not yet been established. Vitamin E deficiency is uncommon, occurring mainly in people with genetic defects or absorptive disorders. Symptoms include myopathy, hemolytic anemia, and neurological problems. Toxicity is also uncommon, though vitamin E can cause bleeding as well as other symptoms, such as gastrointestinal problems, reduced coagulation of the blood, and muscle weakness. A UL of 1,000 mg of α-tocopherol has been established based on the risk of bleeding [1].

11.3.8. Vitamin D

Vitamin D has long been associated with bone protection and improving skeletal integrity. The interaction of vitamin D and calcium relative to bone formation was discussed in chapter 6. However, vitamin D has many other health benefits. For example, its functions in preventing diabetes, cancer, osteoporosis, and heart disease and in improving neurocognitive functions.

11.3.8.1. Vitamin D and calcium

Vitamin D along with parathyroid hormone plays a major role in maintaining blood calcium homeostasis. When the blood calcium level drops, it triggers the secretion of parathyroid hormone from chief cells of the parathyroid gland. Parathyroid hormone increases the levels of the active vitamin D hormone in the body by stimulating the enzyme 1-α-hydroxylase, which converts 25 hydroxycholecalciferol into 1,25 dihydroxy- cholecalciferol, or calcitriol (the active form of vitamin D). Parathyroid hormone and calcitriol together increase calcium absorption from the intestinal lumen, increase calcium reabsorption from the kidneys while decreasing its excretion in the urine, and promote resorption of calcium and phosphate from bone. All these metabolic effects of parathyroid hormone and vitamin D cumulatively increase blood calcium concentration.

Calcitriol interacts with vitamin D receptors in the cell membrane and nucleus of various tissues. The mechanism of action is best elucidated in the intestine. The process begins with interaction of vitamin D with vitamin D receptors present in the mucosal epithelial cells of intestine. Vitamin D binds with these high affinity receptors, vitamin D binding receptors (VDR) and makes a complex called VDR calcitriol complex. The complex travels to the nucleus where it up-regulates the genes responsible for the production of calcium transport proteins. Vitamin D-VDR complex makes heterodimer complex with the retinoic acid receptor RXR which then binds to the promoter region of DNA on a specific gene. One such gene codes for a protein called Calbindin D9K, a protein responsible for increasing enterocyte calcium absorption and also transporting calcium across the intestinal mucosal cells towards the basolateral membrane. Calcium channels are also up-regulated, such as TRPV6 in the brush border of enterocytes [1].

In the kidney, another calcium transport protein may be synthesized in response to calcitriol to increase reabsorption of calcium. In the bone, calcitriol stimulates osteoblasts to produce a receptor activator that in turn increases production and maturation of osteoclasts. Osteoclasts then increase their activity to break down bone and release calcium and phosphorous into the blood [1].

11.3.8.2. Other roles for calcitriol

Vitamin D has a wide variety of other functions, some of which have more evidence than others. Calcitriol has been shown to stimulate differentiation of blood cells and stem cells while also being able to prevent proliferation of certain cell types, such as fibroblasts, keratinocytes, and lymphocytes. Calcitriol also may have a role in preventing abnormal proliferation in certain cancers. Autoimmune disorders may be connected to calcitriol levels, as it can decrease production of certain inflammatory cytokines. Vitamin D deficiency has potential links with many other diseases, such as rheumatoid arthritis, multiple sclerosis, and type 1 diabetes, among others [1].

11.3.8.3. Vitamin D Imbalance

An AI has been set for vitamin D instead of RDA because of the difficulty in assessing cutaneous synthesis of vitamin D, which depends on several variables and significantly differs from person to person. The RDA for vitamin D is 600 I.U. (15 μg) per day for individual 1 to 70 years old, and increases to 800 I.U (20 μg) for people over 70 years. Deficiency of vitamin D results in serious problems with bone development and structure. In children, seizure, slow growth, and soft, unmineralized bones occur in a disease called rickets. Long bones and the spine tend to curve, and joints are large as bone formation does not occur properly. In adults, vitamin D deficiency results in osteomalacia, a condition that weakens the bone as osteoclasts resorb calcium and phosphate, leading to bones lacking sufficient mineralization. Bones become softer and can lead to pain and fracturing. Adequate sunlight can correct a vitamin D deficiency, but malabsorptive conditions such as Crohn's disease can reduce vitamin D absorption, even though intake is normal. Large doses of vitamin D can boost vitamin D status over time [1].

Vitamin D toxicity can occur in response to high dietary intake or supplements, but not from overexposure to the sun. Symptoms of toxicity include anorexia, vomiting, high blood pressure, and a general failure to thrive. This hypercalcemia can lead to calcification of soft tissues, high levels of phosphate in the blood, renal problems, and death if the high level of intake continues over a period of months. The UL is set at 100 μg or 4000 I.U. per day [56].

11.3.9. Vitamin E in immune differentiation

Studies have shown that vitamin E influences many aspects of immune function. Vitamin E controls the gene expression of various proteins, factors, interleukins and cytokines that take part during the process of inflammation. For example, vitamin E reduces the expression of genes responsible for making integrin, which plays a major role in leucocyte adhesion during the process of inflammation [3]. The active form of vitamin E, α-tocopherol, also reduces the gene expression and hence the formation of a receptor protein CD 11 b, resulting in reduced adhesion of monocytes to the vascular endothelial cells. Alpha-tocopherol also decreases the expression of genes responsible for making Interleukin 1 B (IL-1B), which is a pro-inflammatory cytokine and an important mediator of inflammation. Vitamin E also reduces the expression of genes encoding Glycoprotein II B, a stimulator (a receptor) for the aggregation of platelets. By this mechanism, vitamin E reduces platelet aggregation, diminishing another contributing factor in the development of atherosclerosis.

Vitamin E has also been shown to increase the secretion of IL-2 and interferon γ by T cells, cytokines exhibiting low serum levels in advanced colorectal cancer patients. Hence vitamin E may have an anticancer role via immune regulation as well [57].

11.3.10. Iodine

Iodine only has one known function, which involves its incorporation to the thyroid hormones, triiodothryronine and thyroxine. Thyroxine has important roles in regulation of metabolic rate and cellular functions during growth and development. Iodine is essential for normal growth and development in utero and in early life. Deficiencies can lead to the enlargement of the thyroid gland, referred to as a goiter. Many of the effects of iodide on growth appear to work through growth hormone (GH) and insulin-like growth factor (IGF) [58]. While it is clear

these other hormones can affect insulin signaling and the development of metabolic diseases, there does not appear to be a specific role for iodine outside of its necessity for thyroid function.

Iodine that is taken in as part of diet can be either bound with amino acids, or alternatively, exist as free forms of iodate or iodide. Organically bound iodide can also become free through the process of digestion. Free iodine in the form of iodate (often contained in bread products) can be reduced to iodide with the aid of glutathione. Iodinated amino acids are absorbed inefficiently compared to free iodine in the anionic forms [1].

Poor dietary supply of iodine is the most common cause of endemic goiter and cretinism. The antithyroid actions of the goitrogens are related to the existence of thioglucosides. After digestion, they release thiocyanate and isothiocyanate. Thiocyanate is a goitrogenic agent that inhibits thyroid iodide transport. Cyanoglucosides are other important groups of goitrogens that release cyanide after ingestion, which is detoxified to thiocyanate [59].

There are health consequences beyond goiter that can occur from an iodine deficiency. In a fetus, iodine deficiency can result in abortion, stillbirth, congenital anomalies, and perinatal mortality. In a neonate, iodine deficiency can result in infant mortality and endemic cretinism. In a child or adolescent, these deficiencies can result in impaired mental function and delayed physical development. Finally, in adults, these iodine deficiencies could result in reduced work productivity, impaired mental function, decreased educability, and apathy.

More than 90% of dietary iodine will eventually appear in urine. Because of this, urinary iodine (UI) is an outstanding indicator of the recent intake of iodine. The UI can be expressed compared to creatinine excretion (microgram iodine per gram creatinine) or as 24-hour excretion (micrograms per day). In some populations, it could be difficult and impractical to collect 24-hour samples in field studies. In these populations, UI can be measures in spot urine specimens for a sample group. The median UI from a sample can be used to classify a population's iodine sample. The UI can sometimes be misunderstood because individual iodine intakes can be very different from day to day. One common mistake that is made is assuming that any subject with a spot UI less than 100 μg per day is iodine deficient.

To get a more accurate collection, several 24-hour collections are preferable, but would be very difficult to obtain. Also, creatinine, for daily iodine excretion, may be unreliable with spot samples. In malnourished populations, creatinine concentration may be low [59].

There are only a few countries that were completely iodine sufficient before 1990. These countries include Switzerland, some of the Scandinavian countries, the United States, and Canada. At least twelve countries now have optimum iodine status. Iodine deficiency still remains a public-health problem in 47 countries. Even in Australia and the United States the iodine intake is decreasing. More than 17 million babies who have brain damage caused by iodine deficiency are born in the region of south Asia every year. Iodized salt is a major source of iodine, but in this region, it is a challenge to increase the coverage.

11.3.11. Chloride

There are approximately 105 grams of chloride in the body. Chloride is almost always ingested with sodium, as sodium chloride. It can also be ingested as potassium chloride salt, magnesium salt, and calcium chloride. Potassium chloride is used as a substitute for table salt. It is a major electrolyte that aids in normal function of the digestive tract, phagocytosis, and pH balance [60].

During digestion, chloride is secreted from the parietal cells of the stomach accompanied by protons that are secreted as well. Because chloride and hydrogen ions do not readily bind, the result is hydrochloric acid, a powerful digestive acid that is secreted into the stomach to begin the breakdown of food. Cells also secrete chloride as a defense mechanism; it is used to fight foreign substances found in the plasma [1]. Lastly, it plays a part in the excretion of CO_2 from the blood. This is known as the chloride bicarbonate exchanger and is illustrated in **figure 11.3-10 [61]**. The entrance of chloride into the cell in exchange for bicarbonate allows for the bicarbonate to be excreted as CO_2 from the lungs. A recent study by Hilgen *et al.* has shown that inhibition of the chloride bicarbonate exchange in the retina may cause visual damage in mice [62]. The effect of lowered chloride-bicarbonate exchange activity within individuals in relation to visual impairments deserves further study.

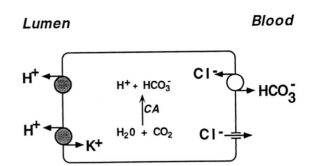

Figure 11.3-10: Chloride-bicarbonate exchange.

Dietary chloride deficiency has occurred in infants fed chloride deficient infant formula for a period of time in the 1978-79, and more recently (2005-2008) in older children or adults in Japan. Symptoms include metabolic alkalosis, loss of appetite, failure to thrive or weight loss, muscle weakness, and lethargy [63,64]. These products that were designed as total diet replacements have largely been withdrawn form markets or reformulated. Chloride deficiency in a free living population is rare, since intakes of salt, mostly from processed food, usually exceeds sodium or chloride needs by a wide margin [42].

11.3.12. Zinc

Most zinc is stored within cells. Zinc has broad effect on metabolism as a whole. It is essential for catalytic activity, structure, and regulation. Due to the fact that zinc is involved in such a large variety of functions, it is difficult to identify an exact function that is most limiting or affected first by a zinc deficiency. It interacts with multiple proteins, including zinc-finger proteins that bind DNA and regulate gene transcription, and modulates the kinetics of many enzymes. The body goes to great lengths to conserve zinc once it is removed from the diet, including the catabolism of muscle to reach intracellular stores [65].

Removal of zinc from the diet results in multiple effects including skin lesions and diarrhea. Zinc is especially important for growth. Malnourished children are often zinc deficient and supplementation, provided there is adequate protein, can restore weight gain [66]. It may also have cardiovascular effects that could reflect metabolic mechanisms. Men given zinc supplementation as part of a normal diet displayed marginally improved exercise performance compared to their performance on a low zinc diet [67].

Perhaps the most profound effects of zinc occur in the immune system. Zinc deficiency leads to lymphopenia and predisposes individuals to infection. Mouse models of zinc deficiency show a dramatic increase in cell apoptosis in developing T cells [68]. It is also critical for normal immune cell development, including B and T cells. It affects cells of the innate immune system as well, including neutrophils and macrophages [69]. Studies are just beginning to tread upon the importance of immune cell metabolism in generating adequate responses, such as the development of memory T cells [70]. Future research will likely identify ways in which zinc modulates these processes.

Aside from modulating the immune system and being an essential nutrient for growth and development, there is some evidence that zinc can affect glucose metabolism. Mice with a targeted deletion of ZnT8 in pancreatic β cells provide evidence for a zinc requirement in glucose homeostasis. ZnT8 deficient mice had impaired glucose tolerance and fewer insulin crystals [71]. A meta-analysis of zinc supplementation concluded that zinc supplementation had a small but significant effect on fasting glucose in type II diabetic and obese individuals [72].

11.4.1. Vitamin A and vision

Vitamin A makes up part of the pigment rhodopsin that is required in the rods of the retina for night vision. When light hits the retina in a dark environment, rhodopsin is split into opsin and *cis*-retinal, which is then converted to *trans*-retinal. To maintain vision, rhodopsin must be reformed by the reattachment of *cis*-retinal, made from the *trans*-retinal in the retina (**Figure 11.4.1**) [1].

11.4.2. Vitamin A imbalances

The RDA for vitamin A is 625 mg RAE for adult men and 500 mg RAE for adult women. Deficiency has a range of symptoms, including xerophthalmia, which involves dryness and other abonormalities of the eye, anorexia, slow growth, and epithelial conditions such as keratinization and lack of differentiation. Night blindness is also common in cases of inadequate vitamin A intake. Vitamin A deficiency leads to the formation of fewer numbers of goblet cells which results in inadequate amount of mucus production [1]. Vitamin A deficiency has also been

shown to have a strong correlation with the development of infections. There are consistent data showing that patients suffering from xerophthalmia also tend to have increased incidence of respiratory tract infections, for example, pneumonia and other

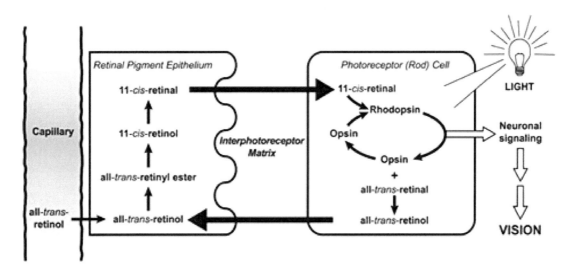

Figure 11.4-1: Role of Vitamin A in the visual cycle.
From lpi.oregonstate.edu

diseases of infectious origin such as measles and diarrhea [51]. Due to vitamin A's effects on the immune system, vitamin A deficient patients also have impaired phagocytic activity of neutrophils.

Excess intake of vitamin A can also cause health problems. Short-term high intake leads to acute hypervitaminosis A that involves gastrointestinal upset, headache, lightheadedness, double vision, and skin problems. High intake in the long term results in hypervitaminosis A, the symptoms of which include skin dryness, itchiness, anorexia, hair loss, headache, bone and muscle pain, fractures, eye pain, and liver damage. In pregnant women, high levels of vitamin A can induce birth defects. The UL for preformed vitamin A is 3,000 μg/day [1].

11.5. Ultratrace Minerals

11.5.1. Introduction

This section will explain the role that the ultratrace minerals, arsenic and vanadium, play in metabolic functioning. The manner in which the body absorbs, utilizes, and excretes these crucial nutrients will be examined. The implications of a deficiency of these ultratrace nutrients are not well understood for humans, because both the concentrations in tissues and the apparent requirement, if essentiality even exists, is extremely small.

11.5.2. Arsenic

Arsenic strikes fear into the minds of many at its very mention, as the mineral has been associated with toxicity and a variety of serious maladies in the industrial world. However, arsenic does play a nutritional role in the human body, specifically with regard to forming and usage of the methyl groups [1].

Arsenic is found in variety of places on earth in different concentrations. Arsenic's presence in the geographical features of different regions depends greatly on the geological history and formation of a region's water, rocks, and soil. Human activity has also resulted in arsenic intake in the bodies of humans. Chemical sources, such as pesticides, have caused the mineral to seep into food stores. Both organic and inorganic forms of arsenic are prevalent in water and food. Arsenic chiefly comes in the form of either trivalent arsenic or pentavalent arsenic. Arsenic present in water is predominantly found in the pentavalent arsenate or trivalent arsenite compositions [1].

Moreover, methylated arsenic is also a prevalent form of the mineral. This form of arsenic is heavily associated with rice, which is consumed in large quantities the world over, but especially so in Asia. Methylated arsenic happens to be less toxic than other forms of the mineral, and is commonly found in plant foods, but potentially comes from microorganisms and is not produced by the plant itself [73]. While inorganic forms of arsenite and trivalent organoarsenicals are found to be the most toxic forms, the pentavalent, methylated arsenic forms are less damaging [1].

11.5.2.1. Absorption

The absorption of the various compounds of arsenic depends on the specific chemistry and solubility of the compound being ingested by the body. Inorganic arsenic enters the body as arsenate and arsenite [1]. Much of the absorption from these two inorganic compounds comes from the ingestion of water.

Beer is an example of a food source containing arsenical compounds [74], in both inorganic and organic forms of the element. Arsenical levels different brands of beers were between 1.5 and 12.4 μg/l. While inorganic arsenicals are present in beer as legacy from the production process, organic species of the element are far more predominant.

Absorption of arsenicals occurs by simple diffusion into intestinal mucosa [1]. Lipid solubility varies among arsenical compounds, and this trait helps to aid absorption by diffusion [75]. Both organic and inorganic arsenicals travel from the intestines through the blood to the liver. Organic arsenic is not heavily metabolized in the liver, while inorganic arsenicals are reduced to trivalent arsenite and then become methylated into monomethylarsonic acid by the enzyme arsenite methyltransferase. Other metabolites of inorganic arsenicals include dimethylarsinic acid, formed by monomethylarsonic acid methyltransferase.

Glutathione, choline, and S-adenosylmethionine donate the methyl groups to form arsenical compounds. The last step in a significant proportion of arsenical metabolism includes the formation of toxic dimethylarsenious acid [1].

11.5.2.2. Function

Research indicates that arsenic is an important part of forming and utilizing the methyl groups from S-adenosylmethonine, which helps the body to synthesize important compounds. S-adenosylmethionine, or 'SAM', also functions to methylate compounds in preparation for DNA synthesis [1]. Deficiencies of arsenic can result in metabolic stress when the trace amounts of the mineral required by the body are not present. Arsenic deficiency in humans manifests as impairment in the metabolism of methionine, which causes a lower SAM concentration and less actvity of its enzyme [1]. Arsenic deficient rodents have been found to exhibit a lower production of the nutrient taurine from the process of methionine [75, 76]. General lack of growth was evident in arsenic deficient rats [77]. Arsenic deficiency can result in an impaired sythesis of polyamines, which depends on SAM [1]. Furthermore, arsenic has been found to play a role in gene expression, as arsenic deficiencies have been shown to affect heat shock proteins, a secondary effect on histone methylation [78].

11.5.2.3. Interactions, Excretion, and Nutriture

Arsenic metabolites may compete with selenium for uptake and tissue retention compete due to the fact that selenate and arsenate are oxyanions with strikingly similar chemical makeup [1]. Arsenic exits the body mainly through the kidneys, with monomethylarsinic acid, dimethylarsinic acid, and trimethylated arsenic all present in urine [1, 79]. Organic arsenites result in arsenobetaine and arsenocholine being present in the urinary excretion as well [80]. The amount of urine excreted daily by healthy adults is extremely low, at less than 50 μg per day [1]. Data are insufficient to set any of the Dietary Reference Intake values for arsenic [23]. Arsenic toxicity, is often initially felt in the gastrointestinal system in the form of gastrointestinal distress. Chronic toxicity symptoms include but are not limited to hyperpigmentation of the skin, hyperkeratosis, weakness in the muscles, neuropathy in the peripheral regions, uncontrolled sweating in large amounts, damage to the liver, psychological distress including delirium, encephalopathy, changes to vascular functioning in the body, and a variety of cancers including oral, skin, colon, lungs, kidney, and bladder cancers [1].

11.5.3. Vanadium

Vanadium (V) is an ultra trace mineral that has long been shown to be present in nearly all-living tissues of plants and animals. As far as minerals go, V is one of the more mysterious elements. The essentiality of V to humans has not been proven and specific roles in metabolism are not fully clear; yet the presence of V does appear to influence human health. V has been investigated continually due to an observed ability to mimic the effects of insulin in cell and animal models. There is danger of V toxicity, but is not relevant because of the amounts found in food are much lower than the UL.

V is a group 5 transition metal with complexes that exist in 8 oxidation states (-3, -1, 0, +1, +2, +3, +4 and +5), under physiological pH the only relevant oxidation states are +5, +4 and +3. Many foods contain low levels of V, but the foods with the highest concentration of V (greater than 100 ng/g) are mushrooms, parsley, dill, oysters, and black pepper [81]. Absorption of V is very inefficient, with only about 5% of ingested V entering circulation, with the majority of absorption located in the upper GI tract. Unabsorbed V will move through the GI tract and will be excreted in feces. When absorbed V is bound to transferrin or phosphate binding proteins and approximately 40- 60% is excreted through the urine in 24 hours. The normal serum concentrations of V are 1-2 μg V/L. So far there have yet to be any known homeostatic regulation mechanisms in humans for V.

In higher animals there has yet to be an identified specific biochemical function. However, there have been outlined functions of V in microbes in nitrogenase that functions to reduce nitrogen to ammonia as well as haloperoxidase function allowing for oxidation of halide ions [81]. Because there have been no definitive outlined functions of V in humans there have been no definitive nutritional deficiency symptoms of V.

Some reported deficiency symptoms in goats have shown higher rates of spontaneous abortion and lower levels of milk production during lactation. Also V deficiency in rats was found to increase thyroid weight and decrease the activity of thyroid peroxidase. This suggests that V plays a role in thyroid function. Data show that V can be an inhibitor of potassium sodium ATPase pumps [82].

In patients with insulin problems V supplementation has been investigated as a therapy for lowering high blood glucose levels. This action has been attributed to the ability of V to compete with phosphate for the active site of certain phosphatases, tyrosine phosphorylases, and phosphate transport proteins. In experimental models when V was administered in absence of insulin it was able to lower blood glucose levels [83, 84]. V does not appear to be able to replace insulin action, but rather activates insulin receptors [81]. The multiple physiological valence states of V provide different supplementation options in diabetic patients. The major obstacle to outright supplementation of V to diabetic patients has been determining an adequate treatment dose and managing the symptoms of V toxicity [84].

The toxicity of V requires greater than 10 mg/day. The signs of toxicity are gastrointestinal distress and tongue turning green. Different types of V offer different levels of toxicity, generally the higher the valence the more toxic the form. There is concern about V accumulation into bones over chronic exposure; however there is no evidence that proves this association to be outright harmful. No DRI values have been set for V, so there are many recommended levels of V consumption. On average US adults take in 10-60 µg/day [85]; suggestions for adequate V consumption levels are anywhere from 10-100 µg/day [81, 85], so most people in the US meet the required amount.

11.6. Summary – Mineral Nutrients

The major macro-minerals that were discussed are essential to the homeostatic function of the human body. They comprise the skeletal structure, as well as nerve and muscle functions. Many of the major minerals are interrelated in their functions. The calcium, phosphorus, and magnesium macro-minerals are interconnected due to their influence on pH and electrolyte balance. Lastly, sulfur plays an integral role in antioxidant functions, protecting our cells from oxidative damage and free radicals that are produced from other metabolic functions.

Trace minerals are an essential component of nutrition. Many metabolic processes rely on trace elements to act as cofactors for specific enzymes. The effect of these nutrients on different aspects of metabolic disease ranges from extensive, with respect to iron and chromium, to poorly understood, with respect molybdenum. Translating much of the basic biochemical work from model microbial systems remains a challenge. In general, these minerals work by changing oxidation states, allowing them to bind free electrons, or stabilize structures via charge based interactions. Future work will examine how metabolic diseases, such as type II diabetes, are affected by these minerals, and what role these minerals can play in disease prevention. The central role of metabolism in many cellular processes, from immune function to carcinogenesis, makes the elucidation of the nutrients that drive these processes of critical importance.

Less is known about recommended intakes and roles of ultratrace minerals in metabolic functioning. Arsenic for example, plays a role in sustaining life through S- adenosyl-methionine functions, but is more commonly viewed as a serious toxic mineral.

11.7. References Cited

1. Jacob, R. A. and Sotoudeh, G. (2002), Vitamin C function and status in chronic disease. *Nutrition in Clinical Care*, 5(2): 66-74. doi: 10.1046/j.1523-5408.2002.00005.x

2. Azzi A, Gysin R, Kempná P, Munteanu A, Negis Y, Villacorta L, Visarius T, Zingg J-M. (2006) Vitamin E mediates cell signaling and regulation of gene expression, *Annals of the New York Academy of Sciences*. 1031(1), 86 – 95

3. Mehdi,Y, Hornick J-L, Istasse LI, and Dufrasne I. (2013) Selenium in the environment, metabolism and involvement in body functions." *Molecules* 18(3): 3292-3311..

4. Beckett GJ & Arthur JR (2005) Selenium and endocrine systems. *J Endocrinol* 184: 455-465.

5. Haas, R H. Thiamin and the Brain. (1988) *Annual Review of Nutrition* 8(1):483-515-

6. Mattevi A, Obmolova G, Schulze E, Kalk KH, Westphal AH, de Kok A, Hol WG. (1992) Atomic structure of the cubic core of the pyruvate dehydrogenase multienzyme complex. *Science.* 255(5051):1544-50.

7. Schenk G, Duggleby RG, Nixon PF, (1998) Properties and functions of the thiamin diphosphate dependent enzyme transketolase, *The International Journal of Biochemistry & Cell Biology*, 30(12): 1297-1318,

8. Lonsdale D, (2006) A review of the biochemistry, metabolism and clinical benefits of thiamin(e) and its derivatives. *Evid Based Complement Alternat Med.* 3(1): 49–59.

9. Food and Nutrition Board, Institute of Medicine. *Thiamin. Dietary Reference Intakes: Thiamin, Riboflavin, Niacin, Vitamin B$_6$, Vitamin B$_{12}$, Pantothenic Acid, Biotin, and Choline.* Washington D.C.: National Academy Press; 1998:58- 86.

10. Russell RM, Suter PM. (1993) Vitamin requirements of elderly people: an update. *American Journal of Clinical Nutrition.* 58(1):4 14.

11. Vuorilehto K , Lutz S., Wandrey C, (2004) Indirect electrochemical reduction of nicotinamide coenzymes, *Bioelectrochemistry*, 65,(1):1-7,

12. Lutsenko S, Barnes NL, Bartee MY et al. (2007) Function and regulation of human copper-transporting ATPases. *Physiol Rev* 87, 1011-1046.

13. Tumer Z & Moller LB (2010) Menkes disease. *Eur J Hum Genet* 18: 511-518.

14. Huster D (2010) Wilson disease. *Best Pract Res Clin Gastroenterol* 24: 531-539.

15. Matoba S, Kang JG, Patino WD et al. (2006) p53 regulates mitochondrial respiration. *Science* 312, 1650-1653.

16. Freund H, Atamian S & Fischer JE (1979) Chromium deficiency during total parenteral nutrition. *JAMA* 241: 496-498.

17. Wang H, Kruszewski A & Brautigan DL (2005) Cellular chromium enhances activation of insulin receptor kinase. *Biochemistry* 44, 8167-8175.

18. Peng Z, Qiao W, Wang Z et al. (2010) Chromium improves protein deposition through regulating the mRNA levels of IGF-1, IGF-1R, and Ub in rat skeletal muscle cells. *Biol Trace Elem Res* 137: 226-234. 348

19. Tuzcu M, Sahin N, Orhan C et al. (2011) Impact of chromium histidinate on high fat diet induced obesity in rats. *Nutrition & Metabolism* 8:28-36.

20. Diaz ML, Watkins BA, Li Y et al. (2008) Chromium picolinate and conjugated linoleic acid do not synergistically influence diet- and exercise-induced changes in body composition and health indexes in overweight women. *J Nutr Biochem* 19: 61- 68.

21. Balk EM, Tatsioni A, Lichtenstein AH et al. (2007) Effect of chromium supplementation on glucose metabolism and lipids: a systematic review of randomized controlled trials. *Diabetes Care* 30: 2154-2163.

22. Institute of Medicine, Food and Nutrition Board, *Dietary Reference Intakes for Vitamin A, Vitamin K, Arsenic, Boron, Chromium, Copper, Iodine, Iron, Manganese, Molybdenum, Nickel, Silicon, Vanadium, and Zinc.* Washington, D.C.: National Academy Press. 2001.

23. Kones, R. (1990). Molybdenum in human nutrition. *Journal of the National Medical Association*, *82*(1):11,32,40,53. Retrieved from http://www.ncbi.nlm.nih.gov/pmc/articles/PMC2625930/?page=5

24. Schwarz, G. (2006). Molybdenum cofactor biosynthesis and molybdenum enzymes. *Annual Review of Plant Biology*, *57*: 623-647. Retrieved from http://www.annualreviews.org.ezproxy.lib.vt.edu:8080/doi/full/10.1146/annurev.arplant.57.032905.105437

25. Schwarz G, Mendel RR & Ribbe MW (2009) Molybdenum cofactors, enzymes and pathways. *Nature* 460: 839-847.

26. Rajagopalan, K. V. (1988). Molybdenum: An essential trace element in human nutrition. *Annual Review of Nutrition*, 8: 401-427. Retrieved

from http://www.annualreviews.org.ezproxy. lib.vt.edu:8080/doi/pdf/10.1146/annurev.nu. 08.070188.002153

27. Turnland, J. (2004). Plasma molybdenum reflects dietary molybdenum intake. *The Journal of Nutritional Biochemistry, 15*(2): 90-95.

28. Reiss, J. (1999). Molybdenum cofactor deficiency: first prenatal genetic analysis. *Prenatal Diagnosis, 4*: 386-388.

29. Dhar SK & St Clair DK (2012) Manganese superoxide dismutase regulation and cancer. *Free Radic Biol Med* 52: 2209-2222.

30. Sarsour EH, Kalen AL, Xiao Z et al. (2012) Manganese superoxide dismutase regulates a metabolic switch during the mammalian cell cycle. *Cancer Res* 72: 3807-3816.

31. Cullen JJ, Weydert C, Hinkhouse MM et al. (2003) The role of manganese superoxide dismutase in the growth of pancreatic adenocarcinoma. *Cancer Res* 63, 1297-1303.

32. Appel, LJ., Baker DJ, Bar-Or O, Morris C, Resnick LM, Sawka MN, Volpe SL, Weinberger MH, and Whelton PK. *Dietary Reference Intakes for Water, Potassium, Sodium, Chloride, and Sulfate.* Washington DC: Nation Academic Pres, 2005. PDF file. <http://www.nap.edu/catalog/10925. html>.

33. Pamnani M, Bryant H, Clough D, & Schooley J. (2003). Increased dietary potassium and magnesium attenuate experimental volume dependent hypertension possibly through endogenous sodium-potassium pump inhibitor. *Clinical & Experimental Hypertension, 25*(2): 103.

34. Martini, L. A., Catania, A. S., & Ferreira, S. G. (2010). Role of vitamins and minerals in prevention and management of type 2 diabetes mellitus. *Nutrition Reviews, 68*(6): 341-354. doi:10.1111/ j.1753-4887.2010.00296.x

35. Lehnhardt, A., & Kemper, M. (2011). Pathogenesis, diagnosis and management of hyperkalemia. *Pediatric Nephrology, 26*(3): 377-384. doi:10.1007/ s00467-010-1699- 3

36. Me, HH, Rice TK, Gu DD, Hixson JE, Jaquish C E, Qi Z, & ... He JJ. (2011). Genetic correlation of blood pressure responses to dietary sodium and potassium intervention and cold pressor test in Chinese population. *Journal of Human Hypertension,* 25(8): 500-508. doi:10.1038/jhh.2010.88

37. Wang ZM, Pierson RN,Heymsfield SB. (1992) The five-level model: a new approach to organizing body composition research. *Am J. Clin Nutr.* 56: 19-28..

38. Knight GS, Beddoe AH, Streat SL, Hill GL. Body composition of two human cadavers by neutron activation and chemical analysis. *Am J Physiol Endocrinol Metab* [internet]. 1986; 250(2):E179-185.

39. Ellis KJ. Human body composition: in vivo methods. (2000) *Physiol Rev Suppl* [internet]. 80(2):649-680.

40. 41. Wang AM, Shen W, Kotler DP, Heshka S, Wielopolski L, Aloia JF, Nelson ME, Pierson RN, Heymsfield SB. (2003) Total body protein: a new cellular level mass and distribution prediction model. *Am J Clin Nutr* [internet].78:979-984.

41. Otten JJ, Hellwig JP, Meyers L. *Dietary Reference Intakes: The Essential Guide to Nutrient Requirements.* The National Academies; 2006. Available from http://www.nap.edu/ catalog/11537.html.

42. Gelse K, Pöschl E, AignerT. (2003). Collagens—structure, function, and biosynthesis. *Advanced Drug Delivery Reviews,* 55(12): 1531-1546, Retrieved from: <http:// www.sciencedirect.com/science/article/pii/ S0169409X03001820>

43. Gaine PC, Pikosky MA, Martin WF, Bolster DR, Maresh CM, Rodriguez NR. (2006) Level of dietary protein impacts whole body protein turnover in trained males at rest. *Metabolism* [internet]. 55: 501-507.

44. Woodley DT, Keene DR, Atha T, Huang Y, Lipman K., Li W, Chen M (2004) Injection of recombinant human Type VII collagen restores collagen

function in Dystrophic Epidermolysis Bullosa." *Nature Medicine* 10(7): 693-5

45. Hubbard S, Till J. (2000). Protein tyrosine kinase structure and function." *Annual Review of Biochemistry*, 69:373-98.

46. Mertins P, Eberl HC, Renkawitz J, et. al. (2008). Investigation of protein-tyrosine phosphatase 1B function by quantitative proteomics." *Molecular & Cellular Proteomics*, 7(9): 1763-777. Retrieved from: <http://www.mcponline.org.prox.lib.ncsu.edu/content/7/9/1763.full>.

47. Wyatt L, Wadham C, Crocker LA, Lardelli M., Khew-Goodall Y. (2007). The protein tyrosine phosphatase Pez regulates TGFβ, epithelial–mesenchymal transition, and organ development." *Journal of Cell Biology*, 178(7): 1223-1235.

48. Love JM, Gudas LJ. (1994) Vitamin A, differentiation and cancer, *Current Opinion in Cell Biology*, 6(6): 825 - 831.

49. Allende LM, Corell A, Madrono A, Gongor R, Rodriguez-Gallego C, Lopez-Goyanes A, Rosal M, Arnaiz-Villena A. (1997) Retinol (vitamin A) is a cofactor in CD3-induced human T- lymphocyte activation. *Immunology* 90(3): 388-96.51. Stephensen CB. (2001) Vitamin A, infection, and immune function, *Annual Review of Nutrition* 21(1): 167-192.52. Shane B. (2012) Folate responsive birth defects: of mice and women. *Am J Clin Nutr* 95(1): 1-2. DOI 10.3945/AJCN.111.0295015.

50. Klee GG. (2000) Cobalamin and folate evaluation: measurement of methyl- malonic acid and homocysteine vs vitamin B_{12} and folate. *Clin Chem* 46:12771277

51. Hébert, A., Forquin-Gomez, M., Roux, A., Aubert, J., Junot, C., Loux, V., & ... Landaud, S. (2011). Exploration of sulfur metabolism in the yeast *Kluyveromyces lactis*. *Applied Microbiology & Biotechnology*, 91(5), 1409-1423. doi:10.1007/s00253-011-3481-2

52. Waggiallah H, & Alzohairy M. (2011). The effect of oxidative stress on human red cells glutathione peroxidase, glutathione reductase level, and prevalence of anemia among diabetics. *North American Journal of Medical Sciences*, 3(7), 344-347. doi:10.4297/najms.2011.3344

53. Klein EA, Lippman SM, Thompson IM, Goodman PJ, Albanes D, Taylor P. (2003) The selenium and vitamin E cancer prevention trial *World journal of urology*, 21(1): 21– 27

54. Ross AC, Taylor CL, Yaktine AL, DelValle HB. (2011) *Dietary Reference Intakes: Calcium, Vitamin D.* Washington DC: National Academies Press.

55. Pekmezci D. (2011) Vitamin E and immunity. *Vitamins and hormones*, 86:179-215.

56. 58. Zimmermann MB (2009) Iodine deficiency. *Endocr Rev* 30, 376-408.

57. Delange, F. (1994). The disorders induced by iodine deficiency. Thyroid, 4(1), 107- 128.60. EFSA Panel on Dietetic Products, Nutrition and Allergies (NDA) Scientific Opinion on the substantiation of health claims related to chloride as Na-, K-

58. , Ca-, or Mg-salt and contribution to normal digestion by production of hydrochloric acid in the stomach (ID 326) pursuant to Article 13(1) of Regulation (EC) No 1924/2006: Chloride as Na-, K-, Ca- or Mg salt and contribution to normal digestion by production of hydrochloric acid in the stomach. *EFSA Journal*, 8(10):1764.

59. 61. Karet FE; Gainza FJ; Györy AZ; Unwin RJ; Wrong O; Tanner MJ; Nayir A; Alpay H; Santos F; Hulton SA; Bakkaloglu A; Ozen S; Cunningham MJ; di Pietro A; Walker WG; Lifton, R. (1998). Mutations in the chloride-bicarbonate exchanger gene AE1 cause autosomal dominant but not autosomal recessive distal renal tubular acidosis. *Proceedings of the National Academy of Sciences*, 95(11):6337-6342.

60. Hilgen G; Huebner AK; Tanimoto N; Sothilingam V; Seide C; Garrido MG; Schmidt KF; Seeliger MW; Löwel S; Weiler R; Hübner CA; Dedek, K. (2012). Lack of the sodium-driven chloride bicarbonate exchanger NCBE impairs visual function in the mouse retina. *Plos One*, 7(10): e46155. doi:10.1371/journal.pone.0046155346(1980)

61. King JC (2011) Zinc: an essential but elusive nutrient. *Am J Clin Nutr* 94: 679S- 684S.

62. Golden MH & Golden BE (1981) Effect of zinc supplementation on the dietary intake, rate of weight gain, and energy cost of tissue deposition in children recovering from severe malnutrition. *Am J Clin Nutr* 34: 900-908.

63. Lukaski HC (2005) Low dietary zinc decreases erythrocyte carbonic anhydrase activities and impairs cardiorespiratory function in men during exercise. *Am J Clin Nutr* 81: 1045-1051.

64. Fraker PJ (2005) Roles for cell death in zinc deficiency. *J Nutr* 135: 359-362.

65. Shankar AH & Prasad AS (1998) Zinc and immune function: the biological basis of altered resistance to infection. *Am J Clin Nutr* 68: 447S-463S.

66. van der Windt GJ, Everts B, Chang CH et al. (2012) Mitochondrial respiratory capacity is a critical regulator of CD8+ T cell memory development. *Immunity* 36: 68-78.

67. Wijesekara N, Dai FF, Hardy AB et al. (2010) Beta cell-specific Znt8 deletion in mice causes marked defects in insulin processing, crystallisation and secretion. *Diabetologia* 53: 1656-1668.

68. Capdor J, Foster M, Petocz P Sammon S. (2012) Zinc and glycemic control: A meta-analysis of randomised placebo controlled supplementation trials in humans. *J*

69. *Trace Elem Med Biol.* 27(2): 137-142.

70. Lomax C, Liu W., Wu L., Xue K, Xiong J, Zhou J, et al. (2012) Methylated arsenic species in plants originate from soil microorganisms. *New Phytologist* 193(3): 665– 672.

71. Herce-Pagliai C, González G, Camean,AM., & Repetto M. (1999) Presence and distribution of arsenical species in beers. *Food additives and contaminants*, 16(6): 267–71. doi:10.1080/026520399284037

72. Nielsen, F. (1993) Ultratrace elements of possible importance for human health: An update. In: Prasad AS (ed.) *Essential and Toxic Trace Elements in Human Health*.Wiley-Liss., Inc. (Prog Clin Biol Res. 1993;380:355-76.)

73. Uthus E. (1992) Evidence for arsenic essentiality. *Environmental Geochemistry and Health*, 14(2):55-58.

74. Uthus E. (1993) Determination of the possible requirement and reference dose level for arsenic in humans. *Scandanavian Journal of Work Environment Health*, 19: 137– 8.

75. Desrosiers R, & Tanguay R. (1986) Further characterization of the posttranslational modifications of core histones in response to heat and arsenite stress. *Biochemical Cellular Biology*, 64(8):750-751.

76. Yamato N. (1988). Concentrations and chemical species of arsenic in human urine and hair. *Bulletin of Enviromental Contaminant Toxicology*, 40(5):.633-40.

77. Vahter M, Concha G, Nermell B. Factors influencing arsenic methylation in humans. *J Trace Elem Exp Med* 13:173–84.

78. French RJ, and Jones PJH. (1993). Role of vanadium in nutrition: metabolism, essentiality and dietary considerations. *Life Sciences* 52 (4): 339– 346. doi:10.1016/0024-3205(93)90146-T.

79. Macara IG. (1980) Vanadium — an element in search of a role." *Trends in Biochemical Sciences* 5(4): 92–94. doi:10.1016/0968-0004(80)90256-X.

80. Goldfine AB, Simonson DC, Folli F, Patti ME, and Kahn CR. (1995). Metabolic Effects of sodium metavanadate in humans with insulin-dependent and noninsulin-dependent diabetes mellitus in vivo and in vitro studies. *Journal of Clinical Endocrinology & Metabolism* 80(11): 3311–3320. doi:10.1210/jc.80.11.3311.

81. Gummow B. (2011) Vanadium: Environmental pollution and health effects. <u>Vanadium: Environmental Pollution and Health Effects</u>. **In:** *Reference Module in Earth Systems and Environmental Sciences, from Encyclopedia of Environmental Health, 2011, Pages 628-636.* http://eprints.jcu.edu.au/16593/. DOI: <u>10.1016/B978-0-444-52272-6.00661-9</u>

82. Kohlmeier M. (2003). Vanadium. In *Nutrient Metabolism*, edited by Martin Kohlmeier, 762–766. Food Science and Technology. London: Academic Press. http://www.sciencedirect.com/science/article/pii/B9780124177628501125.

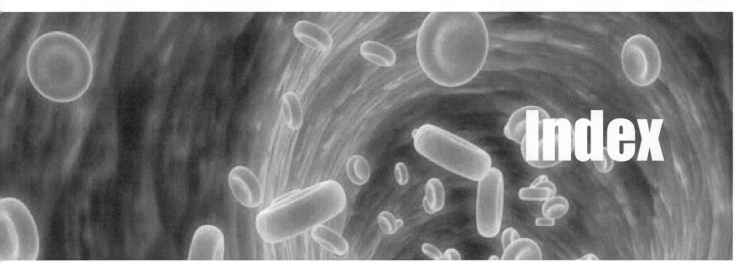